PRACTICAL BUSINESS FORECASTING

Practical Business Forecasting

John A. Saunders, John A. Sharp and
Stephen F. Witt

Gower

Published by
Gower Publishing Company Limited,
Gower House,
Croft Road,
Aldershot,
Hants GU11 3HR,
England

Gower Publishing Company,
Old Post Road,
Brookfield,
Vermont 05036,
USA

British Library Cataloguing in Publication Data

Saunders, John A.
   Practical business forecasting.
   1. Business forecasting
   I. Title   II. Sharp, John A.   III. Witt,
   Stephen F.
   658.4'0355   HD30.27

Library of Congress Cataloging-in-Publication Data

Saunders, John A.
   Practical business forecasting.
   Includes index.
   1. Business forecasting.   I. Sharp, John A.
   II. Witt, Stephen F.   III. Title.
   HD30.27.S28   1986   658.4'0355   86–19564

ISBN 0–566–02516–7

Typeset in Great Britain by
Guildford Graphics Limited, Petworth, West Sussex.
Printed in Great Britain by
Blackmore Press, Longmead, Shaftesbury, Dorset.

Contents

List of illustrations   vii

Preface   xi

1   Introduction   1

2   Data preparation   29

3   Time series models   53

4   Ratio models   111

5   Regression analysis   155

6   Extensions of regression   193

7   Subjective estimation   225

8   New product forecasting   257

9   Trend analysis   285

10 Subjective forecasting   313

Appendix: Software for business forecasting   329

Index   333

Illustrations

Figures

1.1	Forecasts of prices and price changes	8
1.2a	Basic behaviours of a time series	11
1.2b	Seasonality of a time series	12
1.2c	Non-seasonal cycle with a physical cause	12
1.2d	Infrequent events – breakdowns of a large computer	12
1.3	Measures of forecast accuracy	18
1.4	*Ex ante* and *ex post* forecasts	20
1.5	The effect of changing the data point in period 8 on the forecasts for periods 9–12	22
2.1	Time series unadjusted for inflation	40
2.2	Time series adjusted for inflation	41
2.3	Time series unadjusted for trading days	45
2.4	Time series adjusted for trading days	45
2.5	Plot of standard deviation against mean for stationary series	51
2.6	Plot of standard deviation against mean for non-stationary series	51
3.1	Time series A – petrol station sales	58
3.2	Time series B – sales of a photocopying agency	60
3.3	Time series C – engineering company orders	61
3.4	Time series D – process industry output	62
3.5	Seasonal naive model – series A	65
3.6	Autocorrelation function for series B	72
3.7	Autocorrelation function for series C	72
3.8	Forecast versus actual values calculated by Census XII model	76

3.9	Singly differenced time series	86
5.1	Theoretical simple linear regression model	162
5.2	Estimated simple linear regression model	164
5.3	Split of total deviation into explained and unexplained	178
6.1	Durbin–Watson test for autocorrelation	213
7.1	Plausible shapes	230
7.2	A mythical shape	233
7.3	Promotional responses	235
7.4	Decision calculus response	238
7.5	A decision calculus shape	241
7.6	The fit of three shapes	244
7.7	The implications of three shapes	245
7.8	Normally distributed probabilities	248
8.1	New product process	259
8.2	Typical new product sales	260
8.3	Flow chart of TRACKER	264
8.4	New product sales projection	269
9.1	VCR sales forecast using quadratic trend analysis	286
9.2	Typical trend patterns	290
9.3	The fit of four curves to VCR sales data	292
9.4	Penetration of VCRs and forecast	295
9.5	Diffusion: innovation only	297
9.6	Trends in US butter and margarine consumption	301
9.7	Fisher–Pry substitution	303
9.8	Substitution colour TVs for black and white in the UK	304
9.9	The decrease in computation time for computers	304
9.10	Maximum speed of operational military aircraft	306
9.11	Maximum speed of operational helicopters	307
9.12	Economic cruise speed of commercial aircraft	308
9.13	The advance of typesetting technology	309
10.1	First ownership as a tied leading indicator of replacement colour TV sales – UK market	318
10.2	Cross-impact analysis	323
10.3	The hockey stick effect	325

Tables

1.0	Seven groups of forecasting applications	25
1.1	Group 1 applications	26

1.2	Group 2 applications	26
1.3	Group 3 applications	26
1.4	Group 4 applications	27
1.5	Group 5 applications	27
1.6	Group 6 applications	27
1.7	Group 7 applications	28
3.1	Forecast and corresponding actuals	64
3.2	Moving average values for year 2	66
3.3	Classical decomposition model – series B	68
3.4	Forecasts for May–December, year 4	71
3.5	Forecasts for year 6 generated by ORION	74
3.6	Computed values of irregular term	75
3.7	Comparison of results using XII and classical decomposition	78
3.8	Forecasts and actuals for year 6	79
3.9	Mean square errors for k	81
3.10	Forecasts using transformed data	82
3.11	Forecasts using regular differencing	85
3.12	Actual values for years 28–34	89
3.13	Forecasts for years 21–26 and years 29–34	90
3.14	Forecasts for months 41–52	91
3.15	Comparison of Holt–Winters' and single exponential smoothing results, 16–22 January	92
3.16	Comparison of Holt–Winters' and single exponential smoothing results, February	93
3.17	Forecasts for years 1–20	95
3.18	Forecasts for years 29–34	95
3.19	Forecasts for years 21–26	97
3.20	Forecasts for years 29–34	98
3.21	Decision table for choosing time series methods	100
4.1	Cash inflows and outflows over a month	115
4.2	Variables in cash flow model	116
4.3	Ratio modelling by manual computation	117
4.4	Data needed to run model	120
4.5	Result of changes made to Table 4.4	122
4.6	Data for sales turnover and direct cost	123
4.7	Estimation of ratio	124
4.8	Variables appearing in model	128
4.9	Values of variables for years 0–3	133
4.10	Results of calculating the model	134
4.11	Application of random errors to the model	137

4.12	Four sets of values	140
4.13	Number of cars and spare parts sold	142
4.14	Forecasts for original equipment and spares sales	144
4.15	Sales ratios between industries	146
4.16	The complete model	147
4.17	Estimated sales and growth rates	149
4.18	Forecasts generated by model	149
4.19	I/O Manufacturing's estimate of ratios	150
4.20	I/O's sales to consumers and additional ratios	151
5.1	Initial estimation of market share model	172
5.2	Final estimation of market share model	185
6.1	Estimation of cigarette demand model	196
6.2	Full set of estimated coefficients and t values for cigarette demand model	202
6.3	Market share model showing Durbin–Watson statistic	215
6.4	Market share model showing variable correlation matrix	220
7.1	Curve fit expressions and shapes	242
7.2	The fit of ten expressions	243
7.3	Competitive bidding expected payoff	247
8.1	Reasons why sales are low, and solution	268
8.2	Pre-test marketing	274
9.1	VCR sales forecast using quadratic trend analysis	285
9.2	Trend expressions and characteristics	288
9.3	Automatic fit of VCR sales series	291
9.4	Penetration of VCRs: per cent of households	294

Preface

Planning is generally recognized as one of the most important functions of the manager at all levels in the organization and every stage in his career. Planning creates a substantial need for forecasts. This book is intended primarily for those who use, or will use, forecasts and those who are involved in their preparation. It is directed to the concerns of managers and students of management rather than to the specialist. In forecasting, as elsewhere in management, Pareto effects apply. A small proportion of the available techniques is adequate to deal with the great majority of applications. This is reflected in this book. It does not attempt to deal with every technique of interest to the specialist forecaster. It confines itself to those methods that non-specialists can apply successfully.

The structure of the book is as follows. The first two chapters are concerned with topics of general relevance. Thus, from the overview of forecasting provided by the first chapter we move in Chapter 2 to the preparation of data for forecasting. The remainder of the book is concerned with different forecasting techniques and their applications. Chapters 3–9 are devoted to broad categories of forecasting techniques. Thus Chapter 3 deals with what are often referred to as time series analysis techniques or extrapolative and decomposition methods. Chapter 4 covers ratio models that are used for financial forecasting but which also have other applications. Chapters 5, 6 and 7 deal with forecasting for policy making. Regression methods which are particularly useful for these purposes are dealt with in Chapters 5 and 6. Chapter 7 deals with a problem that frequently arises in such applications. For a variety of reasons, from novelty of the product/service through to confidentiality, some of the data needed must be derived subjectively by managers, e.g.

the maximum potential demand for a product.

Chapters 8 and 9 are concerned with strategic forecasts; in particular, approaches to new product forecasting (Chapter 8), forecasting how one product will substitute for another and the forecasting of technological trends. The two latter applications make use of a variety of trend curve projection techniques, which are discussed in Chapter 9. Finally, Chapter 10 addresses an important question that arises once we admit that particular techniques may serve many different forecasting purposes. There are good theoretical, and even better practical, reasons for combining a number of forecasts of a variable derived in different ways to arrive at a 'composite forecast'. Chapter 10 considers how this can be done and the benefits it offers.

The reasoning behind the various forecasting techniques will be discussed but mathematical derivations of formulae will not be presented. It is assumed that the user of the book will have access to one or more of the many suitable computer packages that are available. Without such access it is difficult to make substantial use of many of the forecasting techniques discussed. Given the availability of such packages the reader does not need to be particularly concerned about the details of the calculations. On the other hand, he does need some idea of the validity of the different forecasting methods in particular situations and needs to be able to interpret and use the computer output. The book is intended to provide this knowledge.

Wherever possible, we describe applications of interest to managers and illustrate the use of computer packages for producing the necessary forecasts. Many of the examples described were run using two commercial forecasting packages: the Comshare ORION package and the Comshare SYSTEM W (WIZARD in the UK) package. Further details of these and other software are given in the Appendix.

John A. Saunders
John A. Sharp
Stephen F. Witt

1 Introduction

Do we need to forecast? While it may seem somewhat paradoxical, it is worth drawing attention at the outset to the fact that forecasting is not always worthwhile. However the reader is entitled to expect two things at least: guidance as to when to dispense with forecasts altogether; discussion of when existing forecasting systems should be abandoned to avoid collapse of the management information system due to the strain of producing redundant forecasts. The second point will be covered later in this chapter, with the more general question of monitoring forecasts. For the moment we confine ourselves to the first.

TO FORECAST OR NOT TO FORECAST

There are five common situations in which *not* forecasting a particular variable may be the most sensible course:

1 other readily available information allows the organization to function just as effectively without a forecast;
2 the forecast can be purchased from some external body;
3 the risk that the forecast is supposed to reduce can be insured/hedged against at low cost;
4 all the information the forecast provides is available through studying some publicly available variable;
5 experimentation is possible.

The use of other information

Forecasting is a natural activity for managers. It is noteworthy, however, that when we turn to the management (or, more usually, control) of hardware systems forecasts are little used. Thus an auto-pilot does not require a minute by minute forecast of the weather conditions it will encounter to fly a plane across the Atlantic. Instead it responds to changes in the surrounding conditions such as air pockets. It can do this because the altitude or direction of a plane can be changed very quickly. Conversely, a manager needs forecasts because organizations normally react rather slowly to change. It is, therefore, usually necessary to have reasonable forecasts so that action can be taken in advance. If the delivery time for the special steels used in products is 16 weeks and delivery of those products is either ex stock or in a shorter period than 16 weeks then it will be essential to have a forecast of changing patterns of demand. This will enable stocks to be held at a lower level. On the other hand, it would be unusual to forecast the needs for mild steel washers used on such products. It is more cost effective to keep a large stock and reorder whenever that stock drops below a specified high level. Thus instead of using a forecast, different information, namely the approximate stock level of the washers, provides an effective and cheaper way of managing the system.

Purchase of the forecast from some external body

Managers are often unaware of the huge variety of different forecasts available from government bodies, industry associations, market research agencies, and so on. In general, forecasting is not the business of a manager's organization. It therefore makes sense to obtain what forecasts he can from organizations who specialize in forecasting. This point will be taken up in more detail in Chapter 2.

Insurance/hedging against risk

In business it is often possible to insure against risks, e.g. export credit guarantees. Similarly, in commodity markets it may be possible to hedge against future price changes by buying/selling forward rather than attempting to forecast them. Even if the relevant variables can be forecast, the preparation of the forecasts is expensive and their accuracy indifferent. If the variables concerned are peripheral to the main activities of the organization, paying the costs of hedging/ insurance is likely to be far more efficient.

Studying some publicly available variable

Economic theory suggests that prices determined by an efficient market are sometimes the best forecasts that can be obtained. Thus the price of IBM shares appears to be an excellent predictor of IBM's future profits. If this is true, there is no point in trying to devise systems to forecast IBM's profits. Substantial research may be needed to determine whether there is a market price that provides good predictions of a variable of interest to an organization. In large, free, financial markets like those of the USA, such information is often readily available. For a discussion of the efficient market hypothesis, see Dobbins and Witt (1983).

Experimentation

Because the preparation of some forecasts, such as sales of a new product, can mean considerable expense and often poor results, it may well be cheaper to dispense with these forecasts and conduct an experiment instead. This might involve a selective launch to a particular region or customer group or a full scale launch that will rapidly be abandoned unless sales are promising. While such an approach is common in the marketing of consumer products, it is less widely applied in industrial marketing or in the provision of public services.

MANAGEMENT USES OF FORECASTS

When is it worth setting up a forecasting system? The short answer is whenever the variables concerned are central to the main activities of the organization and the use of the forecasts is likely to provide significant benefits. Thus, where the forecasts are of key variables relating to the organization's 'markets' or to the main resources it uses then they are likely to be worthwhile. There is no point in producing forecasts that scarcely pay for themselves. Where key activities are concerned, however, savings of even a few per cent are often enough to justify the cost.

The typical accuracy achieved in forecasting can be very poor, e.g. errors of 50 per cent or more in medium term forecasting of foreign exchange rate changes or the costs of large projects with a life of ten years or over. On the other hand, in many sales forecasting applications for mature products errors may be only a few per cent even two or three years ahead, provided the stability of the market is little affected by competitor action.

Forecasting by managers fulfils five different broad purposes. These are:

1 resource allocation;
2 policy determination;
3 performance appraisal;
4 strategic planning;
5 contingency planning.

The purpose(s) to be fulfilled by a forecast determine which forecasting techniques are appropriate. Thus, forecasts intended for policy making must be able to represent the effects of policy changes on the variable of interest. Therefore they must embody some attempt to model causes and effects. For many resource allocation purposes, however, the variable of interest is outside the forecaster's control, e.g. forecasting commodity prices for planning raw material purchases, and therefore a method that successfully extrapolates or projects existing trends may be all that is required.

A consequence of this is that forecasts derived for one set of purposes may well be capable of meeting 'lower level' purposes. That is, forecasts intended for purposes later in the list may also meet part or all of the purposes earlier in the list. Of course, this usually means that the purposes later in the list require a greater effort. With this in mind the different purposes will now be examined in greater depth.

Forecasting for resource allocation

The role of forecasts in resource allocation is obvious. Without a realistic appraisal of what is to be done and its resource implications any kind of management, whether of day-to-day operations or the long term future of the organization, would be impossible. A pension fund, for example, must attempt to forecast both inflows of contributions and income from existing investments, since these constitute the source of new investments. Much of what is to be done is, however, conditioned by changes taking place in the environment in which the organization functions, so these changes must be forecast, too. The manager of a pension fund, for example, must consider the changing age structure of fund members and hence the changing proportion of those receiving pensions. Also, if the fund's pensions are to some extent adjusted for inflation, there will be a need for longer term forecasts of inflation. Equally, in a firm that sells ex stock, forecasts of future demand are needed to enable stocks to be built up ahead of periods of high demand and to be run down when demand is low.

The time series methods discussed in Chapter 3 and the ratio models of Chapter 4 are probably the main type of forecast used for resource allocation. Following our remarks above, however, that certainly does not mean they are the only suitable techniques. That question is addressed at the end of this chapter. Similar remarks apply to the other purposes considered below.

Forecasting for policy determination

In some cases management can have a significant effect on the value of a variable, through decisions about advertising expenditure, and so on. In this case, a mere projection of past trends in the variable is of little use. What is desirable is some type of 'causal model' that will allow management to see what the impact of policy changes will be on the variable concerned. Inevitably, such a forecasting model will need to predict future values of the variable of interest on the basis of the values of a number of other variables. The principal tool for such forecasting is regression analysis which is covered in Chapters 5 and 6.

Forecasting for performance appraisal

Forecasting for performance appraisal is perhaps even more common in organizations under the guise of budgeting. Until recent years this may not have been obvious, since the preparation of budgets was the province of the accountant. With the advent of computer 'spreadsheet' packages, however, it has become an important activity of managers and its forecasting content has become much more widely recognized. Hence Chapter 4 of this book has been devoted to the topic of ratio models, which are the basis of financial planning models.

Similarly, an important tool for the achievement of corporate plans is trend curves (discussed in Chapter 9); for example, fitting S-shaped growth curves to technological advances.

Forecasting for strategic planning

By strategic planning we mean those decisions that determine in the longer term the major goals of the organization and the technology and systems used to attain them. It is harder to systematize such forecasting. The variables to forecast are often less obvious and the necessary data more difficult to come by. Because of the complexity of such applications, a variety of approaches are appropriate. Trend curves (see Chapter 9), e.g. S-shaped market growth, are suited to projections of what will happen without major changes in the organization's policies. Regression models may be favoured for determining how the organization can best attack particular markets. Financial models of the type discussed in Chapter 4 will undoubtedly have their place in assessing the balance between the flow of resources into the organization and its usage of resources in developing itself. Finally, a number of 'subjective' techniques that rely on executive experience rather than other data sources may well be favoured for the more speculative aspects of strategy formulation. These are covered in Chapters 7, 8 and 10.

Forecasting unexpected events and contingency planning

The oil price shocks of 1973 and 1979 provide examples of unexpected events that can have a great impact on organizations. Contingency planning against such eventualities may be warranted at two levels: the operational level of production planning or sales target setting so that business can continue 'as usual'; and the strategic level so that shifts of strategy can be introduced quickly and smoothly, e.g. the introduction of car engines that use less fuel.

CLASSIFYING FORECASTS

Later we shall provide guidelines to determine which approaches to forecasting are best suited to particular applications. To this end, it is useful to classify the forecasts needed by management by:

1 which variables are forecast;
2 the time span of the decisions for which they are used;
3 whether they are of point events or time series;
4 the 'nature' of the time series;
5 the method(s) used to prepare the forecasts.

Of these categories, the variable forecast, the time span of decision, and the methods used will form the basis of the first stage of forecast method selection presented later in this chapter. The 'nature' category will be used in subsequent chapters for refining the selection of forecast method. We shall also refer from time to time to the distinction between the forecasting of time series and the forecasting of point events.

Variables to be forecast

As far as the manager is concerned this is probably the most natural way of categorizing forecasts. The forecasting methods that are appropriate to determining wage costs five years hence are unlikely to be the same as those for forecasting journey times for delivery vehicles in the next week. What is to be forecast therefore affects technique selection. More importantly, a key step in establishing a solution to a manager's planning problem is to decide what variables need to be forecast. This can often be a rather more subtle question than first appears. In short term commodity purchasing, for instance, it is usually *changes* to prices that are most important. If the manager believes the price will shortly drop he can reduce his purchases temporarily to take advantage of the fall. Conversely, if he anticipates a rise in prices he will purchase more than immediately required. What the manager needs, then, is good forecasts of future price changes. This is by no means the same as forecasting future price levels. As Figure 1.1 shows, a forecasting method can deliver apparently accurate forecasts of price levels, and yet be more or less useless for predicting the real variable of interest, i.e. price changes. The margin of error between the forecast and the actual

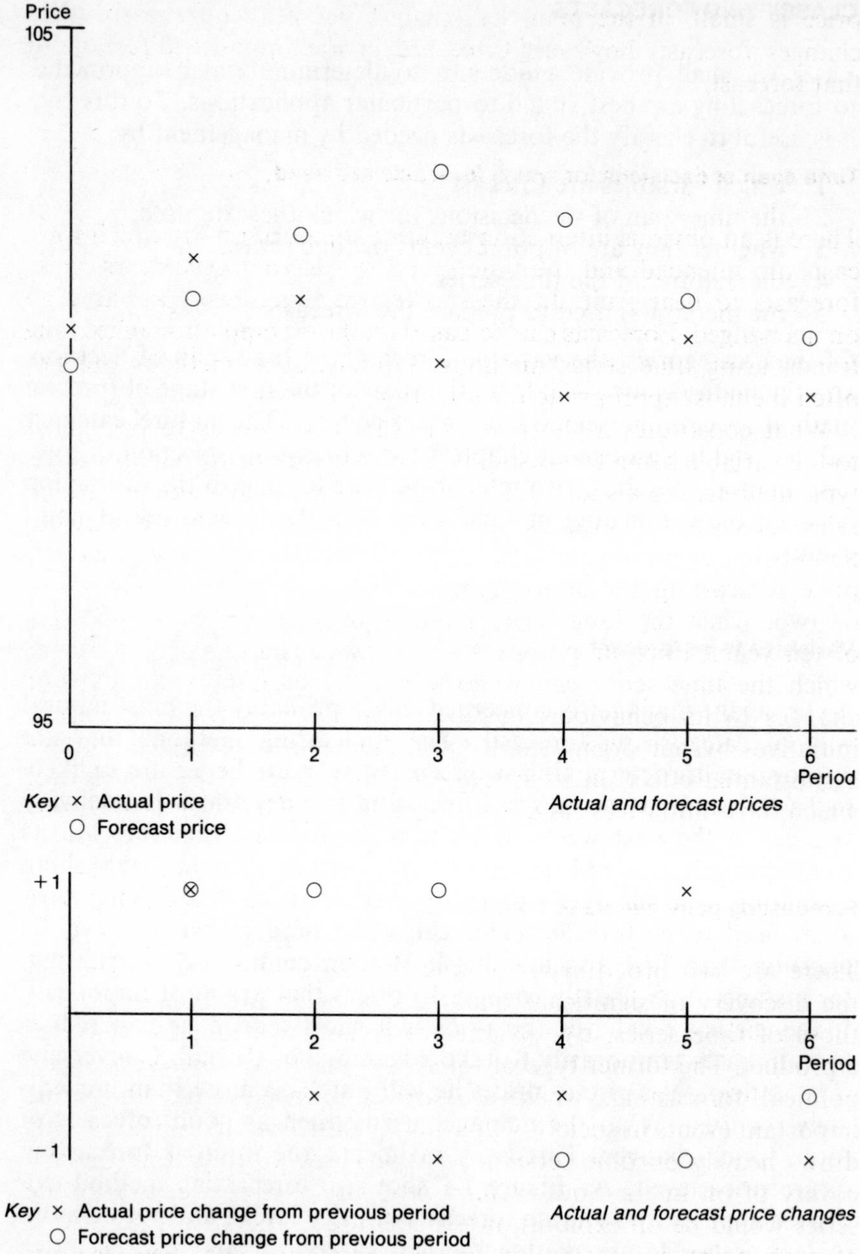
Price
105
95
0
1
2
3
4
5
6
Period
Key × Actual price
○ Forecast price
Actual and forecast prices
+1
−1
1
2
3
4
5
6
Period
Key × Actual price change from previous period
○ Forecast price change from previous period
Actual and forecast price changes

Figure 1.1 Forecasts of prices and price changes

price is small, in the main less than 1 per cent. Of the six price changes forecast, however, three are in the opposite direction to that forecast.

Time span of decisions for which forecasts are used

There is an obvious interaction between the purpose for which forecasts are intended and the time taken for decisions based on those forecasts to bear fruit. In the short term things will probably go on unchanged. Forecasts can be based on the extrapolation of existing trends using time series methods. Equally, such methods are not often the most appropriate for long time horizons.

What constitutes a short or long time span needs to be related to the variable being forecast. Sales forcasts for operational purposes typically relate to a short time horizon of the next 12 months. Many sales forecasts for strategic decisions on the other hand relate to periods ten or more years ahead. By way of contrast, in commodity price forecasting the short term usually relates to the next week or two, while the long term might well mean a period in excess of ten years. For our purposes short term means that period over which the time series can be expected to continue without major changes to its behaviour; medium term is the period over which initiatives by our organization and others can be expected to have a substantial effect on its values; and long term is the period over which those initiatives cannot be foreseen with any accuracy.

Forecasting point events or time series

There are two broad types of forecast: those of point events, e.g. the discovery of significant quantities of oil in the China Sea, and those of time series, e.g. a series of consecutive months' sales for a product. The former type of forecast is mainly of interest in socio-political forecasting, where we are concerned with anticipating important events in society. Typically, the forecasting of point events draws heavily on time series forecasts. Thus in forecasting the discovery of oil in the South China Sea, one obviously relevant time series would be oil exploration expenditure in the area. Forecasting of such point events is also far less common. For these reasons we shall be mainly concerned in this book with the forecasting of time series, though we shall refer from time to time to the identification of turning points in time series. This is of interest in a variety of contexts, since the successful prediction that our sales are about to turn down or that the loan interest rates are about to increase can make substantial savings possible. Hereafter we shall assume, unless noted to the contrary, that we wish to forecast several future values of a time series based on the past values of one or more time series.

The nature of the time series

A time series may take a number of characteristic forms. The 'nature' of the time series can affect the choice of method for forecasting it. In practice, the behaviour of a particular time series can normally be regarded as a combination of the following 'basic behaviours', illustrated in Figures 1.2a, 1.2b, 1.2c and 1.2d.

Fluctuation about a constant level: the time series is essentially constant.

Steps: the time series exhibits discontinuities where it jumps up or down to a new level.

Linear trend: the time series shows a steady rate of increase or decrease from one period to the next. This is a frequent form of behaviour, if a manager is doing an effective job of increasing sales or reducing costs!

Non-linear trend: similar to above except the rate of increase is non-linear.

Saturation: the time series eventually declines to zero. A plot of the cumulative (total to date) value of the time series thus levels off. Typically, if the complete history of, say, sales of a limited life product is plotted the cumulative curve is S-shaped: the product life cycle.

Volatility (noise): the time series is erratic and shifts markedly from one period to the next.

Seasonality: the time series values are markedly influenced by the season. This is true not only of most retail time series but also of series such as industrial production that are affected by holidays.

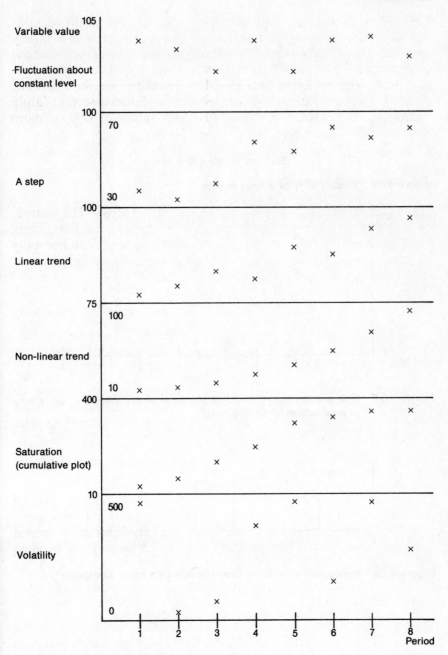

Figure 1.2a   Basic behaviours of a time series

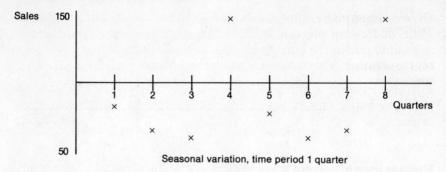

Figure 1.2b   Seasonality of a time series

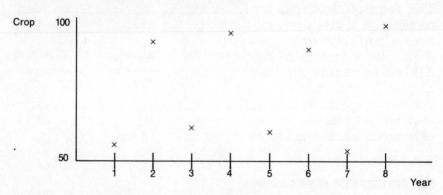

Figure 1.2c   Non-seasonal cycle with a physical cause (biennial variation in production of an orchard)

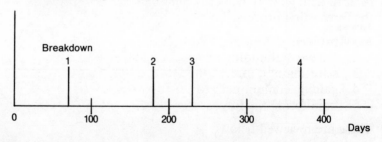

Figure 1.2d   Infrequent events — breakdowns of a large computer

Cycle: occasionally, time series may contain cycles that are due to some underlying physical cycle. Thus there may be 11-year cycles in rainfall due to the corresponding 11-year sunspot cycle's influence on the weather. This would clearly be of interest to a water utility.

Infrequent events: some time series, e.g. breakdowns of equipment requiring major repairs, are concerned with events that do not occur often.

Methods used to prepare the forecasts

This form of classification of forecasts is undoubtedly the most common. It is also the most convenient for writers on forecasting, since a particular technique can usually be used with reasonable success for a number of different purposes involving decisions of different time spans. We accept that this is not the most appropriate division for the manager with a forecasting problem. Later in the chapter, however, we shall attempt to provide the manager with guidance as to the most appropriate techniques for use in a number of common forecasting situations, indicated by chapter.

THE PROCESS OF FORECASTING

Since this book is primarily concerned with a systematic approach to forecasting, it is necessary to consider the various elements of the forecasting process. These are:

1 problem definition;
2 system definition;
3 selection of a forecasting method;
4 gaining commitment to the forecasts;
5 monitoring the forecasting system.

These are reviewed below.

Problem definition

The first step is to establish whether forecasts are needed and, if so, what is expected of them. This necessarily embraces the identification of the variables to be forecast and rough estimates of the accuracy required, if the forecasts are to offer any significant benefits.

This initial feasibility study is also the point at which to establish whether there is some prospect of attaining that accuracy at reasonable cost.

System definition

The next step is to establish what the forecasting system must do and how much work is involved. The level of aggregation at which forecasts are to be prepared must be decided. It matters considerably, for example, whether we forecast sales by product group; by individual product within product group; or by pack size within individual products within product group. For instance, the detergent product group of a company might contain 20 different detergents each of which is sold in ten different pack sizes.

Similarly, the frequency with which forecasts are to be prepared has a substantial impact. In many cases, it will not be possible to produce the volume of forecasts implied by the level of aggregation and the frequency desired unless the process of data gathering can be automated. Such forecasts may only become feasible once the organization has begun to operate a system of information gathering, which involves holding all information on a single central database rather than on individual computer files in a variety of different departments. Economic or industry data from government or other outside sources are also often essential.

Selection of a forecasting method

This will be discussed in depth at the end of the chapter.

Gaining commitment

Though a forecast may be potentially valuable, the benefits will not be obtained unless managers use it. The basic assumption of this book is that the manager who reads it is strongly involved in defining the forecasing system he needs. This is the best way of ensuring that the forecasts are used successfully.

Monitoring the forecasting system

It was noted earlier that there is a need to carry out regular audits to ensure that a forecasting system continues to provide value for money. The simplest way of doing this is to make sure that the costs of running the system are carried on the budget of a manager who has the authority to axe the system, if necessary. In cases where this is not feasible, e.g. where the organization's computer system regularly spews out a mass of different forecasts, the best substitute is an annual audit of forecasting systems. This would at a minimum cover:

1 Whether the forecast is still being used by anyone. Often it no longer is!
2 How the forecast is being used; and whether it is modified in the light of executive judgement, etc.
3 Whether the accuracy/benefits expected of it are still being attained.
4 Whether the benefits obtained from it are greater than the cost of preparing it. If not, it should be dispensed with.
5 Whether the method used to prepare the forecast should be changed.
6 Whether it should be replaced by some other forecast(s) that would now be more useful.
7 Whether expectations about the performance of the forecast should be revised.

SELECTING A FORECASTING METHOD

In general a forecasting method involves the following elements:

1 identification of a suitable model;
2 estimation of the model;
3 use of the model for forecasting;
4 assessment of the forecasts produced;
5 updating the model.

Identification of a suitable model

By model we mean the mathematical equations or procedures used to determine the forecasts. A very simple time series model, for instance, is the single exponential smoothing model. This says that:

$$\text{FORECAST FOR NEXT PERIOD} =$$
$$A \times \text{THIS PERIOD'S ACTUAL VALUE} +$$
$$(1\text{-}A) \times \text{FORECAST FOR THIS PERIOD} \qquad (1.1)$$

where A is a constant. It is discussed in more detail in Chapter 3.

A rather more complex market model would be:

$$\text{SALES} = A + B$$
$$\times \text{OUR PRICE/COMPETITOR'S PRICE} - \text{OUR PRICE} + C$$
$$\times (\text{OUR ADVERTISING BUDGET/COMPETITOR'S}$$
$$\text{ADVERTISING BUDGET}) \qquad (1.2)$$

where A, B and C are constants. This model is conceptually very different from the previous one since it ascribes causality. The ratio of our price to the competitor's and our advertising budget to the competitor's are assumed to determine sales. Models of this type are discussed in more detail in Chapters 5 and 6 in particular. They are usually referred to as *causal* models.

In some cases, e.g. certain subjective forecasting methods, the forecasting model is implicit in that it is concealed in a computer program. The determination of the general type of forecasting model, e.g. exponential smoothing, regression, etc., that is most appropriate to a particular variable is usually referred to in the forecasting literature as *identification*.

Estimation

As we saw in the previous section a forecasting model usually contains a number of constants, e.g. A, B, C in the second example, whose values must be determined. The process by which their values are fixed is usually referred to as *estimation*. The most common approach to estimation is to select the parameter values in such a way that the forecasts produced are close to the corresponding actual values. The effect of this is to adjust the constants of the model so that it fits *past* data well. It will be obvious, however, that there are many circumstances under which such an approach to estimation is inappropriate. It is unlikely to be useful in many strategic applications where we are interested in forecasting for an activity for which no equivalent has existed in the past.

Use of the model for forecasting

Whereas identification and estimation can claim substantial amounts of computer time, the production of forecasts once the forecast model has been obtained usually needs very few calculations. Nonetheless, it is not always easy to obtain the desired forecasts once the forecast model has been derived. The ease with which this can be done indicates how simple it is to use a particular computer forecasting package.

Assessment of the forecasts produced

The most frequently used formal measures of forecast accuracy are mean square error (MSE), mean absolute deviation (MAD) and bias. Mean square error is calculated simply as the average value of the square of the forecast error (the difference between the forecast and the actual value). Mean absolute deviation is the average of the numerical value of the forecast error. Bias is measured by the difference between the average of the actual value of the variable and the average of its forecast value. Or it may be measured by the difference between the total of the actual values and the total of the forecast values. Usually it is considered desirable for the forecast to fluctuate on either side of the actual value. If this is the case, either measurement of bias will give a result close to zero. These different accuracy measures are depicted in Figure 1.3.

It should be recognized that as far as the manager is concerned, there is no virtue in accuracy in itself. Usually, though, it is not possible to measure directly the economic impact of adopting one forecast method rather than another. In cases where this can be done it would appear, in general, that more accurate methods are also more profitable methods, but this may not always be true. Suppose, for example, we are contemplating the purchase of a new computer and need a forecast of future computer requirements.

If the smaller computers in the range from which we intend to purchase cannot be adapted to the full range of purposes served

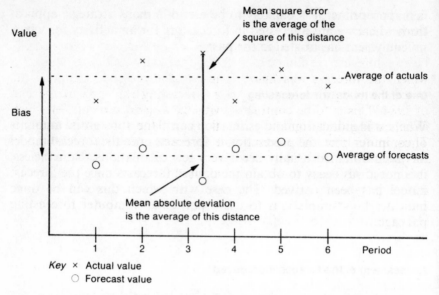

Key × Actual value
○ Forecast value

Figure 1.3 Measures of forecast accuracy

by the larger ones, it may pay us to adopt a forecasting method that is likely to overestimate future usage. This may well lead to purchase of a larger machine than necessary but the consequent losses are unlikely to be great. On the other hand, if a more accurate method happens to underestimate future usage, so that a small machine offering fewer facilities than the larger ones is purchased, the cost of the resulting inconvenience could be enormous.

A further point about accuracy is that what the manager needs is a reasonable estimate of how accurate a forecast method is likely to be in practice. This affects how we go about measuring forecast accuracy. In many types of short and medium term forecasting it is possible to assess how the forecasting model will work in practice by retaining the last few points of the data series and identifying and estimating the model using the remainder. The forecast model is then used to predict the values of the 'held out' data points. Comparison of these predictions with the corresponding actuals provides a good measure of how the forecast method is likely to work in reality. As a more concrete example, suppose we have a time series of monthly data for the period 1980–1984 plus the first six months of 1985. The forecast model could be built using only the data up until the end of 1984. Using this model the values for the first six months of 1985 can then be predicted and compared with the held back actuals.

This type of testing is often referred to by forecasters as *ex ante,* i.e. we forecast certain values using data only up to the point at which the forecast was made. Thus, in the previous example, the process was equivalent to *ex ante* forecasting for 1985 at the end of 1984. This is to be contrasted with the *ex post* type of test which entails using data right up until the point the forecast was made. Thus, in our previous example, the forecasts produced by the model for the period 1980–84 would be *ex post* since the actual data for those periods was used in producing the forecast model. The difference between *ex ante* and *ex post* forecasts is depicted in Figure 1.4.

The difference between *ex ante* and *ex post* testing can be very important in practice. *Ex post* tests often give an over flattering impression of how good the forecast model is. The results of the *ex ante* tests may often be far less favourable. If they are judged unacceptable, it will be necessary to repeat the identification and estimation stages. Forecast method selection is, then, often an iterative process.

Updating the model

Identification and estimation of a forecast model will in general require both more computer time and a higher level of expertise than actually producing the forecasts from the model. For this reason, they are usually only carried out periodically, e.g. once every year for a monthly time series, rather than each time a forecast is to be prepared. In practice, forecast models sometimes perform better if they are updated for each period. The improvement in performance tends to be rather small, however, if the forecasting method is suitable for the application. More frequent updating can even lead to less accurate forecasts! Unless the losses due to inaccurate forecasts are large, updating the forecasting model annually is adequate. Of course, where those costs are high, it will pay to experiment with different update frequencies to determine which performs best. The monitoring of forecasts to determine when the forecast model needs to be reidentified is discussed in Chapter 3.

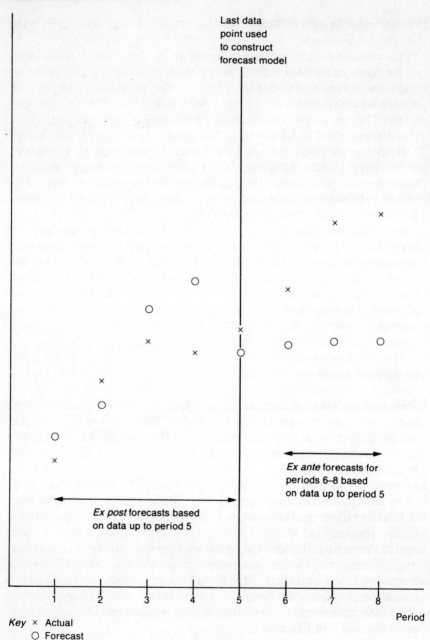

Figure 1.4 *Ex ante* and *ex post* forecasts

Further determinants of forecasting method

We have already reviewed a number of factors that affect choice of forecasting methods. There remain, however, a number of more technical considerations that also help determine the choice. Many methods require more data than are readily available, as for example in the case of forecasting new product sales. Suitable methods for this are discussed in Chapters 7 and 8.

Besides accuracy, another factor to consider is the method's 'robustness'. Some methods are very sensitive to the assumptions made in applying them, or to small changes to some of the data points. An example of this is S-shaped growth curves where, as Figure 1.5 shows, small changes to the data in the early history of the time series can have a big effect on the values forecast. Obviously the results derived by such methods can be markedly affected by inexpert application. By contrast other methods, e.g. some time series methods, are little affected by such maltreatment. In practice, it is hard to use a particular set of forecasts with any confidence, if one is aware that very different figures could be obtained with only slight changes to the way the forecasting method was applied. Robustness is accordingly of great practical concern.

It is often necessary to use a number of forecast methods together to achieve the forecast required. Thus it might be appropriate to forecast total industry sales of a product using a trend curve and then to forecast our company's sales using a regression model that used the industry sales forecast as one of its independent variables. Though there is a large number of forecasting packages available they are never completely comprehensive. Since there are often benefits in standardizing on the use of one package, e.g. being able to obtain advice on its use, compromising on a method that is somewhat less than ideal for our particular application may be justified.

Finally, there are two further related dimensions along which a forecasting method should be judged. First, there is the cost of applying it, including the computer time required for the identification and estimation of the forecast model. However, the costs of computation have fallen, and the typical annual cost of computing a particular forecast may nowadays be only a few pounds. Where, however, there are many thousand forecasts to be prepared, as is often the case in consumer goods industries, banking and finance, etc., the use of complex methods requiring much computation may well be precluded. Obviously a similar situation exists with regard to the costs

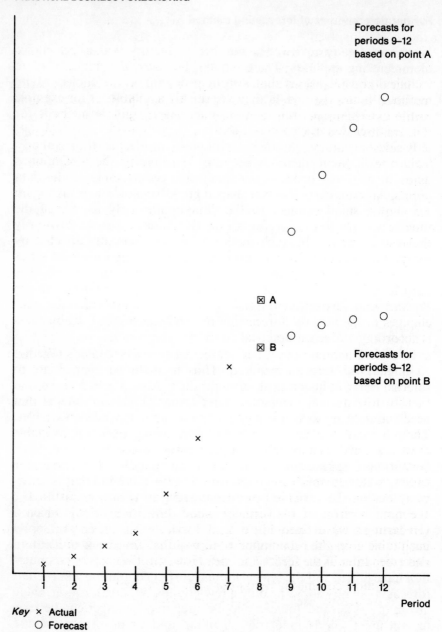

Forecasts for
periods 9–12
based on point A

Forecasts for
periods 9–12
based on point B

Period

Key × Actual
○ Forecast

Figure 1.5   The effect of changing the data point in period 8 on the forecasts for periods 9–12

of data gathering, which nowadays are frequently much higher than the costs involved in actually computing the forecasts. This is currently the case, for example, in obtaining information from commercial computer databases (see Chapter 2).

The other dimension, that tends to be related to cost, is the expertise required to use the forecasting method. Robust techniques and some subjective techniques can be applied without the services of an expert. Others, however, such as regression methods, usually need specialist advice when the forecast model is being derived. Obviously, such expertise is costly. More important, it is in short supply save in large organizations. Though the problem may be circumvented by employing outside consultants, the costs of such methods are clearly far higher than the simple methods the manager can use on his own. This does not mean that such methods never pay. It is essential, however, that they can generate markedly larger savings than the simpler methods.

SELECTING A FORECAST METHOD

Tables 1.0–1.7 are intended to aid the decision about the broad type of forecasting method applicable to the reader's problem. Their main purpose is to guide the manager to those chapters that may contain relevant material.

The procedure for using the tables is as follows. Table 1.0 lists seven groups of forecasting applications in terms of the variables being forecast. Having decided which is the appropriate group, the reader should then refer to the corresponding table number, e.g. for Group 3 applications: Table 1.3. These take the form of decision tables, which further categorize forecasts by the influence the company has on the variable being forecast: great (G) or small (S) and the time horizon of the forecast: short (S), medium (M) or long (L) term as we defined those terms earlier. The lower portion of each table gives the broad applicability of the five groups of methods described later as we see it. The codes used are:

*** most commonly used approach to the problem
** frequently useful alternative approach
* occasionally used in this context
N not suitable for this application

Certain cells of the tables have been left blank. This reflects the fact that, although we know of no applications of the method concerned to this particular problem, it could conceivably be used.

Detailed discussion of the forecasting methods listed in the rows will be found as follows:

Time series methods – Chapter 3
Ratio models – Chapter 4
Regression methods – Chapters 5 and 6
Subjective methods – Chapters 7 and 10
Trend curves – Chapters 8 and 9.

Table 1.0
Seven groups of forecasting applications

Group 1 applications

Own 'sales' consumer markets
Own non-capital equipment sales to industrial markets

Group 2 applications

Capital equipment sales to industrial markets

Group 3 applications

Commodity prices
Stock market prices
Interest rates

Group 4 applications

Wage costs
Costs of purchases
Capital equipment costs

Group 5 applications

Sources and uses of funds

Group 6 applications

Competitor activity

Group 7 applications

Technological progress

Table 1.1

Group 1 applications					
Influence on variable	S	S	S	G	G	G
Forecast horizon	S	M	L	S	M	L
TIME SERIES METHODS	***	**	*	N	N	N
RATIO MODELS			*			
REGRESSION METHODS	*	**	*	**	***	*
SUBJECTIVE METHODS	*	**	***	*	*	**
TREND CURVES	*	**	**	N	N	N

Table 1.2

Group 2 applications					
Influence on variable	S	S	S	G	G	G
Forecast horizon	S	M	L	S	M	L
TIME SERIES METHODS	*	N	N	N	N	N
RATIO MODELS	*	**	*	***	***	*
REGRESSION METHODS	**	**	*	***	***	*
SUBJECTIVE METHODS	*	**	***	**	**	***
TREND CURVES	*	**	*	N	N	N

Table 1.3

Group 3 applications					
Influence on variable	S	S	S	G	G	G
Forecast horizon	S	M	L	S	M	L
TIME SERIES METHODS	**	N	N	N	N	N
RATIO MODELS		*	*			
REGRESSION METHODS		**			**	
SUBJECTIVE METHODS	**	*	**	**	**	**
TREND CURVES				N	N	N

Table 1.4

Group 4 applications					
Influence on variable S	S	S	G	G	G
Forecast horizon S	M	L	S	M	L
TIME SERIES METHODS ***	**	N	N	N	N
RATIO MODELS *	*	*			
REGRESSION METHODS	**			**	
SUBJECTIVE METHODS **	**	**	**	**	**
TREND CURVES			N	N	N

Table 1.5

Group 5 applications					
Influence on variable S	S	S	G	G	G
Forecast horizon S	M	L	S	M	L
TIME SERIES METHODS **	*	N	N	N	N
RATIO MODELS ***	***	*	***	***	*
REGRESSION METHODS					
SUBJECTIVE METHODS *	*	**	*	*	**
TREND CURVES N	N	N	N	N	N

Table 1.6

Group 6 applications					
Influence on variable S	S	S	G	G	G
Forecast horizon S	M	L	S	M	L
TIME SERIES METHODS *	*	N	N	N	N
RATIO MODELS *	**	**	*	**	**
REGRESSION METHODS **	*		**	*	
SUBJECTIVE METHODS ***	***	***	**	**	**
TREND CURVES *			N	N	N

Table 1.7

Group 7 applications						
Influence on variable	S	S	S	G	G	G
Forecast horizon	S	M	L	S	M	L
TIME SERIES METHODS	**	*	N	N	N	N
RATIO MODELS	***	***	*	***	***	*
REGRESSION METHODS						
SUBJECTIVE METHODS	*	**	**	*	**	**
TREND CURVES	***	**	**	*	*	*

FURTHER READING

Dobbins, R. and Witt, S. F., *Portfolio Theory and Investment Management,* Basil Blackwell, Oxford, 1983, 201 pp.

2 Data preparation

When considering sources of data used for forecasting, it is convenient to divide the data used into two types: primary data that the organization itself originates or whose collection it commissions; and secondary data, which are collected by other bodies. The main sources of the two types of data are:

Primary
    Organization's own information systems
    Data collected on behalf of the organization

Secondary
    UK government
    Other government
    International bodies
    Local government
    Official bodies
    Trade associations
    The press
    Multiclient studies
    Econometric models
    Commercial databases

PRIMARY DATA

Primary data are the most likely to be relevant to the organization's forecasting needs at least for shorter term forecasts with horizons of a year or so. Primary data that are generated by the organization's own information systems can be virtually costless if they arise as a by-product of the usual operating systems of the organization, e.g. sales statistics compiled from the order processing system. This, of course, will only be the case if information is viewed as a 'corporate resource' so that data from different parts of the organization, e.g. the sales invoicing and the production system, can be combined for a particular forecasting purpose. In setting up a forecasting system (see Chapter 1), this should be borne in mind.

Often, however, the data required for forecasting purposes may not be available within the organization. As discussed in Chapter 8, this is particularly likely to be the case in new product forecasting, where it is rarely possible for the organization to undertake its own data collection. Rather it must commission some outside specialist agency with the necessary contacts to carry it out. This is a much more expensive proposition in most cases, unless the data requirements are modest and can be met by an omnibus survey of a cross section of the population in which additional questions can be incorporated at a low fee.

SECONDARY SOURCES

Secondary data sources have two main attractions. Often they contain data that no individual organization could hope to collect for reasons of confidentiality or commercial secrecy but which, say, governments can legally require organizations to supply. Since most of these sources are either produced for official purposes or are intended to be sold to many organizations, secondary data have the additional merit of being cheap. Their chief drawback is the bewildering array of sources and the errors or hidden assumptions that may exist in the data, which may not be obvious to the unwary user.

An increasingly important source of secondary data for forecasting is the many commercial databases that have come into existence in the last decade or so. These carry a very wide range of both quantitative and qualitative data that can be useful in almost any type of forecasting. In many cases, they offer the further advantage that the forecaster can 'download' information direct from the commercial database into his own computer system without having laboriously to reenter it.

GOVERNMENT STATISTICS

Like most governments that of the UK provides an enormous range of statistical data that is useful to the forecaster. The following list is by no means exhaustive. Rather, we have attempted to describe those that are most frequently used. For more specialized forecasting purposes, e.g. matters concerned with law and order or education, there are also extensive government statistics. Interested readers are referred to the Central Statistical Office Publication: *A Brief Guide to Government Statistics.*

Population statistics

The Office of Population Censuses and Surveys provides detailed census (and sample census) information in many cases down to ward level. The importance of demographic trends, e.g. the declining birth rate, makes this a good data source for strategic forecasting with time horizons of ten years or more. The population projections regularly produced by the Office of Population Censuses and Surveys is also useful.

The Office is also responsible for the *General Household Survey*. This is conducted on a random sample basis annually. The questions asked vary from year to year. The survey provides important material on changes in society, e.g. the increasing number of working mothers.

The Family Expenditure Survey

As its name implies this survey gives details of expenditures by households on a large variety of items and is compiled by region, by family income and so on. It represents, therefore, an important source of data for forecasting many consumer markets.

Economic statistics

This category is, of course, very large and we can only list some of the main classes within it. The Central Statistical Office produces a wide range of macroeconomic statistics relating to the economy as a whole: from the GNP through interest and exchange rates, to the series of leading and coincident indicators that are intended to chart the state of the economy. These series are of particular interest for econometric forecasting (see Chapters 5 and 6).

The Central Statistical Office also publishes many data series of more specific interest. An example is the series of R and D spending by industry that has obvious applications in forecasting for certain technologically based businesses.

Customs statistics

For products that are mainly imported or that enjoy substantial export markets, customs statistics can be an important data source. Very detailed data are available for quite narrow product groups (mainly at 4-digit Standard Industrial Classification level), e.g. air conditioning equipment, tabulated by country of origin and destination.

Employment related statistics

A variety of employment related data useful to the forecaster are produced by the UK central government. The Department of Employment's *Employment Gazette,* for example, carries data on changes in employment, vacancies, etc. by industry and details of earnings surveys. The latter are of particular use in forecasting wage costs.

Further valuable material can be found in the Inland Revenue Statistics which show the incidence of taxation on incomes. Social security costs, another aspect of labour costs of concern to the forecaster, are to be found in a number of sources including the Central Statistical Office's *Annual Abstract of Statistics.*

Industry statistics

The Business Statistics Office provides an extensive array of statistics, mainly on manufacturing industry. The *Census of Production,* for instance, gives information on the sales, costs, capital investment, employment, etc. of individual industries mainly at 3 digit Standard Industrial Classification level. These are an important source of data for forecasting market potential and for modelling of other companies (see Chapter 4).

The *Census of Distribution,* published by the Business Statistics Office, also gives certain information on wholesale, retail and service industries. This is, however, much less comprehensive than the *Census of Production.*

Extensive statistics are produced for some specific industries, e.g. agriculture, tourism, usually by the Ministry concerned, that are of considerable use to forecasters.

A further set of data useful for detailed industry forecasting is the input/output tables produced by the Business Statistics Office. Applications of input/output modelling are described in Chapter 4.

Company financial data

UK forecasters are fortunate to have data available on the finances and income of all registered companies through Companies' House. These data are of use for many different purposes, e.g. forecasting the growth of particular company sectors.

A by-product of the Companies' House data collection is the MA4 Financial Statistics of broad industry groups that derive, on a sample basis, the income statements, balance sheets, etc. for a number of broad (essentially SIC 2 digit) industry groups. These data have applications in forecasting using ratio models (see Chapter 4). Further useful data for forecasting with ratio models are the *Price Index Numbers for Current Cost Accounting,* published by the Central Statistical Office, which provides a basis for the prediction of future raw material costs, etc.

UK LOCAL GOVERNMENT

Various statistical data relevant to forecasting for local and regional government in the UK are to be found in Department of the Environment publications and those of CIPFA (The Chartered Institute of Public Finance and Accounting).

Some local and regional authorities provide information on aspects of the local economy that are of interest to the forecaster. Unfortunately, there is much variation between one authority and another, so that it is only possible to remind the forecaster that here is a potential data source that should not be overlooked.

OTHER GOVERNMENTS

Most western governments provide similar types of statistical information to that published by the UK government. These are of obvious interest to the forecaster in a multinational or for export forecasting purposes. Though large specialist, e.g. university, libraries will often carry such statistics for countries such as the USA and Common Market countries, a convenient source of such data is very often the commercial attaché of the country concerned.

OFFICIAL BODIES

Some official bodies in the UK are important sources of data for more specialized forecasting purposes. Thus the individual Economic Development Councils of the National Economic Development Office publish many data about their industries that are not readily available elsewhere. Other bodies such as the World Bureau of Metal Statistics can provide data on an international basis.

Many international bodies supply important data for the purposes of the forecaster. The United Nations *Yearbook of International Statistics,* which gives details of trade by commodity between individual member countries is one such source. Similarly the Organization for Economic Cooperation and Development (OECD) collects data on, for example, the foreign trade of member countries (The OECD *Monthly Statistics of Foreign Trade*) and produces independent macroeconomic forecasts for member countries (The OECD *Economic Outlook*). The International Monetary Fund's *International Financial Statistics* again provides important data for the forecasting of balance of payments and related items.

TRADE ASSOCIATIONS

Most major industries have trade associations. These are often in a position to collect data from their members that could not easily be gathered by an individual member. Sometimes this information is published by the trade association concerned, e.g. the *Forecasts of Advertising Expenditure* published by the Advertising Association. Perhaps the best known such source is the quarterly survey conducted by the Confederation of British Industry of the order books, investment intentions, etc. of their members. Where the data are not published it is sometimes possible to gain access to them, if the forecaster can demonstrate that there is no threat to confidentiality.

THE PRESS

The financial press is an important source of data for many forecasting purposes. Information on commodity prices and closing stock prices, for instance, are given in the *Financial Times* along with many other useful series (see *The Guide to FT Statistics*).

There are many different trade journals that produce information indispensable to the forecaster interested in the industries they cover. Thus the *Building Societies' Gazette* provides a large number of series related to house purchase; *Chemical Age International* carries regular surveys of major chemical plant projects being undertaken around the world, etc.

MULTICLIENT STUDIES

Multiclient studies represent a different form of secondary data providing information not available from other sources. Such studies are carried out by one organization, very often a market research agency, on behalf of a number of clients. Sometimes the group of clients is a restricted one, e.g. companies in the same industry. More often it is possible for any organization to purchase the data from the study. Though the fee is typically very high by comparison with the costs of other types of secondary data, such data are still much cheaper than those collected solely for one organization.

One such type of study is the detailed market research survey, for example those produced by the US Agency Frost and Sullivan for various industry markets. Regular industry audits of product purchases by brand (see Chapter 8) or of advertisement recall represent another type of multiclient study of obvious use to the market forecaster, as do the detailed advertising expenditure statistics provided by Media Expenditure Analysis Ltd.

ECONOMETRIC MODELS

Several models of the UK economy are of particular use to those concerned with forecasting using econometric models for which forecasts of future macroeconomic variables are often needed as inputs (see Chapters 5 and 6). Most of the models concerned are associated with academic institutions. Perhaps the best known of these is the London Business School Model. However, there are also macroeconomic forecasts produced by the University of Liverpool Research Group, The Henley Centre for Forecasting and the Cambridge Economic Policy Group. Further models of this type are that of the National Institute for Economic and Social Research and the UK Treasury Model. This latter model has been made available for several years to groups of individuals (e.g. the ITEM Club) who wish to provide alternative forecasts to those of the government based on different assumptions about export growth, etc. to those employed by the Treasury to derive government forecasts.

All these models deal with the macroeconomy and forecast only broad aggregates, e.g. consumer expenditures. A further model that operates on a very different basis is that provided by Cambridge Econometrics. This is an input/output model (see Chapter 4) which can provide much more detailed forecasts of the sales of individual industries. It is also particularly suited to long term econometric forecasts extending 10–20 years into the future, since it can incorporate assumptions about changes to the structure of the economy as time progresses.

COMMERCIAL DATABASES

Commercial databases represent the full span of secondary data sources. A typical commercial database operator will carry databases from many information providers ranging from government sources through to multiclient studies. These databases are rarely unique. They usually have a printed counterpart. Indeed, the databases are often produced as a by-product of publishing the printed source. Nevertheless, they are generally much more convenient to the forecaster than the corresponding printed material and, as the number of such commercial databases grows, this will become even more true. Some major classifications of data of interest for forecasting are listed below.

Macroeconomic forecasts

Macroeconomic forecasts are available through commercial database operators for other countries. Forecasts for the US economy are available, for instance, from the UK computer bureau SIA (which carries forecasts derived from the Wharton Model of the US economy) and from the US DIALOG system, which carries forecasts compiled from a variety of sources produced by PREDICASTS INC. Another useful set of data produced by PREDICASTS is the series of international data and forecasts that covers a number of countries.

Financial databases

Forecasters can use commercial computer databases for a variety of purposes from financial modelling through to prediction of company bankruptcies. Prominent ones in the UK are: EXSTAT and DATASTREAM, both of which provide more or less complete coverage of the quantitative information of companies' accounts listed on the London Stock Exchange. A number of bureaux, e.g. SIA and DATASTREAM, have information on foreign currency quotations and the prices of major commodities. Data drawn from the accounts of smaller, non-listed UK companies are available through the Inter Company Comparisons database on the DIALOG system in the USA. Dun and Bradstreet maintain systems in several countries that cover the payments records of individual companies that are also of interest to the forecaster.

A very different set of data, useful for forecasting in the context of financial markets, is provided by the London Business School. Particularly notable are the data on 'beta coefficients' that are used in forecasting future share values.

Other databases

Other commercially available databases have information of use for particular forecasting purposes. Company directories, e.g. *Dun's Market Identifiers,* available on DIALOG are, for instance, a good source of information on the size of markets and the importance of the main companies operating in those markets. For technological forecasting (see Chapters 9 and 10) databases of patents can often yield valuable information. Finally, bibliographic reference sources can be a valuable aid in finding sources of information on particular topics of interest to the forecaster, ranging from individual markets to applications of specific forecasting techniques.

USES OF DATA IN FORECASTING MODELS

There are two distinct types of managerial forecasting model in which past experience is used as an indicator of the future, and these may be termed *causal* models and *non-causal* models. Non-causal models simply extrapolate past history on the forecast variable, and examples of such models are given in Chapter 3 (time series models) and Chapter 9 (trend analysis). The data required for these models merely consist of a series of historical observations on the variable to be forecast. In general, the more data available, the more accurate the forecasts will be, although if the pattern of data on the forecast variable changes substantially over time, more accurate predictions may be obtained by using only the more recent observations.

The causal model approach to managerial forecasting attempts to discover those variables which appear to have influenced the forecast variable in the past, and then estimates the quantitative relationship between the causal and forecast variables. Future values of the forecast variable are then obtained by using forecasts of the causal variables in conjunction with the estimated relationship. Such models are considered in Chapter 5 (regression analysis) and Chapter 6 (extensions of regression). Data requirements for causal models comprise historical series of observations on each of the causal variables in addition to the forecast variable, and also future values of the causal variables. For a causal model to be of use for forecasting purposes, it must be possible to predict future values of the causal variables relatively easily. In general, the more observations, the more accurate the forecasts will be, although if a *very* long time period is considered there may be a change in the structure of the relationship between the causal and forecast variables.

QUALITY OF DATA

The accuracy of a forecast is influenced by the quality of the data used in preparing it. Hence, it is important that the forecaster is aware of the errors which may arise in the collection of data for a forecasting situation. Measurement errors occur during the data collection and processing phases resulting in inaccurate information being used. For example, data may be suppressed or falsified by survey respondents, incorrect answers may be given on account of misunderstanding what is required in a questionnaire, or key punching errors may occur.

In those forecasting situations involving published sources of data, the degree of accuracy of the data implied by the level of reporting may be greatly exaggerated. Market sales of a product may be reported to the nearest £10,000, even though the error range for the value of the variable suggests that it might be overstated or understated by as much as £1 million. The forecaster needs to be aware of the level of accuracy of the data used to prepare the forecast in order to assess its value. In addition to the prediction error resulting from the application of a particular forecasting technique, even more errors may be present associated with the sources of data being used.

INFLATION ADJUSTMENT

Data are often recorded in terms of current prices and thus real changes in the series are masked by the effects of inflation. The impact of changing price levels may be eliminated by transforming such data into constant prices using an appropriate deflator index, for example the GNP deflator, the Retail Price Index (RPI) or some component of the RPI. By converting current price data into constant price data, a series is obtained which is not affected by inflation and is therefore more appropriate for use in forecasting models.

The effect of correcting a time series to eliminate inflationary movements may be seen by examining Figures 2.1 and 2.2. Figure 2.1 shows an uncorrected series for orders over a six-year period, whereas Figure 2.2 shows the series after adjusting for the effects of inflation. Figure 2.1 suggests that there has been an upward trend in orders over the period and that the variability of orders has been increasing, whereas Figure 2.2 shows clearly that the mean and variance of the time series are stationary. We shall use the inflation adjusted series in Chapter 3 (series C), since it appears markedly more regular than the raw series.

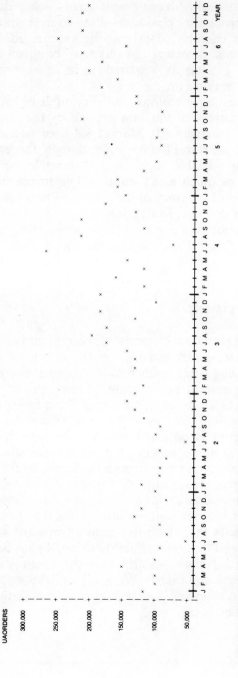

Figure 2.1 Time series unadjusted for inflation

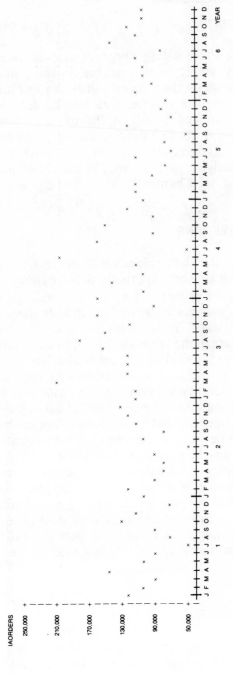

Figure 2.2 Time series adjusted for inflation

MISSING DATA POINTS

Data collected for forecasting purposes may be incomplete: some observations may simply be unavailable. In these situations it may be necessary to estimate the missing values as some forecasting techniques cannot be applied to series with missing data points. Various methods can be applied to fill in the missing values. The most common approach is to use a moving average estimate (see Chapter 3). Alternatively decomposition techniques, which break the series down into its underlying patterns, may be used to estimate the missing data points (again, see Chapter 3).

OUTLYING OBSERVATIONS

Outliers are particular data values which are in some sense extreme; they are cases which the hypothesized forecasting model fails to fit, while the model is satisfactory for the bulk of the data. The unusual events which can cause outliers include the weather, strikes, breakdowns and wars. Such events are not expected to recur or to influence the data in the same way again, so by eliminating outlying observations a more typical data series is obtained.

Outliers may be picked out by examining the estimation error associated with each observation used in estimating the forecasting model, that is the difference between the actual value of the forecast variable and the value yielded by the forecasting model. If an abnormally large absolute value is obtained for the estimation error, then the observation may be regarded as an outlier. To justify the elimination of such freak observations, an attempt should be made to explain the occurrence of the extreme values. The forecasting model is then re-estimated excluding the outlying observation(s). If, however, forecasting techniques are being used which cannot be applied to series with missing data points, the outlying observations need to be replaced by more suitable values (see the previous section) before re-estimation takes place.

AGGREGATION OF DATA

Raw data are frequently recorded at various levels of detail and over varying periods of time. The values can be aggregated (or accumulated) to give the level of detail or periodicity required for the forecasts.

The raw data may be classified by brand name within a product group, but interest may centre on forecasts by product group only. Alternatively, the data may be collected on a quarterly basis, but the forecasts may only be required on an annual basis. In such situations, the nature of the business and the forecaster's understanding of the data will determine whether the raw data should be aggregated first and then forecasts derived or forecasts created from the raw data and then aggregated.

When using a forecasting technique which requires data on more than just one variable (such as regression analysis), aggregation across time may be necessary to match data of different frequencies. For example, in order to estimate a regression model where the data on some variables are available quarterly but on others only annually, the quarterly figures can be added up to obtain annual figures.

TRADING DAY ADJUSTMENTS (CALENDAR EFFECTS)

Different months have different numbers of working days and therefore it may be necessary to normalize monthly or quarterly data to adjust for the actual number of trading days included in each time period. Otherwise, the forecasting technique selected may give misleading results.

To make a trading day adjustment data are collected on the number of working days which fall in each period covered by the series of observations. The average number of working days in a time period is then calculated, and the raw data are adjusted to reflect the values that would have occurred if the time period had contained the average number of trading days. This adjusted series is used to estimate the forecasting model.

If, say, monthly sales data are required to be normalized for different numbers of working days, the following equation may be used:

$$NS_i = \frac{S_i}{WD_i/AWD}; \ i = 1 \text{ (January)},$$
$$2 \text{ (February)}, \ldots, 12 \text{ (December)} \tag{2.1}$$

where

NS_i is normalized sales for month i;
S_i is actual sales for month i;
WD_i is the number of working days in month i;
AWD is the average number of working days per month
$= \sum_{i=1}^{12} WD_i/12$.

For example, if actual sales in January total 1,000, there are 20 working days in January and the average number of working days per month is 21, then trading day adjusted sales in January are given by substituting into equation (2.1) as follows:

$$NS_i = \frac{1,000}{20/21}$$
$$= 1,050$$

In order to obtain a forecast of the actual series, it is necessary to adjust the forecast normalized series by multiplying by WD_i/AWD.

The impact of trading day adjustments on a time series may be seen clearly in Figures 2.3 and 2.4. An uncorrected output series over a two-year period is shown in Figure 2.3 and displays little discernible pattern. When this series is corrected for trading days a much clearer data pattern emerges as shown in Figure 2.4. Correction appears well worthwhile.

ELIMINATION OF TRENDS BY DIFFERENCING

Often the data series encountered in business forecasting situations exhibit trends in the mean level. However, many time series models assume stationarity, and therefore it is necessary first to remove any non-stationarity. Furthermore, where a trend is present in a data series, it can obscure the presence of a seasonal pattern. It is therefore important to remove the trend and then examine the de-trended or stationary series to identify any seasonality.

In order to recognize the presence of non-stationarity in a data series the autocorrelation coefficient should be analysed. The auto-correlation coefficient describes the association among values of the

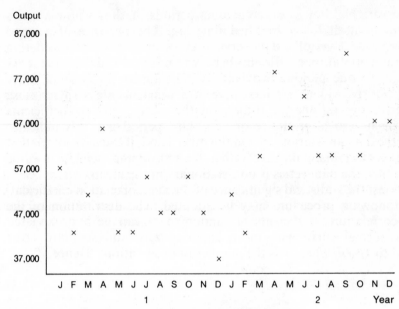

Figure 2.3   Time series unadjusted for trading days

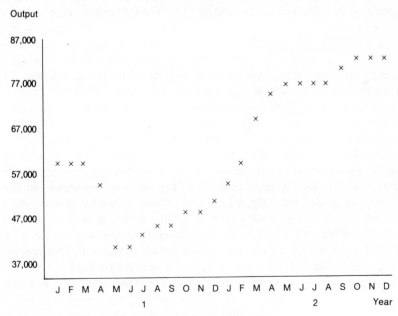

Figure 2.4   Time series adjusted for trading days

same variable, but at different time periods; it shows how a series relates to itself for a specified time lag. The presence of a trend in the mean level of a data series may be examined by considering the autocorrelation coefficients between this series and the same series lagged by one period, two periods, and so on. In general, fairly high positive values are indicative of a trend, whereas values close to zero show stationarity. If therefore the autocorrelation coefficients approach zero after the second or third period lag, this indicates that the data are stationary. On the other hand, if the autocorrelation coefficients remain positive rather than dropping quickly towards zero, then the data series is non-stationary in the mean.

To test the statistical significance of the autocorrelation coefficient, the following procedure may be adopted. The distribution of the autocorrelation coefficients of random data can be approximated by a normal curve with mean equal to zero and standard error equal to $1/\sqrt{n}$, where n is the number of observations. Hence, if

$$|r| > 1.96/\sqrt{n} \tag{2.2}$$

where $|\ |$ denotes absolute value and r is the calculated value of the autocorrelation coefficient, then the autocorrelation coefficient is significantly different from zero at the 5 per cent level. If

$$|r| \leqslant 1.96/\sqrt{n} \tag{2.3}$$

then the autocorrelation coefficient is not statistically significant.

A time series for which the autocorrelation coefficients remain positive and are significantly different from zero at the 5 per cent level for several time periods should be regarded as non-stationary in the mean. A time series for which the autocorrelation coefficients are close to zero after the second or third period lag should be regarded as stationary in the mean.

The most frequently used procedure for eliminating trends in the mean is that of differencing, which consists of subtracting successive values of a series from each other. If a time series of sales is subject to a linear trend, this series can be rendered stationary by forming a second time series which comprises first (regular) differences of the original series. If Y_t, $t = 1, 2, \ldots, n$ represents sales in period t, then the series representing first differences of sales, Z_t, is given by

$$Z_t = Y_t - Y_{t-1}; t = 2, 3, \ldots, n \tag{2.4}$$

Consider the following example:

t	Y_t	$Z_t = Y_t - Y_{t-1}$
1	3	—
2	5	2
3	7	2
4	9	2
5	11	2
6	13	2
7	15	2

Clearly the linear trend in the original series, Y_t, has been removed in the new series, Z_t.

If a time series is subject to a quadratic trend, this series can be rendered stationary by forming a new time series which comprises second differences of the original series, denoted W_t, where

$$W_t = Z_t - Z_{t-1}; t = 3, 4, \ldots, n \tag{2.5}$$

This may be rewritten as

$$\begin{aligned} W_t &= (Y_t - Y_{t-1}) - (Y_{t-1} - Y_{t-2}) \\ &= Y_t - 2Y_{t-1} + Y_{t-2}; t = 3, 4, \ldots, n \end{aligned} \tag{2.6}$$

Consider the following example:

t	Y_t	$Z_t = Y_t - Y_{t-1}$	$W_t = Z_t - Z_{t-1}$
1	1	—	—
2	4	3	·—
3	9	5	2
4	16	7	2
5	25	9	2
6	36	11	2
7	49	13	2

Hence, the quadratic trend in the original series, Y_t, has been removed in the new series, W_t.

In practice, if we have a time series which is non-stationary in the mean, first differences should be taken. If the resulting series is still non-stationary, then second differences should be taken. In almost all practical situations, first or second differences will remove any trends in the mean.

Computer forecasting packages such as ORION incorporate the facility for performing an autocorrelation analysis of a data series. The autocorrelation coefficients are output for a set of time lags together with the corresponding significance limits. In addition, such programs readily permit a series to be differenced.

SEASONALITY

Seasonality in a data series may be identified using autocorrelation analysis. However, where a trend is present in a data series, this can obscure the presence of a seasonal pattern in the autocorrelations. It is therefore necessary first to remove any non-stationarity in the series by regular differencing (see previous section) and then examine the autocorrelations of the de-trended series to identify any seasonality.

If data are recorded at monthly or quarterly intervals, it is likely that they will exhibit seasonal fluctuations; the average in some months (quarters) will be up compared with the overall monthly (quarterly) average, and in some months (quarters) it will be down. For example, sales of consumer goods and services such as clothes, cars and holidays are subject to seasonal variations.

In order to ascertain whether there is a seasonal pattern in the data series, it is necessary to calculate the autocorrelation coefficient (see the previous section) between the (stationary) series and the same series lagged by the number of time periods in a year – for monthly data the lag is 12, and for quarterly data the lag is 4. A fairly high positive value for the autocorrelation coefficient indicates a seasonal pattern, whereas a value close to zero shows the absence of seasonal fluctuations. If the positive autocorrelation coefficient is significantly different from zero at the 5 per cent level, then the data series should be regarded as subject to seasonality, that is, there is a strong relationship among observations drawn from the same month (quarter), but different years. It is also likely that for monthly data the autocorrelation coefficient with a lag of 24 periods will take a fairly high positive value and be statistically significant, and for quarterly data the autocorrelation coefficient with a lag of 8 periods will behave similarly.

If a time series does exhibit seasonal fluctuations various courses of action are possible. If one wishes to eliminate the seasonal component, this may be achieved by seasonal differencing; for monthly (quarterly) data, the value of a series in a given month (quarter) has subtracted from it the value of the series in the same month (quarter) in the previous year. First order seasonal differencing of this nature should convert a time series which is non-stationary with regard to its seasonal component into a stationary series. Thus if Y_t, $t = 1, 2, \ldots, n$ represents sales in month t, then the series representing first seasonal differences of sales, R_t, is given by

$$R_t = Y_t - Y_{t-12}; t = 13, \ldots, n \qquad (2.7)$$

If autocorrelation analysis of the series R_t, $t = 13, \ldots, n$, shows that seasonality is still present, then second order seasonal differencing may be used to yield stationarity in the seasonal component. Thus

$$S_t = R_t - R_{t-12}; t = 25, \ldots, n \qquad (2.8)$$

where S_t is the series representing second seasonal differences of sales.

There are various alternative methods of seasonal adjustment. Seasonality in data series used in regression models can be catered for by the use of dummy variables which measure the seasonal effects (see the relevant section in Chapter 6). Time series forecasting methods applicable to data exhibiting seasonality are discussed in the Methods section in Chapter 3; here decomposition methods are used to divide the basic underlying pattern of a data series into trend, seasonal, random and possibly cyclical components. Knowledge regarding the seasonal component may be useful to a manager since it enables him to forecast the fluctuations resulting from seasonal causes.

LOGARITHMIC TRANSFORMATIONS

Some time series encountered in managerial forecasting are non-stationary in the variance. In such cases, the variability of the time series usually increases as the mean of the time series increases and at approximately the same rate, that is, the standard deviation is proportional to the mean. The presence of non-stationarity in the variance of a time series may be recognized by plotting the observations against time. Visual inspection should give some indication as to whether the variance increases with the mean, that is, whether the observations become more spread out as the mean increases. A somewhat more sophisticated method for detecting non-stationarity in the variance is to divide the observed time series into subsets of, say, 12 observations for monthly data series or four observations for quarterly data series, and calculate the mean and standard deviation of each subset. The standard deviation is then plotted against the mean for each subset of the time series. If a random scatter about a horizontal straight line is obtained, this indicates that the standard deviation is independent of the mean, that is the time series is stationary in the variance (see Figure 2.5). If a random scatter about an upward sloping straight line passing through the origin is obtained, this shows that the standard deviation is proportional to the mean, that is the time series is non-stationary in the variance (see Figure 2.6).

A data series which exhibits this latter characteristic may be rendered stationary in the variance by applying the logarithmic transformation. If the original time series for which the standard deviation is proportional to the mean is denoted by Y_t, then the series representing the logarithmic transformation of this series is given by Z_t, where

$$Z_t = \log_e Y_t \tag{2.9}$$

where $\log_e$ represents natural logarithms. Since it does not matter what base is used for the logarithms as long as we are consistent an equally valid logarithmic transformation is obtained by using logarithms to the base 10, i.e.

$$Z_t = \log_{10} Y_t \tag{2.10}$$

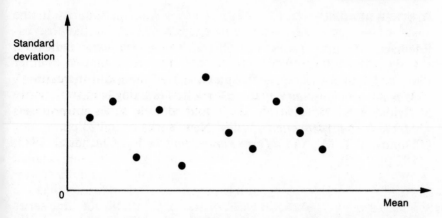

Figure 2.5   Plot of standard deviation against mean for stationary series

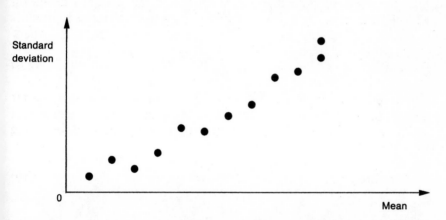

Figure 2.6   Plot of standard deviation against mean for non-stationary series

FURTHER READING

Edelhart, M. and Davies, O., OMNI *Online Database Directory,* Collier Macmillan, 1983.

Eley, P. J. and Sharp, J. A., 'Using On-Line Financial Information', *Management Accounting,* vol. 63, no. 1, 1985, pp. 34–36.

Makridakis, S., Wheelwright, S. C. and McGee, V. E., *Forecasting: Methods and Applications,* Wiley, New York, 1983, 923 pp.

O'Donovan, T. M., *Short Term Forecasting,* Wiley, Chichester, 1983, 282 pp.

3 Time series models

The models dealt with in this chapter are those in which forecasts of future values of a variable are based on the time series' own past values. More strictly we are concerned with single (or univariate) time series models. By a time series we mean a sequence of values of a variable, $x_1, x_2 \ldots x_t$ representing its values at consecutive equally spaced points in time, e.g. weeks, months, etc.

Time series forecasts are produced by applying one or more models to the time series. The models may vary greatly in sophistication. Most, though, involve the two processes described in Chapter 1: the fitting of the model to the time series data and the use of the model thus derived to produce forecasts. Rarely is it possible to justify time series models on the basis of theory. The reasons for their use are essentially pragmatic: they often generate acceptable forecasts at low cost. In practice, the focus in appraising such methods is normally on whether they are capable of meeting the manager's accuracy requirements. It is assumed that readers would not have arrived at this point had not the decision table of Chapter 1 indicated that some at least of their forecasting needs might be met by time series methods.

TYPICAL APPLICATIONS OF TIME SERIES MODELS

Time series models are typically used where there is a large number of forecasts to be produced and/or the expertise required for more sophisticated methods is lacking. They are frequently used for producing operational forecasts, e.g. for forecasting materials requirements. Essentially, they can be applied wherever the past demand series contains useful information about future values. They are, therefore, by no means confined to short term forecasting. They can, for example, often be very successful at predicting macroeconomic variables 12–18 months ahead because the economy takes a long time to adapt to changes in government policy or in the environment. Again in the published results of forecasting competitions, which have concentrated on time series methods, they have proved able, in many cases, to forecast up to five years ahead with mean percentage errors of no more than 20 per cent. Because such methods are cheap and easy to apply they are also well suited to providing forecasts for the use of other types of more complex forecasting model. This is particularly true in the case of the ratio models described in Chapter 4.

DATA CONSIDERATIONS IN TIME SERIES MODELLING

Time series methods apply to 'ideal' time series where the underlying behaviour is regular and, therefore, can be predicted – and where we have values at regular intervals, e.g. weekly or monthly.

In practice, real time series depart from these ideal properties in a variety of ways. It is therefore often necessary to subject the data to preliminary processing as discussed in Chapter 2.

CHOOSING A TIME SERIES METHOD

With most data series more than one time series method may give satisfactory forecasts. In general, we have to go through a two-stage process in which we establish which methods may be suitable and then determine which is likely to prove most satisfactory. The first stage is best carried out using the decision table provided at the end of the chapter. The second stage involves a number of considerations that will be illustrated by examples. The factors affecting choice of a time series method have already been encountered in Chapter 1. Here we consider more closely how they relate to choosing between time series methods.

The data pattern

In Chapter 1 we introduced seven common data patterns that categorize the nature of the time series. These were: fluctuation about an underlying constant value; steps in the data; a linear trend in the data; a non-linear trend; saturation; a cycle and, in particular, a seasonal cycle; infrequent events.

Some of these patterns may be combined. Thus, a seasonal cycle is often superimposed on any one of the previous patterns. The pattern in the data affects the choice of applicable time series methods both directly and indirectly. Some techniques are not suitable for certain patterns. Single exponential smoothing, for example, should not be used on data that contain a trend. They may, therefore, have the indirect effect of requiring that we transform the data in some way before applying our technique to it. Thus we can remove the trend from the data by differencing and then apply single exponential smoothing. More fundamentally, where we are dealing with events that occur only very infrequently, e.g. major plant breakdowns, we need to transform the data by working with the time interval between breakdowns rather than the frequency of breakdown. If, for example, our breakdowns occur on Day 5, Day 95, Day 144, Day 293, etc., our transformed data become: 90, 49, 149, etc.

Length of series

Any specific data series can be fitted as closely as we wish by using a suitably complex model. As discussed in Chapter 1, however, this is not a sensible way to proceed. Simple (parsimonious) models perform better and are much more robust. The implication of this is that the fewer data points we have, the simpler a time series model we must use. In certain applications such as new product forecasting this may mean that, while we still have only a few data points, we should use a simple method and, perhaps, swap to a more complex one later. Conversely, major discontinuities may occur in a series because of some change in the environment. In that case it may make sense to ignore all save the most recent periods of data, since past ones are no longer representative.

Frequency of data collection

Time series data are always collected on a periodic basis. The length of the time period affects what cycles can be detected in the data. Obviously, if data are collected monthly it is not possible to detect variations within the month. In applications such as supermarket sales forecasting, for instance, there are substantial cycles within the week as well as over the year. If such short term cycles are to be built into the forecast the time period over which the data are collected must be suitably short.

Forecast horizon

How far ahead we wish to forecast can also affect the choice of forecast model. Some models that work well when forecasting only one or two periods ahead lack robustness when used for longer time horizons. Under those circumstances, it will usually be better to employ forecast models that are unlikely to give 'peculiar' forecasts.

Model fitting, validation and use

Most of the models to be examined involve the fitting of the model to the past history of the time series. This is done by adjusting the model to give the best possible fit to the data. Often a by-product of the model-fitting process is an estimate of the range within which the true value will lie. As pointed out in Chapter 1, this usually gives an optimistic picture of the accuracy of the forecast. It is also necessary to form an impression of the reliability of the forecast. This can be done in two ways. One is simply to examine how the forecasts are affected by a slight change in the assumptions. If, for example, when we omit the last data point from the time series, the model and the forecasts produced by it are drastically changed, this lack of stability in the model indicates that the forecasts are likely to be unreliable in practice.

An alternative approach which, where possible, should always be applied is the notion of holding back the last few values of the time series to give a test of the forecast as described in Chapter 1. The number of values held back should be related to the time horizon of the forecasts. This will vary markedly from one application to another. For forecasting day to day variations in labour requirements or cash flow the forecast horizon would probably be between a week and a month. For production planning purposes it might vary, depending on the degree of automation of the processes involved, from a week or a month in a process industry to as much as 12 months ahead in heavy engineering fabrication. In planning capital investment for capacity expansion time horizons may well be several years. Here we have tried to use realistic time horizons for the series being forecast. It should be noted, however, that these would not be appropriate in every application and that a different choice of forecast horizon might well suggest a different choice of forecast model.

Hold back (*ex ante*) tests of forecasting ability are intended to give a practical feel for how well a particular time series method works with a particular time series. Sometimes, however, the tests can be somewhat misleading. This is particularly the case for models that are applied to differenced data (see Chapter 2 for a definition of differencing). With such series the forecasting ability of the method may depend critically on the point from which forecasting is begun. For such series it is, therefore, wise to supplement the *ex ante* tests with robustness tests to establish that the forecasting ability of the method is little affected if one or two points are dropped from the end of the data series.

Some time series methods are relatively expensive to re-estimate each time a new data point becomes available. For these it is useful to be able to determine when a model should be re-estimated and when it is safe to continue using an existing model without re-estimation. Examples will be given of the various approaches to assessing forecast error.

In order to test our forecast model or, more importantly, to employ it, we must be able to generate forecasts from it. This is not always straightforward, especially if we wish to forecast several periods ahead, as will be seen in some examples.

EXAMPLE TIME SERIES

Since the choice of time series method and possibly the transformations required are affected by the factors discussed above, there can be no single best forecasting method. The methods will be illustrated on a number of time series with different characteristics so that some idea can be gained of their weaknesses and strengths; where they will work well and where they are likely to work badly.

We shall use four data series. Their lengths range from 34 to 72 data points. Longer data series are surprisingly uncommon in most areas of business outside of financial and commodity markets. They are, therefore, not atypical as far as length goes. Furthermore, other things being equal, longer series are easier to forecast so their comparative shortness probably aids the comparison of different forecasting methods. The actual data values for these series are given in Appendices 3.1–3.4. Here we restrict ourselves to presenting the series in graphical form, since this is an indispensable step in identifying patterns in the data and deciding likely techniques and transformations to apply. A brief description of each is given below along with an indication of which aspects of the time series will be explored here.

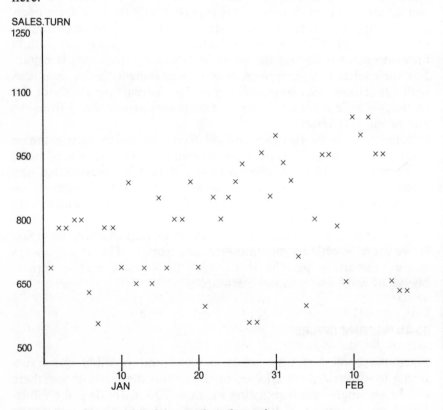

Figure 3.1   Time series A – petrol station sales

Series A – petrol station sales

This series, depicted in Figure 3.1, gives 48 consecutive days' sales of a petrol station open seven days per week. The data series (SALES.TURN), which starts on 1 January, is tabulated in Appendix 3.1. The effects of annual seasonality have been removed from the daily data, by dividing by the appropriate annual seasonal index determined from a weekly model, allowing better identification of the weekly cycle, which Figure 3.1 shows is a marked feature in this case. It will also be noticed that there seems to be little evidence of annual variation over the time span of the data. The removal of seasonal effects appears to have been fairly successful.

Two different forecasting problems will be examined using this series: forecasting sales for the week 16–22 January based on a very short data series extending to either 13 or 15 January; forecasting sales for the first 17 days of February based on data for January.

Series B – sales of a photocopying agency

Figure 3.2 gives 52 consecutive months of sales (SALES) for an agency providing photocopying services, again starting in January of year 1. Here the most obvious features are the strong annual seasonality and a strong upward trend. These data are tabulated in Appendix 3.2.

This series will be used to examine the ability of various forecasting models to forecast the last 12 months of the series based on the first 40 months.

Series C – engineering company orders

Figure 3.3 gives the orders at current prices received by an engineering company over a 72-month period adjusted for the effects of inflation. This series (IAORDERS) is of interest because it shows quite wide fluctuations, about a roughly constant level, without any very obvious pattern. It is tabulated in Appendix 3.3.

The focus for this time series will be on forecasting orders for year 6 based on data for the first five years' sales. This is a difficult series to forecast but some methods are distinctly better than others.

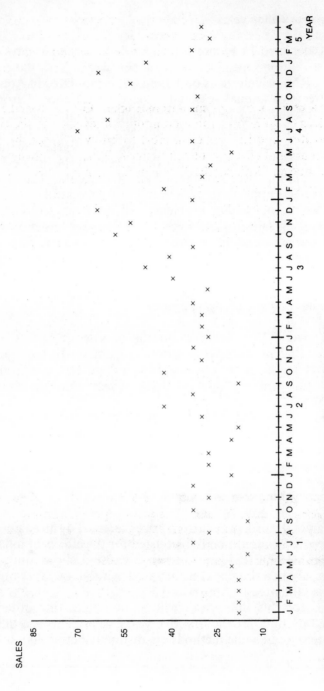

Figure 3.2   Time series B – sales of a photocopying agency

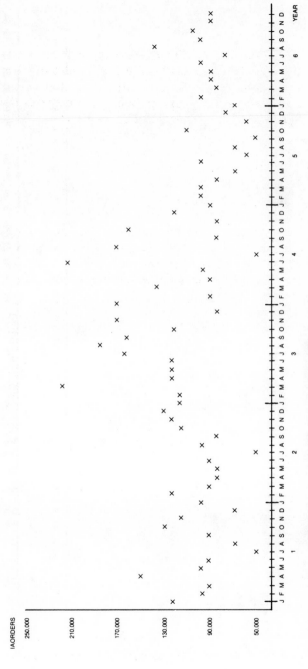

Figure 3.3 Time series C – engineering company orders

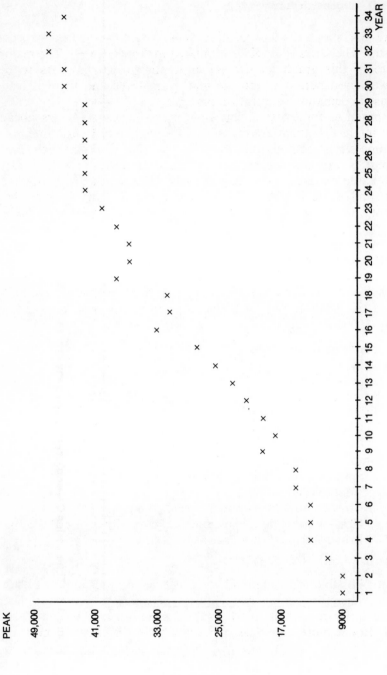

Figure 3.4   Time series D – process industry output

Series D – process industry output

Figure 3.4 shows 34 consecutive years of output for a process industry. The series (PEAK) is tabulated in Appendix 3.4. The major feature of this graph is that initial strong growth appears to be followed by a period where the market matures and there is little increase in demand: a saturation pattern.

In practice, forecasts of this time series up to six years ahead are of interest. It therefore provides an opportunity to examine how well time series methods can work for this type of data series. Two different 6-year ahead forecasts will be examined: those for years 21–26 based on data up to year 20 when there was a strong upward trend; and those for years 29–34 where growth was almost non-existent.

THE METHODS EXAMINED

We shall not attempt to examine every type of time series method. Instead, we shall confine ourselves to commonly used ones. They are:

1 Naive methods
    Naive
    Seasonal naive
2 Moving average
3 Decomposition methods
    Classical decomposition
    Census XII
4 Smoothing methods
    Single exponential smoothing;
    Adaptive smoothing;
    Brown's double exponential smoothing;
    Holt–Winters double exponential smoothing;
    Brown's triple exponential smoothing.
5 Autoregressive methods.

It is not possible to examine every conceivable application of each method. Therefore, unless explicitly noted, methods will be applied to time series for which they would normally be considered well suited. For a more complete picture of where individual methods can be used the reader is referred to the decision table at the end of this chapter.

Naive methods

The basic naive model. This assumes that the next period's value of the time series is the same as this period's. In equation form the forecast value of x_{t+1}, which we denote by $\hat{x}_{t+1}$ (it is customary in the forecasting literature to denote estimates by 'hats'), is given by:

$$\hat{x}_{t+1} = x_t \tag{3.1}$$

More generally, the model takes the form:

$$\hat{x}_{t+3} = \hat{x}_{t+2} = \hat{x}_{t+1} = x_t \tag{3.2}$$

The basic naive model often works well for series without seasonality or trend. The last few periods of series D meet that condition. Some idea of how useful the basic naive model is likely to be in practice may be gained by forecasting the values for periods 31–34 on the basis of the value for year 30 (42110). The forecast and corresponding actuals are given in Table 3.1.

Table 3.1
Forecast and corresponding actuals

Year	31	32	33	34
Forecast	42110	42110	42110	42110
Actual	42800	44100	44230	42600

The maximum error (year 34) is about 4.8 per cent. This would certainly be acceptable for many forecasting purposes. It demonstrates why naive forecasts are often used as a yardstick to assess whether the use of more complex time series methods is justified.

Seasonal naive model. This is a variant on the basic naive model suitable for seasonal series having a season of length s time periods. It takes as a forecast of $x(t)$ the value for the corresponding period last season. More generally the model takes the form:

$$\hat{x}_{t+2s} = \hat{x}_{t+s} = \hat{x}_t = x_{t-s} \text{ etc.} \tag{3.3}$$

This model can be conveniently illustrated with series A, which contains a seven-day seasonal cycle. In accordance with the way most forecasting packages use the term 'seasonality', we shall use it to mean any regular cycle that can be identified with some external cause; in this case, variations in driving activity across the week. Here:

$$\hat{x}_t = x_{t-7} \tag{3.4}$$

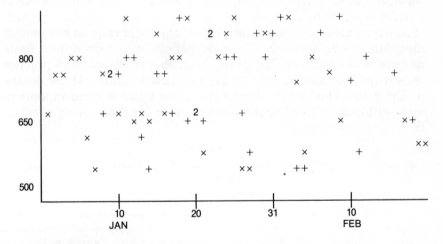

× = SALES TURN (actual)
+ = NAIVE7 (Seasonal naive forecast)
2 = Actual and forecast coincide

Figure 3.5   Seasonal naive model – series A

Figure 3.5 shows actual values against the forecast derived from the previous week's actual, i.e. that could have been made up to seven days in advance. The graph shows that the forecasts are reasonable over much of January but that they deteriorate towards the end of the month. The seasonal naive model is obviously not well suited to these latter data points.

The moving average forecast

For seasonal data with seasonality of s periods, a moving average s periods long is free of seasonal effects. The moving average forecast for periods $t + 1$, $t + 2$, etc. is given by:

$$\hat{x}_{t+2} = \hat{x}_{t+1} = [x_t + x_{t-1} \ldots + x_{t-s+1}]/s \tag{3.5}$$

Such a forecast is of a somewhat different nature from others derived by time series methods, since it basically attempts to estimate the non-seasonal portion of the time series. Such forecasts can be useful, for instance, in determining whether a company has sufficient productive capacity to cope with the average over the year of a highly seasonal demand. The use of moving average forecasts is conveniently illustrated using series B. The first period for which a 12-month moving average can be computed is December of year 1. We have chosen to illustrate the moving average values for year 2, as shown in Table 3.2. This clearly demonstrates the upward trend in annual sales with only May showing a lower value for the moving average than the previous month.

Table 3.2
Moving average values for year 2

Jan	Feb	Mar	Apr	May	Jun	Jul	Aug	Sep	Oct	Nov	Dec
22.3	22.9	23.5	23.8	23.4	24.5	25.3	25.8	26.2	27.0	27.2	27.3

Decomposition methods

These are amongst the oldest forecasting methods in use. They have a strong intuitive appeal because of the way they break down the data series into a number of components that make sense to managers.

Classical decomposition. The starting point of the classical decomposition approach is that the observation of the time series at period t, x_t, can be represented as:

$$x_t = T_t \times S_t \times I_t \tag{3.6}$$

where

T represents the trend value;
S represents the seasonal component;
I represents the irregular (unpredictable) component;
t represents the time period.

Some authors add an additional longer term cycle component to the classical decomposition model. From a theoretical standpoint, such cycles can rarely be justified. Furthermore, there are rarely enough data (three cycles or more) to enable such cycles to be detected anyway. For these reasons this term has been omitted from the classical decomposition model presented here.

In broad terms the classical decomposition method works as follows. Seasonality is removed from the data by taking a moving average with a period of one year. A linear trend is then fitted to the deseasonalized data using regression of the deseasonalized data against time (see Chapter 5). This provides a value T_t for the trend at each time period. The seasonal component is estimated by dividing the time series value x_t by the computed trend value to give a seasonal index for that period. The seasonal component S_t is derived by averaging the values for corresponding periods in the year, e.g. with monthly data the seasonal term for January is derived by averaging all the seasonal indexes corresponding to January. Finally the irregular term I_t is computed using equation (3.6) and the values of T_t and S_t previously derived.

It is usually advised that the method only be used where at least three consecutive years of data exist. Obviously it is best suited where trend or seasonality, and preferably both, are marked. Our photocopying agency data (series B) fits these requirements.

Table 3.3 shows the output of the classical decomposition model when applied to all 52 points of the photocopying agency sales data.

Table 3.3
Classical decomposition model — series B

Year 1

	Jan	Feb	Mar	Apr	May	Jun	Jul	Aug	Sep	Oct	Nov	Dec
SALES SEA	0.88	0.96	0.87	0.83	0.76	0.91	1.40	1.05	0.75	1.38	1.10	1.27
SALES TREND	17.91	18.50	19.04	19.63	20.21	20.80	21.37	21.97	22.56	23.13	23.73	24.30
SALES IRR	1.11	1.00	1.07	1.08	1.28	0.73	1.06	1.03	0.88	0.97	0.99	1.00
SALES ADJ	20.37	18.77	20.81	21.63	26.30	15.34	22.92	22.94	20.10	22.51	23.58	24.38
SALES	18.00	18.00	18.00	18.00	20.00	14.00	32.00	24.00	15.00	31.00	26.00	31.00

Year 2

	Jan	Feb	Mar	Apr	May	Jun	Jul	Aug	Sep	Oct	Nov	Dec
SALES SEA	0.88	0.96	0.87	0.83	0.76	0.91	1.40	1.05	0.75	1.38	1.10	1.27
SALES TREND	24.90	25.49	26.03	26.62	27.19	27.79	28.36	28.96	29.55	30.12	30.72	31.29
SALES IRR	0.95	1.02	1.11	0.95	0.77	1.07	1.04	1.03	0.86	0.99	0.83	0.81
SALES ADJ	23.77	26.07	28.90	25.23	21.04	29.58	29.36	29.64	25.45	29.78	25.39	25.16
SALES	21.00	25.00	25.00	21.00	16.00	27.00	41.00	31.00	19.00	41.00	28.00	32.00

Year 3

	Jan	Feb	Mar	Apr	May	Jun	July	Aug	Sept	Oct	Nov	Dec
SALES SEA	0.88	0.96	0.87	0.83	0.76	0.91	1.40	1.05	0.75	1.38	1.10	1.27
SALES TREND	31.88	32.48	33.01	33.61	34.18	34.78	35.35	35.94	36.54	37.11	37.71	38.28
SALES IRR	0.89	0.94	1.02	1.19	0.93	1.21	0.90	0.94	1.26	1.05	1.19	1.21
SALES ADJ	28.29	30.24	33.52	39.65	31.56	41.63	31.51	33.46	45.55	38.49	44.44	45.61
SALES	25.00	29.00	29.00	33.00	24.00	38.00	44.00	35.00	34.00	53.00	49.00	58.00

Year 4

	Jan	Feb	Mar	Apr
SALES SEA	0.88	0.96	0.87	0.83
SALES TREND	38.87	39.46	40.02	40.61
SALES IRR	1.03	1.04	0.79	0.78
SALES ADJ	39.61	40.66	31.21	31.24
SALES	35.00	39.00	27.00	26.00

The actual sales for each month are shown in the bottom line. The seasonal component, trend component and the irregular component are to be found in the first, second and third lines respectively. It will be noted that the seasonal component for, say, January is the same across all four years. Similarly, allowing for rounding error, the trend term is found to increase by a constant amount of just under 0.6 from one month to the next.

If the time series were completely explained by the trend and seasonal terms, i.e. was always equal to:

$$\text{SALES ADJ} = \text{SALES TREND} \times \text{SALES SEAS} \tag{3.7}$$

then the irregular term would always be 1. In fact, subtracting 1 from the irregular term and multiplying by 100 gives the percentage error in the value of the forecast for the period, as defined in Chapter 1. Thus the error for April in Year 3 is $100 \times (1.19 - 1) = 19$ per cent. This, of course, is *ex post* forecast error. For the reasons explained in Chapter 1 this is likely to give an overly optimistic impression of the accuracy of forecasts of series C produced by the decomposition method.

The derivation of forecasts using the decomposition model is not completely straightforward. It will be illustrated in this case by preparing forecasts for the rest of year 4. The process for the month of May, which is readily generalized, is as follows:

1 Compute the latest estimate of the change in the trend term over a 12-month period. In this case that is the difference between the April year 4 value of SALES TREND and the April year 3 value, i.e.

   $$40.61 - 33.61 = 7.0$$

2 Add this to the value of SALES TREND for the period last season that corresponds to the period being forecast, in this case May year 3. This gives:

   $$34.18 + 7.00 = 41.18$$

3 Multiply this by the latest available value for the seasonal factor for May, i.e. that for May year 3. This gives the desired forecast, in this case:

$$41.18 \times 0.76 = 31.30$$

Table 3.4 gives the forecasts for the remainder (May–December) of year 4 derived in this way.

Table 3.4
Forecasts for May–December, year 4

	May	Jun	Jul	Aug	Sep	Oct	Nov	Dec
Forecasts	31.30	38.02	59.29	45.09	32.66	60.87	49.18	57.51

In series B the seasonality is immediately obvious from the graph. The question arises, however, as to how to test for seasonality in less clearcut situations. One tool for doing this is the autocorrelation function, described in Chapter 2. Essentially this looks at the relationship between values of the time series one period apart, two periods apart, etc. If the series has seasonality of period s, then this will show itself by a markedly stronger relationship between points s time periods apart because they will be moving in the same direction as a result of seasonal effects. Figure 3.6 shows the autocorrelation function (ACF) for series B up to a lag of 12 time periods. The ACF is statistically significant (extends beyond the dashed lines) for lags of one month and 12 months. A significant ACF at lag one says nothing about seasonality. That at 12 months does, since it can readily be identified with variations across the year. It is worth noting that often where annual seasonality is significant the ACF is also significant at lags of four months, three months, etc. that divide into a year an integer number of times. In such cases, these significant values can be ignored if a model with annual seasonality is adopted, since it will automatically take these effects into account. Figure 3.7 shows the ACF for series C. No clear evidence of seasonality is apparent in the graph of that series (Figure 3.3). It is not surprising, then, that the ACF is not significant at lag 12 months. There is no indication of a need for a model incorporating annual seaonality. The significant values at lags of two, four and five months are better handled by the construction of a non-seasonal model.

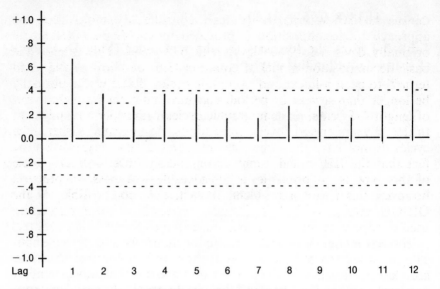

Figure 3.6 Autocorrelation function for series B

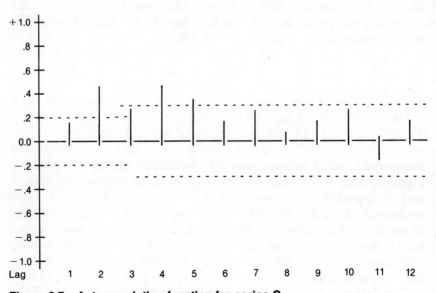

Figure 3.7 Autocorrelation function for series C

Census XII. An alternative (though considerably more complex) approach to decomposition is provided by the Census XII model originally devised for the US Bureau of Census. This extends the basic decomposition model of equation (3.6) by allowing the trend term T_t to be non-linear and to contain cycles. These would normally be longer than a year in period, e.g. medium term business cycles of length 4–5 years, or demographic cycles with a period equivalent to the 20 years or so between generations. As indicated earlier, such cycles do not have the same clear rationale as seasonal cycles. The fact that the XII model might automatically fit a long term cycle of this type is, in principle, a considerable weakness. In practice, however, this is not a problem. In fact, it is not possible for the ORION version of XII to fit such cycles. Non-linear trends are used to cope with more complex, longer term variations in the data.

The XII model deals with monthly or quarterly data. It automatically tests for seasonality so there is no need to examine the autocorrelation function of the data to see whether a seasonal term is required. As for the classical decomposition model, at least three years of data are required to run the model. Series C of inflation adjusted factory orders fits this requirement. The model was applied to the first five years of data only so that the year 6 data could be used to obtain some idea of the model's suitability for use with this series.

The output of the XII model is voluminous. The main features in this case were:

1 No evidence of stable seasonality was found. The model, however, still contains a seasonal term, a trend term, a short term (within year) cycle and an irregular term.
2 The fitted trend term was non-linear with an upward drift until about halfway through the five years followed by a downward drift thereafter.

Because no significant seasonality was detected, the XII model is inappropriate in this case. Nevertheless, a seasonally adjusted model was produced which is given here. Though the XII model is very sophisticated, that does not exempt the manager from attempting to assess its output. Complicated techniques that are wrongly applied are far more likely to give poor forecasts than are simple methods!

Because of the complexity of the XII model any forecasting package that contains it will provide a mechanism to generate forecasts from it. The forecasts for year 6 generated by ORION are shown in Table

3.5 along with the corresponding actual values. With the exception of January, the forecasts are extremely poor, presumably because of the non-linear trend term, even for a time horizon of three months or so. The XII model does not look a very attractive approach to forecasting this series. The within sample errors relating to the five years of data used to build this model give no indication that this problem is likely to arise, however, as shown by the computed values of the irregular term in Table 3.6. In this case a value of the irregular term of 100 indicates perfect agreement between forecast and actual and the difference from 100 the percentage error. This provides a graphic illustration of the differences between *ex ante* and *ex post* tests that are often encountered in practice.

Table 3.5
Forecasts for year 6 generated by ORION

Year 6	Forecast	Actual
Jan	76168.4	74657.00
Feb	65546.9	110686.00
Mar	73389.0	92901.00
Apr	56938.2	104840.00
May	53419.2	98476.00
Jun	65202.3	113520.00
Jul	36677.7	75912.00
Aug	65041.8	143745.00
Sep	45316.7	111625.00
Oct	69775.9	124321.00
Nov	47336.1	97937.00
Dec	49792.7	96151.00

Though the forecasts are poor, it is of great concern that they are almost all pessimistic. The total forecast for the 12 months is about 686,000 against a corresponding actual total of about 1,245,000. As pointed out in Chapter 1, there are many situations in which the cumulative forecast error over a period, e.g. a year as here, may be a more relevant measure. In this case, were the forecasts intended as an input to a production plan for the next

Table 3.6
Computed values of Irregular term

Year	Jan	Feb	Mar	Apr	May	Jun	Jul	Aug	Sept	Oct	Nov	Dec
1	103.5	103.3	91.7	100.0	110.5	100.5	97.9	71.2	103.2	112.6	108.1	85.4
2	99.9	140.0	100.6	104.9	97.0	99.0	96.4	97.2	95.0	85.7	105.9	123.4
3	93.1	93.0	100.0	100.8	95.6	83.0	100.0	113.8	119.9	60.4	108.9	65.7
4	115.1	84.1	101.5	90.7	107.4	100.0	71.8	123.4	89.3	99.6	85.2	106.8
5	89.0	117.1	101.6	102.8	91.1	114.2	108.9	74.0	84.0	128.7	86.4	115.3
S.D.	9.0	21.0	3.9	4.9	7.4	9.9	13.4	21.2				

year, the fact that they underestimate the year's sales by some 45 per cent could be serious.

Updating the model. Both the classical decomposition model and, especially, the XII model involve substantial amounts of computation for estimation. It is desirable, then, to avoid re-estimating them every time period. In some cases the model under consideration generates statistical confidence limits (see Chapter 5) that can be used for this purpose. This is not the case with either the XII model or the classical decomposition model. We shall, therefore, illustrate a simpler, somewhat cruder, approach. Figure 3.8 shows a graph of forecast versus actual values as calculated for year 5 by the previous XII model. This shows that for the last five periods the forecast value is consistently above the actual value. This will happen, by chance, on average one in 32 times. This is too biased against re-estimation for many applications. Re-estimation whenever four, or even three, consecutive forecast errors are all negative or all positive would probably be more suitable in general. This gives a one in

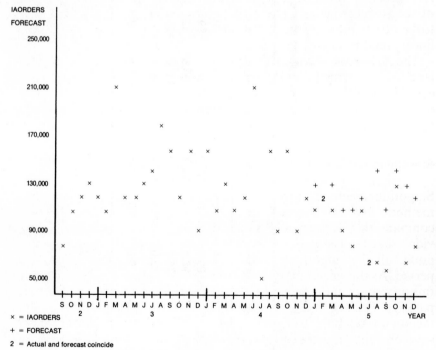

Figure 3.8   Forecast versus actual values calculated by Census XII model

16 probability and one in eight probability, respectively, of embarking on an unnecessary re-estimation, because the observed pattern in the errors is solely due to chance and not to any defects in the model.

A comparison of XII and classical decomposition. Given that the XII model involves considerably more computation even than the classical decomposition model, it is of interest to know whether the additional computational effort results in better forecasts. To throw some light on the matter both methods will now be applied to the first 40 data points of series B and the resulting models used to derive forecasts for the last 12 data points of the series. Series B exhibits marked seasonality and trend and is, therefore, an appropriate one to which to apply these models. The resulting forecasts, and the corresponding actual values are given in Table 3.7. Though there are one or two large percentage errors in the forecasts derived by classical decomposition, they are, on the whole, quite good. The XII forecasts, however, are much poorer, especially towards the end of the forecast period. These large forecast errors once again seem to be attributable to the XII model's predilection for fitting a non-linear trend term.

The XII model is widely used by practitioners because of the excellence of its seasonal decomposition. It would not seem prudent, however, to apply it where seasonality does not appear to be present or to use versions of the model containing non-linear trends. Such applications, as our examples show, can lead to very poor results.

Smoothing methods

Smoothing methods provide a relatively simple set of forecasting methods that perform well in practice. Because they are cheap to compute, they are very well suited to high volume applications. Provided that the last period's model parameters are given as a starting point, all the smoothing models can be cheaply re-estimated each period. As this generally gives slightly better forecasts, we recommend this procedure, if the forecasting package permits, as does the ORION package. Because the process is not expensive of computer time this facility of ORION has been used in all the smoothing examples save one that illustrates how the estimation is done. The forecast error function minimized in all cases was mean square error.

Table 3.7
Comparison of results using XII and classical decomposition

Year 4	XII forecast	Classical decomposition forecast	Actual
May	30.7	31.3	16.0
June	48.5	38.0	38.0
July	70.5	59.3	68.0
Aug	52.2	45.1	55.0
Sept	34.8	32.7	38.0
Oct	72.2	60.9	32.0
Nov	59.2	49.2	50.0
Dec	71.5	57.5	60.0
Year 5			
Jan	51.3	49.7	42.0
Feb	61.5	44.6	37.0
Mar	58.9	40.9	25.0
Apr	60.5	39.5	29.0

Single exponential smoothing. The simplest smoothing model is single exponential smoothing. Assume for a moment that we have a forecast, F_t, for the value of the time series at time t, x_t. The forecast for period $t + 1$ is generated by the formula:

$$F_{t+1} = F_t + k(x_t - F_t) \qquad (3.8)$$

where k is a constant between 0 and 1. The second term on the right hand side of equation (3.8) is k times last period's forecast error. The single exponential smoothing model can be thought of, then, as attempting to reduce forecast error by correcting last period's forecast by a proportion of last period's error. Equation (3.8) is readily rearranged to give the model in the form in which it is usually presented:

$$F_{t+1} = (1 - k)F_t + kx_t \qquad (3.9)$$

To fit the model the forecaster needs to do two things: estimate a forecast F_1 for the first value of the time series x_1; and choose the 'best' value of k. A simple way to do this is as follows:

1. take $F_1 = x_1$
2. try generating forecasts using equation (3.8) for the whole time series using a number of values of k, e.g. 0.05, 0.15 ... 0.95 and choose the value of k that gives the lowest forecast error. Commonly applied measures of forecast error are mean absolute deviation and mean square error. These were described in Chapter 1.

Applications to series of constant level. The standard application of the single exponential smoothing model is to series without seasonality and trend that fluctuate about a constant level. Our previous investigations and Figure 3.3 suggest that series C comes into this category. The single exponential smoothing model was applied to the first five years' data of the time series. The resulting forecast for each month of year 6 was 79991, since for the single exponential smoothing model, as we shall see in the next example,

$$\hat{x}_{61} = \hat{x}_{62} = \hat{x}_{63} \text{ etc.}$$

where $\hat{x}_{61}$ is the forecast for period 61, i.e. January of year 6, based on the model derived from the first five years of the series. The corresponding forecasts and actuals for year 6 are given in Table 3.8.

Table 3.8
Forecasts and actuals for year 6

	Jan	Feb	Mar	Apr	May	Jun
Forecast	79991	79991	79991	79991	79991	79991
Actual	74657	110686	92901	104840	98476	113520

	July	Aug	Sept	Oct	Nov	Dec
Forecast	79991	79991	79991	79991	79991	79991
Actual	75912	143745	111625	124321	97937	96151

Though these forecasts are still not particularly good, they are considerably better than those given by the XII model as well as much cheaper to derive. The total forecast for the year is 960,000. This represents an underestimate of total demand for year by 23 per cent. This forecast error is only half that obtained from the XII model. Though forecast errors of the size of that in August are uncomfortably large, errors of this magnitude in forecasting demands for industrial products are not uncommon in our experience. Some series cannot be forecast with acceptably low errors using time series methods. In such cases three possible solutions are open to the manager:

1 examine the possibility of using other forecasting methods, most usually econometric modelling, to derive the forecasts and perhaps to construct a composite forecast (see Chapter 10) based on those forecasts and the time series ones;
2 attempt to reduce the sensitivity to forecast error of the system for which the forecast is being made;
3 attempt to control more directly the value of the variable being forecast, e.g. by increased selling effort at certain times of the year, etc.

Applications to transformed data. The single exponential smoothing model only functions satisfactorily on time series that fluctuate about a constant level, i.e. that are without steps, trend or seasonality. Such time series are not often encountered by managers. Therefore the data often need to be transformed, e.g. by differencing or seasonal differencing as discussed in Chapter 2, to remove trends or seasonal cycles, before the model can be applied to them.

Because of its simplicity this model is well suited to use with time series containing only a few data points. A convenient illustration of both these considerations is afforded by the daily sales data of series A. The model will be used to construct a forecast for the period 16–22 January based on data for the period 1–15 January. The first step is to seasonally difference the data. Since the seasonality is seven days, this involves creating a new series d_t where:

$$d_t = x_t - x_{t-7} \qquad (3.10)$$

This reduces our original 15 data points by seven leaving eight on which to base the single exponential smoothing model. Table 3.9 shows the mean square errors for values of k of 0.05, 0.15 and

0.25 respectively. The value at 0.15 is seen to be the lowest, though there is little difference between them: a sign that the resulting forecast model is likely to be robust.

Table 3.9
Mean square errors for k

Value of k	0.05	0.15	0.25
Mean square error	11803	11686	12006
Forecast d_{16}, etc.	65.5	51.1	52.5

This value of k can be used to derive the required forecasts. The process will now be described to make clear the procedure though, in practice, it would be carried out automatically by the ORION system.

The starting point is the actual value of the difference for 15 January, $d_{15} = 77$ and the value of F_{15} printed out by ORION (46.51). The forecast value of d_{16} is then:

$$F_{16} = F_{15} + k(d_{15} - F_{15}) \tag{3.11}$$

i.e. $F_{16} = 46.51 + 0.15 \times (77 - 46.51) = 51.10 \tag{3.12}$

For the single exponential smoothing model the forecasts of d_{17}, d_{18}, etc. are all equal to the forecast of d_{16}. To forecast our actual time series we need to note that from equation (3.10)

$$x_t = x_{t-7} + d_t \tag{3.13}$$

To forecast, say, x_{16} we add the forecast value of the seasonal difference, F_{16}, to the value of the time series seven days previously, x_9. If that value of the time series did not exist, because we were forecasting more than seven days ahead, then we would have to use the forecast value of x_9 rather than the actual value. Applying this process leads to the forecasts shown in the first column of Table 3.10. The largest error is around 19 per cent on 19 January. These forecasts are perfectly adequate for many purposes. Furthermore, such daily time series tend to be difficult to forecast and it must be remembered that only just over two complete cycles of data have been used.

Table 3.10
Forecasts using transformed data

| Date | Actual | Seasonally differenced data | | Forecast based on seasonally differenced log transformed data |
		Forecast based on 1–15 January	Forecast based on 1–13 January	
14 Jan	656	–	567.30	–
15 Jan	838	–	805.30	–
16 Jan	681	796.10	789.30	806.83
17 Jan	787	742.10	735.30	748.35
18 Jan	800	931.10	927.30	956.29
19 Jan	868	701.10	694.30	703.11
20 Jan	688	726.10	732.30	731.56
21 Jan	593	707.10	700.30	710.45
22 Jan	830	889.10	882.30	903.55

Testing the robustness of the model. In Chapter 1 two ways were introduced for testing the robustness of the model. These were: examining the effects of changes to the forecasting model parameters on the forecasts; and examining the effect on the forecasts of dropping one, or more, data points. The forecasts of d_{16} derived from the three different values of k in the above model illustrate the first approach. The values were: 65.5, 51.1 and 52.5 for $k = 0.05$, 0.15 and 0.25 respectively.

The second approach can be illustrated by the use of a model based on the data for 1–13 January only, i.e. that effectively only uses six data points. The forecast for $d_{14} = d_{15} = d_{16}$, etc. is now 44.3. The new forecasts are given in the fourth column of Table 3.10. The change is again very small. The largest error is now about 20 per cent. Whichever approach we use to test robustness we conclude that in this case it is excellent, despite the very small number of data points used.

Using seasonally differenced log transformed data. As described in Chapter 2, a common transform is to generate the time series:

$$L_t = \text{Log}_{10}x_t \tag{3.14}$$

If this transformation is applied to the data of series A the result is a new series (LGSALES). The seasonality obviously remains in the data, so before we can apply the single exponential smoothing model to them, we must seasonally difference the series as above to create a new time series:

$$D_t(t) = L_t - L_{t-7} \tag{3.15}$$

If we now apply the model to these new data for the period from 1–15 January and use it to predict the value $D_{16} = D_{17} = D_{18}$ the prediction turns out to be 0.0347. Our forecast of $Log_{10}(x_t(t))$ accordingly turns out to be:

$$L\hat{o}g_{10}x_t = Log_{10}x_{t-7} + \hat{D}_t \tag{3.16}$$

In this case this gives:

$$L\hat{o}g_{10}x_{16} = Log_{10}x_9 + 0.0347 \text{ etc.} \tag{3.17}$$

Converting equation (3.17) to a forecast of x_t gives:

$$\hat{x}_{16} = x_9 \times 10^{0.0347}$$
$$= 1.083x_9$$

Similarly $\hat{x}_{17} = 1.083x_{10}$, etc. The results from these forecasts are also shown in the fifth column of Table 3.10. The largest of the errors is around 20 per cent; a good performance when account is taken of the small quantity of data used.

When used in conjunction with simple time series models the log transformation usually gives, as here, perfectly acceptable forecasts, though on average forecasts derived using the untransformed raw data are somewhat better. When used in conjunction with more complex models greater problems may arise. On balance, in time series work log transformations are best avoided save where the variance of the series is not constant, i.e. where the variability of the series appears to be changing with time.

Regular (or single) differencing. This was another common transformation described in Chapter 2. It has two common applications: to remove trend from data to enable them to be handled by methods such as single exponential smoothing; and as a possible way of making series that show no coherent pattern into ones exhibiting fluctuation around a constant level.

The use of regular differencing to remove trend from data is most conveniently illustrated using the data of series D. The data were first differenced to create a new time series d_t given by:

$$d_t = x_t - x_{t-1} \tag{3.18}$$

It will be recalled that the forecast horizon of interest here is six years. Two such sets of forecasts will be illustrated: the first for years 21–26 based on the data for years 1–20; the second for the years 29–34 based on data up to year 28. The first model corresponds to the period of rapid growth in the variable PEAK, the second to a period when growth was very slow. The process of deriving a forecast from a model using differenced data will be illustrated using the first model based on data for the years 1–20. Application of the single exponential smoothing model gives a forecast for d_{21}, d_{22} and the other differences as 1302.3. The forecast for x_{21}, year 21, is generated by:

$$\hat{x}_{21} = x_{20} + \hat{d}_{21} \tag{3.19}$$
$$= 34560 + 1302.3 = 35862.3$$

Since we are supposing for the purpose of this forecast that the actual value of x_{21} is unknown, to forecast x_{22} we use the value of $\hat{x}_{21}$ instead, in accordance with the equation:

$$\hat{x}_{22} = \hat{x}_{21} + \hat{d}_{22} \tag{3.20}$$
$$= 35862.3 + 1302.3 = 37164.6$$

Repetition of this process allows the remaining forecasts for years 23–26 to be generated as shown in Table 3.11.

These forecasts exhibit relatively low errors, though the errors for the set of forecasts for years 29–34 are on the whole somewhat greater than those obtained using naive forecasts. However, the acceptability of the forecasts depends on the purpose for which they are intended. For capacity planning purposes, it is usually the increase in demand from one year to the next that is of interest. Judged by this criterion the forecasts of Table 3.11 are not too bad. Both sets do, however, clearly exhibit one of the difficulties of all time

Table 3.11
Forecasts using regular differencing

Forecasts for years 21–26

Year	21	22	23	24	25	26
Forecast	35862.3	37164.6	38466.9	39769.2	41071.5	42373.8
Actual	35820	37740	39650	41110	40510	40640

Forecasts for years 29–34

Year	29	30	31	32	33	34
Forecast	41957.6	42945.2	43932.8	44920.4	45908.0	46895.6
Actual	41350	42110	42800	44100	44230	42600

series models that deal with trends. Trends will be extrapolated into the future and as demand levels off this becomes more inappropriate. The exponential smoothing models do recognize changes in trend but they adjust in arrear of those changes. Long time horizon forecasts based on them therefore tend to lead to overestimation of future demands as saturation begins.

The use of single differencing in conjunction with series without trend can be illustrated using series C, which shows no particular pattern of fluctuation. Previous analysis has established that it is non-seasonal. Earlier attempts to forecast it were unsatisfactory. Figure 3.9 shows the singly differenced time series. It will be noted that with three exceptions – June, July, August, year 4 – the transform seems to have had the desired effect. Those particular points appear to be 'obvious' outliers. It will be assumed that some reason, e.g. a general election, can be found to suppose that they are, indeed, so.

With series like series C, single differencing may or may not help to give better forecasts. A convenient test as to whether differencing is indicated is to compute the standard deviations of the undifferenced and differenced series. Differencing is indicated if the differenced series has a standard deviation that is lower than that of the undifferenced series. In this case the standard deviation of the undifferenced series is 35181 whereas the standard deviation of the differenced series is 47380.

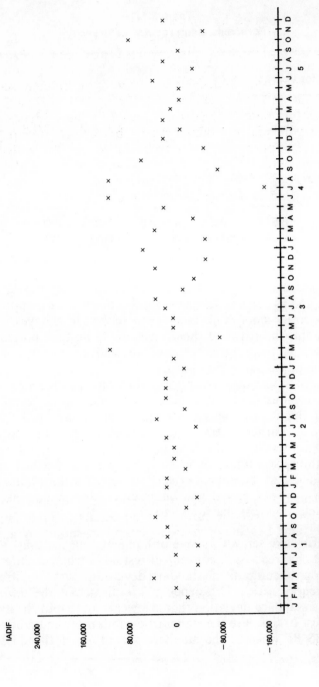

Figure 3.9   Singly differenced time series

Given that three of the points appear to be outliers, the question arises as to whether differencing might be indicated, if more 'reasonable' values were adopted for them. This provides a convenient point at which to illustrate the procedure used for replacing outliers. The classical decomposition model is often useful for filling in such missing values. In this case, the absence of trend and seasonality makes its use inappropriate. Instead the values have been 'forecast' using a single exponential smoothing model based on data up to May of year 4. The appropriate value turns out to be -1523. Even when the apparent outliers are replaced in this way, the standard deviation of the differenced series (38177) remains higher than that of the undifferenced series. It is still better to model the actual data series rather than the differenced one. No forecast model will, therefore, be constructed in this case.

Adaptive smoothing. A variant on the single exponential smoothing model is adaptive smoothing. This is based on the single exponential smoothing model of equations (3.8) and (3.9). However, instead of using a constant value for k, this model adapts its value in the light of the forecast error. Where the forecast error is large, the value of k is set close to 1 implying a rapid adjustment of the forecast to the previous actual value. Under these circumstances the adaptive smoothing model mimics the naive forecast. When the forecast error is small, the value of k is set close to zero, implying little change to the forecast. The means whereby the adjustment is carried out is based on making the value of k depend on the ratio of the smoothed forecast error to the smoothed absolute forecast error (i.e. the numeric value of the forecast error ignoring sign). If the forecast error is consistently in one direction because of consistent under- or over-forecasting this ratio will be close to 1. Where the forecasts show no consistent bias then the smoothed error will fluctuate about zero and therefore so will the ratio. The equations for the commonly used Trigg and Leach approach to adaptive smoothing are given below.

$$E_{t-1} = X_{t-1} - F_{t-1} \tag{3.21}$$
$$SE_{t-1} = aE_{t-1} + (1 - a)SE_{t-2} \tag{3.22}$$
$$SAE_{t-1} = a|E_{t-1}| + (1 - a)SAE_{t-2} \tag{3.23}$$
$$k_t = \left| \frac{SE_{t-1}}{SAE_{t-1}} \right| \tag{3.24}$$
$$F_t = k_t x_{t-1} + (1 - k_t)F_{t-1} \tag{3.25}$$

where E_{t-1} denotes the forecast error in period $t - 1$, SE_{t-1} the smoothed forecast error in $t - 1$, SAE_{t-1}, the smoothed absolute forecast error for period $t - 1$, k_t is the smoothing constant for period t, F_t is the forecast for period t and a is a constant between 0 and 1. The notation $|v|$ denotes the numerical (absolute) value of the variable v. Thus k_t is set equal to the numerical value of the ratio SE_{t-1}/SAE_{t-1}.

Adaptive smoothing contains no trend term. Just as with the single exponential smoothing model, the forecasts for one period ahead, two periods ahead, etc. are identical. Thus the method will not give good results, if the data contain trend and it is required to forecast several periods ahead. Essentially it is intended to detect sudden upward or downward steps in the data of the type discussed in Chapter 1.

The method can be demonstrated using series D, which exhibits something like this form of behaviour in the last third of the series. Specifically, we shall examine how an adaptive smoothing model based on data for the years 24–31 is able to detect the change in level occurring about year 30. Note that the adaptive smoothing model would not be appropriate before year 24. Though all the other examples of the chapter have used the complete data series from the start to the point from which forecasts are to be generated this is not always desirable. If the series changes its nature, e.g. saturates as here, it may be necessary to restrict the data used to build the model to those which it can operate with, otherwise the 'best' values of the model parameters determined by the forecasting package may well be inappropriate. A further example would be where a step change occurs in a data series that is being modelled as fluctuating about a constant level. If such a model is to continue to be applied, data prior to the step will have to be disregarded.

The forecast generated by the adaptive smoothing model, in this case, is 42108. The actual values are shown in Table 3.12 for years 28–34 so as to demonstrate how the method detects the upward step in year 30 and carries it forward into the forecasts for years 32–34.

It can be seen that the jump in the actual value in period 30 is translated into the forecasts once it is sustained in period 31.

Brown's double exponential smoothing. Single exponential smoothing cannot deal with data containing a trend. Double exponential smoothing methods can. These models produce a forecast containing

Table 3.12
Actual values for years 28–34

Year	28	29	30	31	32	33	34
Forecast	–	–	–	–	42108	42108	42108
Actual	40970	41350	42110	42800	44100	44230	42600

two terms: a constant level and a linear trend. Both the constant level and the trend term are continually re-estimated as further data become available.

There are two common double smoothing methods for use with non-seasonal data: Holt's method and Brown's method. Here we shall illustrate Brown's method using series D. As earlier, we give two sets of forecasts for six years ahead: one based on the data for years 1–20 and the second on the data for years 1–28. The forecasts thus cover years 21–26 and years 29–34, respectively. These are shown in Table 3.13.

The approach used to forecasts are given in equations (3.26–3.30).

$$S'_t = kx_t + (1 - k) S'_{t-1} \tag{3.26}$$
$$S''_t = kS'_t + (1 - k) S''_{t-1} \tag{3.27}$$
$$T_t = k(S'_t - S''_t)/(1-k) \tag{3.28}$$
$$C_t = 2S'_t - S''_t \tag{3.29}$$
$$F_{t+h} = C_t + hT_t \tag{3.30}$$

where T_t is the estimate of the trend at period t, C_t is the estimate of the constant term at period t, F_{t+h} is the forecast for period $(t + h)$ and k is a constant between 0 and 1.

Both sets of forecasts are better than those produced by applying single exponential smoothing to the differenced series. This tends to be true in general. In fact, save for the forecasts for years 25–26 in the first set, all the forecasts here are very good. The over-forecasts in years 25 and 26 are, as before, due to an extrapolation of the previously strong trend beyond the point where it began to slacken.

Holt–Winters' double exponential smoothing. Holt's double exponential smoothing method, though marginally more complex, tends to give

Table 3.13
Forecasts for years 21–26 and years 29–34

Year	21	22	23	24	25	26
Forecast	36841	38269	39697	41125	42553	43981
Actual	35820	37740	39650	41110	40510	40640

Year	29	30	31	32	33	34
Forecast	41934	42363	42792	43222	43651	44081
Actual	41350	42110	42800	44100	44230	42600

similar results to Brown's. In fact, Holt's method is more usually used in conjunction with Winters' method to deal with seasonal time series. This model contains a constant level, a trend and seasonal factors all of which are re-estimated as new data become available. It is, therefore, essentially a smoothed version of the classical decomposition model. The conditions under which it can be applied are similar to those for the classical decomposition model. Holt–Winters' method, however, requires much less computation than classical decomposition. Though it would usually be considered desirable to have at least two complete seasons of data for use with the model, it can function with only a few data points provided good estimates of the seasonal factors can be made. This is often possible, for instance, where the product being forecast is expected to exhibit similar seasonality to existing ones. Just as in single exponential smoothing it was necessary to provide an initial estimate of the constant level, here initial estimates must be provided of the constant level, the trend and the seasonal factors. The equations used to compute the forecasts are:

$$C_t = k_1 x_t/S_{t-L} + (1 - k_1)(C_{t-L} + T_{t-L}) \qquad (3.31)$$
$$T_t = k_2 (C_t - C_{t-1}) + (1 - k_2) T_{t-1} \qquad (3.32)$$
$$S_t = k_3 x_t/C_t + (1 - k_3) S_{t-L} \qquad (3.33)$$
$$F_{t+h} = (C_t + hT_t) S_{t-L+h} \qquad (3.34)$$

where C_t is the estimate of the constant term at period t, T_t is the estimate of the trend term, S_t is the estimate of the seasonal factor for period t, F_{t+h} is the forecast for period $t + h$, L is the length of the seasonal cycle, and k is a constant between 0 and 1.

The method will first be illustrated by applying it to the first 40 months' data for series B. All the seasonal factors are initially set equal. We are supposing in this case, and subsequent ones, that no information about seasonality is available. The forecasts generated by the model for months 41–52 are shown in Table 3.14.

Table 3.14
Forecasts for months 41–52

Period	Holt-Winters' forecast	Actual	Classical decomposition forecast	XII forecast
		Year 4		
May	36.8	16.0	31.3	30.7
June	29.9	38.0	38.0	48.5
July	63.2	68.0	59.3	70.5
Aug	48.2	55.0	45.1	52.2
Sept	31.2	38.0	32.7	34.8
Oct	64.4	32.0	60.9	72.2
Nov	54.0	50.0	49.2	59.2
Dec	65.0	60.0	57.5	71.5
		Year 5		
Jan	40.1	42.0	49.7	51.3
Feb	41.8	37.0	44.6	61.5
Mar	41.6	25.0	40.9	58.9
Apr	41.5	29.0	39.5	60.5

Some of the individual forecasts, e.g. May year 4, show errors of more than 100 per cent. This, however, is yet another situation in which cumulative error over the year is likely to be of more interest. Comparison of the forecast and actual totals for the year shows that the latter are overestimated by some 14 per cent. Examination of Figure 3.2 shows that this is, again, a result of a change in trend (in this case about month 38) leading to slower growth than forecast.

To give some idea of how Holt–Winters' method compares with classical decomposition and census XII, the corresponding forecasts for those two models are also repeated in Table 3.14. In this case, classical decomposition is slightly better than Holt–Winters'. In general, it is somewhat inferior on average to Holt–Winters'. The XII forecasts, of course, are much the worst: particularly when account is taken of the much greater computational effort they involve.

To gain some feel for the difference in results between Holt–Winters' method and the application of single exponential smoothing to seasonally differenced data and to demonstrate another useful feature of the Holt–Winters' model, it will now be applied to series A. This, of course, exhibits weekly seasonality. This causes no problems with Holt–Winters' method. As we have seen, decomposition methods cannot usually deal with other than yearly seasonality. The first application uses data for 1–15 January to build the model. Forecasts are produced for the following week. These are compared in Table 3.15 with the single exponential smoothing results derived earlier. The exercise is then repeated using data for the whole of January to build the model and a longer forecast horizon, i.e. the first 17 days of February. The results are as shown in Table 3.16.

Table 3.15
Comparison of Holt–Winters' and single exponential smoothing results, 16–22 January

| | January | | | | | | |
	16	17	18	19	20	21	22
Single exp. smoothing + sea. diff.	791.1	833.1	929.1	696.1	721.1	702.1	884.1
Sales turn (actual)	681.0	787.0	800.0	868.0	688.0	593.0	830.0
Holt–Winters	821.0	859.2	846.7	652.3	566.4	733.6	820.2

Table 3.16
Comparison of Holt–Winters' and single exponential smoothing results, February

	February								
	1	2	3	4	5	6	7	8	9
Single exp. smoothing + sea. diff.	901.7	957.7	584.7	587.7	993.7	867.7	1020.7	966.7	916.7
Sales turn (actual)	926.0	876.0	737.0	560.0	814.0	936.0	945.0	770.0	668.0
Holt–Winters	847.8	666.2	589.4	775.9	815.5	828.8	876.0	852.3	669.7

	February							
	10	11	12	13	14	15	16	17
Single exp. smoothing + sea. diff.	777.7	600.7	854.7	976.7	985.7	810.7	708.7	1076.0
Sales turn (actual)	1036.0	990.0	1024.0	949.0	961.0	641.0	627.0	628.0
Holt–Winters	592.4	779.9	819.9	833.2	880.6	856.8	673.2	595.6

For the forecasts based only on the first 15 days of the month, the forecasts based on single exponential smoothing of the seasonally differenced data are rather better than those produced by the Holt–Winters' model. Both sets of forecasts are, however, good. In the case of the February forecasts, which are based on a larger number of complete seasons of data, the Holt–Winters' forecasts are marginally better. This is usually so, in practice, where a reasonable number of data points are available. Again, however, both sets of forecasts are very good.

Brown's triple exponential smoothing. Smoothing models with a non-linear trend are also available. Brown's triple exponential smoothing method is, perhaps, the commonest and will now be considered. The method estimates a constant level, linear trend and non-linear trend as follows:

$$S'_t = kx_t + (1 - k) S'_{t-1} \tag{3.35}$$
$$S''_t = kS'_t + (1 - k) S''_{t-1} \tag{3.36}$$
$$S'''_t = kS''_t + (1 - k) S'''_{t-1} \tag{3.37}$$
$$C_t = 3S'_t - 3S''_t + S'''_{t-1} \tag{3.38}$$
$$T_t = k[(6 - 5k)S'_t - (10 - 8k) + (4 - 3k)S'''_t]/2(1 - k)^2 \tag{3.39}$$
$$Q_t = k^2(S'_t - 2S''_t + S'''_t)/(1 - k)^2 \tag{3.40}$$
$$F_{t+h} = C_t + hT_t + \tfrac{1}{2}h^2Q_t \tag{3.41}$$

where C_t is the estimate of the constant level at period t, T_t is the estimate of the trend term at period t, Q_t is the estimate of the non-linear (quadratic) term at period t, F_{t+h} is the forecast for period $t + h$ and k is a constant between 0 and 1. The method will be applied to series D. Table 3.17 gives forecasts derived by the method based on data for the years 1–20 along with the corresponding actuals. The forecasts for years 21–24 are reasonable, though there is clearly a tendency to overestimate the actual values. The forecasts for years 25 and 26 are markedly poorer. Overall the forecasts are inferior to those derived earlier by the simpler smoothing methods.

An even worse set of forecasts results for the forecasts for years 29–34 based on the first 28 data points. These are given in Table 3.18. Comment is scarcely required here. The problems that can arise from non-linear trend terms are once more clearly revealed.

Table 3.17
Forecasts for years 1–20

Year	Actual	Forecast
21	35820	37811
22	37740	39706
23	39650	41637
24	41110	43611
25	40510	45625
26	40640	47680

Table 3.18
Forecasts for years 29–34

Year	Actual	Forecast
29	41350	40145
30	42110	38153
31	42800	35749
32	44100	32935
33	44230	29709
34	42600	26072

Autoregressive models

In many business time series, there is a strong relationship between this period's value and next period's. More generally, the last few periods' values may serve as a very good basis on which to forecast next period's value. Autoregressive models attempt to exploit this fact. One of their useful properties is that they can follow non-linear trends. Regression methods as described in Chapter 5 are used to estimate the autoregressive model. Here our concern is solely to illustrate their use in time series modelling. Any series with trend is likely to be well suited to forecasting by means of this model. Series D is such a series. As before, forecasts for years 21–26 and years 29–34 will be presented.

The autoregressive model takes the form:

$$\hat{x}_t = a_0 + a_1 x_{t-1} + a_2 x_{t-2} \ldots + a_n x_{t-n} \tag{3.42}$$

Where the time series is seasonal the past values x_{t-1}, x_{t-2}, etc. should comprise a complete past year of data. An alternative approach, that is almost always better, is to seasonally difference the data first. It will be assumed here that seaonality has been removed in this way. Where the data are non-seasonal, no more than four or five immediate past values should be used. Furthermore, the regression package should be allowed to select only the minimum set of independent variables necessary by means of stepwise regression, i.e. the addition of independent variables one at a time by the regression package until no further variables would be statistically significant.

A useful feature of the autoregressive model is that it provides a statistical confidence interval for its forecasts. As always, these tend to give an optimistic picture of the accuracy of the forecasts, even though the width of the confidence interval is frequently dispiritingly large!

In the models of series D the independent variables were confined to the last five periods' values, i.e. x_{t-1}, x_{t-2}, x_{t-3}, x_{t-4} and x_{t-5}. For the model based on the first 20 data points, the independent variables selected by the regression package were x_{t-1} and x_{t-3} only. The forecasts for years 21–24 were, therefore, based on the values for the previous time period and the value two time periods previously or their forecast values. Thus the forecast for the year 21 was given by:

$$\hat{x}_{21} = 1832.1 + 0.48797 x_{20} + 0.57005 x_{18} \tag{3.43}$$

whereas that for x_{22} was given by:

$$\hat{x}_{22} = 1832.1 + 0.48797 \hat{x}_{21} + 0.57005 x_{19} \tag{3.44}$$

and that for x_{24} by:

$$\hat{x}_{24} = 1832.1 + 0.48797 \hat{x}_{23} + 0.57005 \hat{x}_{21} \tag{3.45}$$

The results are given in Table 3.19 along with the confidence limits and corresponding actuals.

Table 3.19
Forecasts for years 21–26

Year	Forecast	95% confidence		Actual
		Lower	Upper	
21	36813	32878	40747	35820
22	39879	35151	44607	37740
23	39949	35851	44048	39650
24	41600	37436	45763	41110
25	43406	39071	47742	40510
26	44202	39384	49021	40640

The forecasts for years 25 and 26 are not as good as the others, which are excellent. Even these are, however, better than those derived by triple smoothing. All the actuals lie within the stated confidence intervals which thus provide good guidance as to the accuracy of the forecasts in this case.

The model derived from the data for years 1–28 was found to depend only on the previous time period's data point. The forecasts derived from this model are given in Table 3.20. They are even better than in the previous case although the time series had changed from one with a marked trend to fluctuating around a near constant level. Of course, the forecasts were derived using different models. These results do, however, show the flexibility of autoregressive models. They often work extremely well in practice. They do, however, require substantial amounts of computation and do not lend themselves to re-estimation each time period. Furthermore, in our experience they can sometimes give rise to somewhat peculiar forecasts at longer time horizons because of their ability to follow non-linear trends.

A DECISION TABLE FOR CHOOSING TIME SERIES METHODS

Table 3.21, which is split into four sections, provides the information required to select the time series methods that are most likely to be appropriate for a particular series. By method is meant, in this context, combinations of time series models and transforms. The

Table 3.20
Forecasts for years 29–34

Year	Forecast	95% confidence		Actual
		Upper	Lower	
29	41702	38290	45114	41350
30	42067	38648	45485	42110
31	42796	39363	46229	42800
32	43459	40013	46904	44100
33	44707	41234	48179	44230
34	44831	41356	48307	42600

models considered are those discussed in this chapter, except that Brown's and Holt's double exponential smoothing methods have been treated as one because of the similarity of their performance, in practice. The transformations considered in the table are those discussed earlier, i.e. seasonal differencing, regular or single differencing and log transformation along with combinations of the first two with the third. It does not take into account the costs of the various methods, merely their likely suitability. In judging this we have made use of the results of various time series forecasting competitions, our own experience of the different methods and the general notion agreed by most forecasting practitioners that simple methods are likely to give better and more robust forecasts. In accordance with these principles, certain combinations of forecasting models and transforms have been omitted from the table on the grounds that they may give rise to problems in practice without offering any significant advantages over other model/transform combinations. The combinations omitted are: double smoothing + log transformation; triple smoothing + log transformation; autoregressive + log transformation; adaptive smoothing + single differencing; double smoothing + single differencing and triple smoothing + single differencing. Furthermore, the table will be found to reflect the findings of this chapter that are confirmed by wider experience. Even where they are apparently most appropriate, i.e. in the case of non-linear trends and saturation, the triple exponential smoothing and autoregressive models can give very poor results for forecasts at longer time horizons. On the whole, they are outperformed by models that assume a linear trend. These are much less likely to go disastrously wrong. It is also assumed that the version of XII used will be restricted to fitting a linear trend only. The problems of allowing it to fit non-linear trends have been illustrated in our discussions of that method.

It is assumed that the data series to be forecast has already been examined to determine what data patterns appear to exist in it. The table is divided into four sections depending on whether the data appear to fluctuate about a constant level; whether the data appear to exhibit fairly frequent steps; whether the data seem to exhibit a linear trend, or whether there appears to be evidence of non-linear trend or saturation. The seasonal movements that can be super-imposed on these patterns are covered in the tables. As far as the part of the table dealing with fluctuation about a constant level is concerned, it is worth bearing in mind that few business series are strictly constant. If the steps are relatively infrequent, however, e.g. every 20 periods, and the manager is willing to monitor the series a little more rigorously, we would suggest consideration be given to treating it as fluctuating about a constant level and abandoning the past series whenever a step occurs.

In general, combining time series forecasts in the way described in Chapter 10 leads to substantially more accuracy. This is particu-larly so if the time series models are fairly different in the way they work. If cost permits we would accordingly advise the use of several or all of those methods that appear to be appropriate for a particular series. It is assumed that the information in the table will be used only as first stage in determining which methods these are. Having selected those which appear from Table 3.21 to be likely to be suitable, the reader is expected to test their forecasting performance on a representative sample of time series (on occasions, of course, there may be several hundred) to establish which are appropriate.

To use the decision table it is necessary to establish the seasonality of the data, i.e. none, annual or non-annual, e.g. weekly; the forecast horizon required and the length of the series. The latter is measured in terms of the number of data points or the number of complete seasons of data, if the data are seasonal. It should be remembered that major changes to competitive conditions or other environmental upheavals can cause substantial changes to the nature of a series. Under those circumstances it may be necessary to consider abandon-ing past data as discussed above for the case of occasional steps in the series.

Table 3.21
Decision table for choosing time series methods

	Data with constant level									
PATTERN										
Annual seasonality	N	N	N	Y/N	Y/N	Y/N	Y	Y	N	N
Non-annual seasonality	N	N	N	Y/N	Y/N	Y/N	N	N	Y	Y
FORECAST HORIZON										
1–3 periods	Y	Y	N	Y/N	Y	N	Y	N	Y	N
4–12 periods	N	N	Y/N	Y/N	N	Y/N	N	Y/N	N	Y/N
12+ periods	N	N	Y/N	XXX	N	Y/N	N	Y/N	N	Y/N
LENGTH SERIES										
< 10 points or 1 season	Y	N	Y/N	Y	N	N	N	N	N	N
< 20 points or 2 seasons	N	Y/N	Y/N	N	Y/N	Y/N	N	N	N	N
< 30 points or 3 seasons	N	Y/N	Y/N	N	Y/N	Y/N	N	N	N	N
≥ 30 points or 3 seasons	N	Y/N	Y/N	N	N	N	Y	Y	Y	Y
Naive basic	**	**	**	NA	NA	NA	NA	NA	NA	NA
Seasonal naive	NA	NA	NA	NA	**	**	**	**	**	**
Naive sing. diff.	NR	NR	NA	NA	NA	NA	NA	NA	NA	NA
Classical decomposition	NA	NA	NA	NA	NA	NA	***	***	†NA	†NA
XII decomposition	NA	NA	NA	NA	NA	NA	***	***	NA	NA
Single exp. smoothing	***	***	***	NA	NA	NA	NA	NA	NA	NA
Single exp. + sea. diff.	NA	NA	NA	NA	***	***	***	***	***	***
Single + sing. diff.	VT	VT	VT	NA	NA	NA	NA	NA	NA	NA
Single exp. + LT	**	**	**	NA	NA	NA	NA	NA	NA	NA
Single exp. + sea. diff. + LT	NA	NA	NA	NA	**	**	**	**	**	**
Single exp. + singl diff. + LT	NR	NR	NR	NA	NA	NA	NA	NA	NA	NA
Adaptive	*	*	*	NA	NA	NA	NA	NA	NA	NA
Adaptive + sea. diff.	NA	NA	NA	NA	*	*	*	*	*	*
Adaptive + LT	*	*	*	NA	NA	NA	NA	NA	NA	NA
Adaptive + sea. diff. + LT	NA	NA	NA	NA	*	*	*	*	*	*
Double Holt/Brown exp. smo.	NR	NR	NR	NA	NA	NA	NA	NA	NA	NA
Double Holt/ Brown + sea. diff.	NA	NA	NA	NA	NR	NR	NR	NR	NR	NR
Holt–Winters'	NA	NA	NA	IT	NR	NR	NR	NR	NR	NR
Brown's triple exp.	NA	NA	NA	NA	NA	NA	NA	NA	NA	NA
Brown's triple + sea. diff.	NA	NA	NA	NA	NA	NA	NA	NA	NA	NA
Autoregressive	*	NR	NA	NA	NA	NA	NA	NA	NA	NA
Autoregressive + sea. diff.	NA	NA	NA	NA	*	NR	*	NR	*	NR

KEY

Y	– Yes
N	– No
Y/N	– Yes or no
{	– Y to one implies N to remaining yoked questions
XXX	– Unwise to attempt
IT	– Good initial guesses for seasonal factors + trend suppression required
LT	– Log transformed data used
NA	– Not appropriate
NR	– Not recommended
VT	– Only if variance/standard deviation differenced series less than that of undifferenced
*	– Sometimes useful
**	– Normally satisfactory
***	– First choice method
†NA	– Assumes only versions that deal with annual seasonality available

Table 3.21 (continued)

	Data with steps									
Naive basic	**	**	**	NA	NA	NA	NA	NA	NA	NA
Seasonal naive	NA	NA	NA	NA	*	*	*	*	*	*
Naive sing. diff.	**	**	**	NA	NA	NA	NA	NA	NA	NA
Classical decomposition	NA	NA	NA	NA	NA	NA	NA	NA	†NA	†NA
XII decomposition	NA	NA	NA	NA	NA	NA	NA	NA	NA	NA
Single exp. smoothing	NA	NA	NA	NA	NA	NA	NA	NA	NA	NA
Single exp. + sea. diff.	NA	NA	NA	NA	**	**	**	**	**	**
Single + sing. diff.	***	***	***	NA	NA	NA	NA	NA	NA	NA
Single exp. + LT	NA	NA	NA	NA	NA	NA	NA	NA	NA	NA
Single exp. + sea. diff. + LT	NA	NA	NA	NA	*	*	*	*	*	*
Single exp. + sing. diff. + LT	*	*	*	NA	NA	NA	NA	NA	NA	NA
Adaptive	**	**	**	NA	NA	NA	NA	NA	NA	NA
Adaptive + sea. diff.	NA	NA	NA	NA	*	*	*	*	*	*
Adaptive + LT	*	*	*	NA	NA	NA	NA	NA	NA	NA
Adaptive + sea. diff. + LT	NA	NA	NA	NA	*	*	*	*	*	*
Double Holt/Brown exp. smo.	*	*	*	NA	NA	NA	NA	NA	NA	NA
Double Holt/Brown + sea. diff.	NA	NA	NA	NA	NR	NR	NR	NR	NR	NR
Holt–Winters'	NA	NA	NA	IT	NR	NR	NR	NR	NR	NR
Brown's triple exp.	NA	NA	NA	NA	NA	NA	NA	NA	NA	NA
Brown's triple + sea. diff.	NA	NA	NA	NA	NA	NA	NA	NA	NA	NA
Autoregressive	NA	NA	NA	NA	NA	NA	NA	NA	NA	NA
Autoregressive + sea. diff.	NA	NA	NA	NA	NA	NR	NA	NA	NA	NA

KEY
Y   – Yes
N   – No
Y/N   – Yes or no
{   – Y to one implies N to remaining yoked questions
XXX   – Unwise to attempt
IT   – Good initial guesses for seasonal factors + trend suppression required
LT   – Log transformed data used
NA   – Not appropriate
NR   – Not recommended
VT   – Only if variance/standard deviation differenced series less than that of undifferenced
*   – Sometimes useful
**   – Normally satisfactory
***   – First choice method
†NA   – Assumes only versions that deal with annual seasonality available

Table 3.21 (continued)

Data with linear trends

Naive basic	NR	NR	NA	NA	NA	NA	NA	NA	NA	NA
Seasonal naive	NA	NA	NA	NA	NA	NA	NA	NA	NA	NA
Naive sing. diff.	*	*	*	NA	NA	NA	NA	NA	NA	NA
Classical decomposition	NA	NA	NA	NA	NA	NA	***	***	†NA	†NA
XII decomposition	NA	NA	NA	NA	NA	NA	***	***	NA	NA
Single exp. smoothing	NA	NA	NA	NA	NA	NA	NA	NA	NA	NA
Single exp. + sea. diff.	NA	NA	NA	NA	***	***	***	***	***	***
Single + sing. diff.	***	***	***	NA	NA	NA	NA	NA	NA	NA
Single exp. + LT	NA	NA	NA	NA	NA	NA	NA	NA	NA	NA
Single exp. + sea. diff. + LT	NA	NA	NA	NA	**	**	**	**	**	**
Single exp. + sing. diff. + LT	**	**	**	NA	NA	NA	NA	NA	NA	NA
Adaptive	NA	NA	NA	NA	NA	NA	NA	NA	NA	NA
Adaptive + sea. diff.	NA	NA	NA	NA	*	*	*	*	*	*
Adaptive + LT	NA	NA	NA	NA	NA	NA	NA	NA	NA	NA
Adaptive + sea. diff. + LT	NA	NA	NA	NA	*	*	*	*	*	*
Double Holt/Brown exp. smo.	***	***	***	NA	NA	NA	NA	NA	NA	NA
Double Holt/Brown + sea. diff.	NA	NA	NA	NA	***	***	***	***	***	***
Holt Winters'	NA	NA	NA	IT	**	**	***	***	***	***
Brown's triple exp.	NR	*	NR	NA	NA	NA	NA	NA	NA	NA
Brown's triple + sea. diff.	NA	NA	NA	NA	*	NR	*	NR	*	NR
Autoregressive	*	**	NR	NA	NA	NA	NA	NA	NA	NA
Autoregressive + sea. diff.	NA	NA	NA	NA	**	NR	**	NR	**	NR

KEY

Y	– Yes
N	– No
Y/N	– Yes or no
{	– Y to one implies N to remaining yoked questions
XXX	– Unwise to attempt
IT	– Good initial guesses for seasonal factors + trend suppression required
LT	– Log transformed data used
NA	– Not appropriate
NR	– Not recommended
VT	– Only if variance/standard deviation differenced series less than that of undifferenced
*	– Sometimes useful
**	– Normally satisfactory
***	– First choice method
†NA	– Assumes only versions that deal with annual seasonality available

Table 3.21 (concluded)

Data with non-linear trends/saturation

Naive basic	NR	NR	NA	NA	NA	NA	NA	NA	NA	NA
Seasonal naive	NA	NA	NA	NA	NA	NA	NA	NA	NA	NA
Naive sing. diff.	**	**	**	NA	NA	NA	NA	NA	NA	NA
Classical decomposition	NA	NA	NA	NA	NA	NA	***	***	†NA	†NA
XII decomposition	NA	NA	NA	NA	NA	NA	***	***	NA	NA
Single exp. smoothing	NA	NA	NA	NA	NA	NA	NA	NA	NA	NA
Single exp. + sea. diff.	NA	NA	NA	NA	***	***	***	***	***	***
Single + sing. diff.	***	***	***	NA	NA	NA	NA	NA	NA	NA
Single exp. + LT	NA	NA	NA	NA	NA	NA	NA	NA	NA	NA
Single exp. + sea. diff + LT	NA	NA	NA	NA	**	**	**	**	**	**
Single exp. + sing. diff. + LT	**	**	**	NA	NA	NA	NA	NA	NA	NA
Adaptive	NA	NA	NA	NA	NA	NA	NA	NA	NA	NA
Adaptive + sea. diff.	NA	NA	NA	NA	*	*	*	*	*	*
Adaptive + LT	NA	NA	NA	NA	NA	NA	NA	NA	NA	NA
Adaptive + sea. diff. + LT	NA	NA	NA	NA	*	*	*	*	*	*
Double Holt/Brown exp. smo.	***	***	***	NA	NA	NA	NA	NA	NA	NA
Double Holt/Brown + sea. diff.	NA	NA	NA	NA	***	***	***	***	***	***
Holt Winters'	NA	NA	NA	IT	**	**	***	***	***	***
Brown's triple exp.	NR	**	NR	NA	NA	NA	NA	NA	NA	NA
Brown's triple + sea. diff.	NA	NA	NA	NR	**	NR	**	NR	**	NR
Autoregressive	*	**	NR	NA	NA	NA	NA	NA	NA	NA
Autoregressive + sea. diff.	NA	NA	NA	NA	**	NR	**	NR	**	NR

Key
Y	– Yes
N	– No
Y/N	– Yes or no
{	– Y to one implies N to remaining yoked questions
XXX	– Unwise to attempt
IT	– Good initial guesses for seasonal factors + trend suppression required
LT	– Log transformed data used
NA	– Not appropriate
NR	– Not recommended
VT	– Only if variance/standard deviation differenced series less than that of undifferenced
*	– Sometimes useful
**	– Normally satisfactory
***	– First choice method
†NA	– Assumes only versions that deal with annual seasonality available

Using the decision table

The use of the decision table will be illustrated by examples. Consider first a series that:

1 appears to fluctuate about a constant level;
2 appears to have weekly seasonality;
3 for which our forecast horizon is 14 days;
4 for which we have 30 datapoints.

Reference to that portion of the table dealing with series fluctuating about a constant level shows that the relevant column is the very last one in that we have non-annual seasonality, a forecast horizon of 12+ periods and more than three seasons' of data. Note that to compress the table only one of the Y/N entries corresponding to forecast horizons of 4–12 periods or 12+ periods will be Y, in any given case. The other will be N. However, we are indifferent which is the case.

Examination of the methods portion of the table shows that the most highly recommended method is single exponential smoothing applied to seasonally differenced data. Naive seasonal differencing is also likely to be suitable, as are single exponential smoothing + seasonal differencing of the log transformed data, adaptive smoothing + seasonal differencing and adaptive smoothing + seasonal differencing of the log transformed data.

As a second example we consider a series for which:

1 the data appear to have non-linear trend;
2 the data appear to be non-seasonal;
3 the forecast horizon is 15 periods;
4 nine data points are available.

Reference to the portion of the table dealing with non-linear trends and saturation shows that the fourth column is now the relevant one but that no time series method is advised for such a long forecast horizon with so few data points.

For the next example we consider the case of:

1 a series apparently fluctuating about a constant level;
2 apparently non-seasonal;
3 a forecast horizon of eight periods;
4 16 data points.

The relevant column in the constant level section of the table is now the third. The most preferred method is single exponential smoothing and the next most recommended method single exponential smoothing of the log transformed data and naive basic. Adaptive smoothing with and without log transformation may also sometimes be useful. Finally, single exponential smoothing + single differencing may be useful but the standard deviation test described earlier in the chapter should be applied to establish that the differenced series has a lower standard deviation than the undifferenced series.

For the next example, we consider the case of a series where:

1 the data appear to fluctuate about a constant level;
2 they appear to exhibit weekly seasonality;
3 the forecast horizon is seven periods;
4 there are only five data points.

The relevant column in the constant level section of the table is now the fourth. Only one method is recommended, Holt–Winters', and that only if good initial estimates of the seasonal factors are available and the trend term of the model is suppressed by putting the relevant model parameter equal to zero.

For a final example we consider the case where:

1 the time series appears to contain a non-linear trend;
2 annual seasonality appears to exist;
3 the forecast horizon is 12 periods;
4 there are 40 data points.

The relevant column in the section of the table dealing with non-linear trends is the third from the right. Strongly recommended methods are: classical decomposition, XII (with a linear trend term only), single exponential smoothing + seasonal differencing, double exponential smoothing + seasonal differencing and Holt–Winters'. Given this range of possibilities there seems little need to examine the single starred methods. Single exponential smoothing of seasonally differenced log transformed data might well be worth examining, however.

ADVANTAGES AND DRAWBACKS OF TIME SERIES MODELS

Time series methods are by comparison with most other forecasting methods quick, simple and cheap to apply provided the necessary software is available. They are therefore suited to 'semi-automatic' operation. Once an appropriate method is identified for a particular time series, it can be used to produce forecasts at regular intervals. These can be used as an input to forecasting by managers. Sometimes they will be accepted as they stand. Often, they will need modification in the light of changes in external circumstancs such as promotion campaigns by competitors or interruptions in raw materials supplies, which no forecasting model that focuses on a single variable can take into account. This sums up the advantages and disadvantages of these methods. Because they are cheap to apply they are suited to high volume applications that are typical of production and market planning. On the other hand, they are unable to take into account the many other factors that determine the value of the variable being forecast besides its own past values. This disadvantage can, however, be a source of strength. Since the idea behind them is very different from that which underlies most other forecasting methods, they are well suited to being combined with another forecast based on some other method to obtain a combined forecast that may be more accurate than either alone. This will be discussed in more detail in Chapter 10.

FURTHER READING

Makridakis, S. et al., 'The Accuracy of Extrapolation (Time Series) Methods', *Journal of Forecasting*, vol. 1, no. 2, 1982.

'Commentary on the Makridakis Time Series Competition', (M. Competition), *Journal of Forecasting,* vol. 2, no. 3, 1983.

Scott Armstrong, J., 'Forecasting by Extrapolation: Conclusions from 25 years of Research', *Interfaces,* vol. 14, no. 6, 1984.

SALES TURN	1 678.00	2 763.00	3 763.00	Jan 4 795.00	5 789.00	6 604.00
SALES TURN	7 523.00	8 761.00	9 745.00	Jan 10 691.00	11 883.00	12 650.00
SALES TURN	13 675.00	14 656.00	15 838.00	Jan 16 681.00	17 787.00	18 800.00
SALES TURN	19 868.00	20 688.00	21 593.00	Jan 22 830.00	23 805.00	24 832.00
SALES TURN	25 861.00	26 917.00	27 544.00	Jan 28 547.00	29 953.00	30 827.00
SALES TURN	Jan 31 980.00	1 926.00	2 876.00	Feb 3 737.00	4 560.00	5 814.00
SALES TURN	6 936.00	7 945.00	8 770.00	Feb 9 668.00	10 1036.00	11 990.00
SALES TURN	12 1024.00	13 949.00	14 961.00	Feb 15 641.00	16 627.00	17 628.00

APPENDIX 3.2

Year 1

SALES	Jan	Feb	Mar	Apr	May	Jun	Jul	Aug	Sep	Oct	Nov	Dec
	18.00	18.00	18.00	18.00	20.00	14.00	32.00	24.00	15.00	31.00	26.00	31.00

Year 2

SALES	Jan	Feb	Mar	Apr	May	Jun	Jul	Aug	Sep	Oct	Nov	Dec
	21.00	25.00	25.00	21.00	16.00	27.00	41.00	31.00	19.00	41.00	28.00	32.00

Year 3

SALES	Jan	Feb	Mar	Apr	May	Jun	Jul	Aug	Sep	Oct	Nov	Dec
	25.00	29.00	29.00	33.00	24.00	38.00	44.00	35.00	34.00	53.00	49.00	58.00

Year 4

SALES	Jan	Feb	Mar	Apr	May	Jun	Jul	Aug	Sep	Oct	Nov	Dec
	35.00	39.00	27.00	26.00	16.00	38.00	68.00	55.00	38.00	32.00	50.00	60.00

Year 5

SALES	Jan	Feb	Mar	Apr
	42.00	37.00	25.00	29.00

APPENDIX 3.3

	Jan	Feb	Mar	Apr	May	Jun	Jul	Aug	Sep	Oct	Nov	Dec
Year 1												
IAORDERS	116879.00	98278.00	94296.00	144179.00	95916.00	91973.00	54148.00	70848.00	86000.00	126354.00	108093.00	72775.00
Year 2												
IAORDERS	95492.00	115282.00	91322.00	81978.00	75954.00	86867.00	51908.00	97810.00	82093.00	109856.00	120602.00	133438.00
Year 3												
IAORDERS	114663.00	107617.00	207346.00	120273.00	117167.00	123525.00	147767.00	179166.00	152006.00	116321.00	159432.00	91848.00
Year 4												
IAORDERS	161330.00	101819.00	135435.00	97811.00	111706.00	208515.00	52369.00	161028.00	87258.00	150300.00	93827.00	120555.00
Year 5												
IAORDERS	98106.00	111575.00	107711.00	85363.00	70887.00	106390.00	56692.00	67102.00	53415.00	124616.00	57106.00	79260.00
Year 6												
IAORDERS	74657.00	110686.00	92901.00	104840.00	98476.00	113520.00	75912.00	143745.00	111625.00	124321.00	97937.00	96151.00

APPENDIX 3.4

Year	1	2	3	4	5	6
PEAK	9100.00	9800.00	11400.00	12430.00	12500.00	13700.00

Year	7	8	9	10	11	12
PEAK	15100.00	16000.00	18090.00	17670.00	19310.00	20900.00

Year	13	14	15	16	17	18
PEAK	23090.00	24450.00	27860.00	32100.00	30490.00	31780.00

Year	19	20	21	22	23	24
PEAK	36080.00	34560.00	35820.00	37740.00	39650.00	41110.00

Year	25	26	27	28	29	30
PEAK	40510.00	40640.00	41980.00	40970.00	41350.00	42110.00

Year	31	32	33	34		
PEAK	42800.00	44100.00	44230.00	42600.00		

4 Ratio models

The models dealt with in this chapter have not traditionally been regarded as forecasting models. This position has changed, however, in recent years with the widespread adoption of 'spreadsheet' modelling packages, which very often use ratio models as the basis on which to model business situations. By a ratio model we mean quite simply one that contains a number of variables that are observed to move in a reasonably predictable ratio to each other, so that given a forecast of one variable, we can derive through these ratios forecasts of the values of other variables. As a simple illustration, consider the problem of a company's closing balance sheet value of inventory. Examination of published accounts of larger companies shows that the ratio:

$$\text{closing value of inventory:sales} = \frac{\text{closing value of inventory}}{\text{sales}}$$

usually has a fairly constant value – r. So, if we wish to forecast next year's closing inventory, we can do so provided we have a forecast of next year's sales by the formula:

$$\text{forecast closing inventory} = r \times \text{forecast sales} \qquad (4.1)$$

This simple idea is at the heart of all ratio models. The example also brings out a number of features of this type of model. First, the models only work if there is some regularity in the behaviour of the ratios involved. Most usually this is simply that they remain reasonably constant over time. As our second model in this chapter will show, however, all that is really necessary is to be able to give a rule that describes how the ratios vary with time. Second, the ratios have to be estimated. Third, ratio models usually require a number of forecasts of other variables. A consequence of these latter two points is that the application of ratio models is often strongly dependent on the various forecasting methods described elsewhere in this book. To avoid repetition, the appropriate methods will be mentioned as the need arises in the discussions of the individual models of this chapter but will be described in detail in other chapters.

PREDICTING RATIOS

There would be no point in using ratio models if the ratios on which they were based could not be predicted. There are two major reasons why it is usually possible to do this: ratios often reflect actual physical processes within the organization; and many ratios are used as a basis for exerting managerial control.

Ratios such as that of inventory:sales are, in essence, determined by lags in the distribution, manufacturing and raw material purchasing systems of the firm. Since the times required for delivery or manufacture will not usually change dramatically without major changes in operating technology, the ratios are likely to show only a gentle and predictable downward drift due to continuous improvements in operating efficiency. Management control of key performance ratios such as return on assets is often achieved by means of setting target values for each of the individual ratios, e.g. direct cost:sales, which affect them. If ratios deviate from their target values, they become the focus of managerial efforts directed to restoring them to the intended value. The upshot is again to ensure that the values of the ratios can be predicted.

COMPUTING RATIO MODELS

On the whole, ratio models are more complex than most of the forecasting models described in other chapters. They usually contain several variables and occasionally several hundred. Since data need to be entered for many of these variables, they often involve substantial data management problems. Though they are mainly used to forecast accurately the outcome of certain decisions or events, they are frequently used to answer 'What if?' questions, i.e. to explore the consequences of some event that may or may not happen. They can, therefore, also be used in contingency planning applications as described in Chapter 1. This contrasts with time series modelling, for example, where the focus is on predicting what will happen in the future. A further rather special feature is their integrative nature. They tend to provide a broader picture of an organization suited to a wider range of managerial needs, including forecasting, than most of the other approaches we discuss.

During the 1960s and early 1970s a number of what we would now recognize as ratio models, but which were then called corporate models, were developed by large companies on their own computer systems. On the whole, they were far too expensive for most companies to construct; nor were they particularly simple to use. In banking and finance, on the other hand, there was a substantial tradition of building ratio models to forecast the cash requirements of new or expanding companies. These were a great deal simpler to apply than corporate models since they were much less ambitious. The way modelling was done, however, varied from one company to another and there was no standardization of software. This situation was changed by the advent of a number of special purpose software packages produced during the 1970s to develop ratio models primarily for the purposes of financial planning. The discovery that these packages could be made more accessible for the new user by the use of a 'spreadsheet' format has led over the last five years or so to an enormous expansion of their use. Typical examples of such packages are VISICALC and its derivatives and LOTUS 1-2-3. As the market for such packages has developed, they have tended to revert to the use of a formally defined model rather than the rows or columns of a spreadsheet which can be somewhat restrictive when models become larger. For more sophisticated uses of ratio models there are considerable advantages to such an approach. Giving the variables mnemonic names and writing equations to define the forecast model makes the model much easier to understand for other managers or when the model builder returns to them after an interval of several months. For this reason, just such a language, SYSTEM W, was used to develop the models in this chapter. Since, however, we wish to explore ratio models from a more general point of view, they will be presented in this chapter in longhand, i.e. variables and ratios appearing in the equations will be written out in full. Those familiar with other languages or spreadsheet packages should readily be able to formulate the models by reference to the model descriptions presented in this chapter.

USES OF RATIO MODELS

Though the impetus for the development of software has come from its use in financial modelling, ratio models are certainly not only of interest to accountants. There are many reasons why managers concerned with, say, marketing or production might wish to build financial models. Furthermore the fact that variables move in a fairly constant ratio to each other is a very widespread phenomenon in business, economic and social systems. Indeed in, for example, modelling the effects of inflation through the use of forecasts of future price indices, we are essentially defining ratio models as the appropriate ones to use. These models can then be applied to many other types of situation relevant to managers. We shall examine two here: so-called 'vehicle park' models and input/output models.

Traditionally, ratio models were mainly used in finance, for determining future cash needs. A more comprehensive, though scarcely complete, list of their uses would be:

1 forecasting for the purposes of budgeting or target setting, including manpower planning;
2 assessing the creditworthiness of companies;
3 forecasting future uses of and sources of financial resources for determining the timing of new equity issues, etc.;
4 appraising takeover candidates and their fit with the company;
5 evaluating the strengths and weaknesses of competitors or the benefits that adoption of specific products of our organization can bring customers;
6 contingency planning: the examination of the implications of major threats and opportunities posed by the environment.

We have already noted that ratio models can incorporate inflation effects in a natural way. This ability to account for a pressing managerial concern for much of the past decade is probably one reason for the growth in their popularity. For simplicity we shall omit those effects from the examples presented. The reader should bear in mind, therefore, that in practice most such models require additional equations representing the effects of inflation.

Since this is a book on forecasting rather than finance, it will be assumed that the reader is familiar with basic accounting concepts.

PAYBACK MANUFACTURING LTD

As our first example we consider the case of John Smith, Managing Director and Chairman of Payback Manufacturing Ltd. Some 20 months ago the company took out a bank loan to finance partially the start-up of the company, which manufactures products for sale to the retail trade. It is only in the past few months, however, that the company has been able to start building up its sales. It was a condition of the original loan that the company repay it within two years. Therefore John Smith wishes to examine whether that can be accomplished during the next four months, i.e. to forecast when the loan will be repaid.

In this type of modelling there is always a choice of basis on which to develop the model. It can be done in terms of the cash flows of the business or in terms of sources and uses of funds. Broadly speaking the cash flow approach is better suited to smaller businesses where the major cash flows are relatively few in number, whereas the flow of funds approach is usually simpler for larger businesses. We shall give an example of each approach. For Payback Manufacturing a cash flow model will be constructed. The starting point is to identify the cash inflows and outflows as listed in Table 4.1. In this case, the natural time period is a month.

Table 4.1
Cash inflows and outflows over a month

CASH INFLOWS	CASH OUTFLOWS
Cash from sales	Payments to suppliers
	Wages and fixed costs, e.g. rent
	Loan interest payments
	Tax payments
	Capital expenditure
	Loan repayments

The model is a very simple one intended to focus on John Smith's specific problem. The variables involved are listed in Table 4.2. Those that are directly computed using ratios have been italicized. The names of ratios are shown in lower case. The names of other variables are shown in upper case. This convention will be adhered to throughout the remainder of the chapter. It is assumed that forecasts of sales and variables such as wages and fixed costs over the next four months (months 1–4) have already been derived by John Smith by some other means and that the values of the relevant ratios have already been estimated, too.

Table 4.2
Variables in cash flow model

SALES
CASH FROM SALES
DIRECT COSTS (RAW MATERIALS, ETC.)
PAYMENTS TO SUPPLIERS
WAGES AND FIXED COSTS
INTEREST PAYMENTS
TAX PAYMENTS
CAPITAL INVESTMENT
LOAN REPAYMENTS
CASH
LOAN
proportion of sales paid same month
proportion of sales paid following month
direct costs:sales ratio
proportion of direct costs paid same month
proportion of direct costs paid following month
interest rate (per month)

Before presenting the equations for the model it will be convenient to illustrate the process of ratio modelling by considering a simplified version that will be computed manually. The computations are given in Table 4.3. The basis of them will now be discussed.

The starting point of the computations is the actual sales for the past month (month 0) and the forecast sales for months 1–4 (i.e. the next four months), as entered in the first row of the table. The next row gives the cash inflow from sales. This is assumed to be 95 per cent of this month's sales plus 5 per cent of last month's

Table 4.3
Ratio modelling by manual computation

| | Month | | | | |
	0	1	2	3	4
SALES	801.00	865.00	930.00	1003.00	1075.00
CASH FROM SALES	–	861.80	926.75	999.35	1071.40
DIRECT COSTS	744.93	804.45	864.90	932.79	999.75
PAYMENTS TO SUPPLIERS	–	751.48	811.10	872.37	940.16
WAGES AND FIXED COSTS	–	32.00	32.00	33.10	33.70
INTEREST PAYMENTS	–	4.24	4.24	4.24	4.24
TAX PAYMENTS	–	28.30	0	0	0
CAPITAL INVESTMENT	–	0	0	25.00	0
LOAN REPAYMENTS	–	0	0	0	212.00
CASH	13.00	58.78	138.19	202.84	84.14
LOAN	212.00	212.00	212.00	212.00	0

sales, i.e. 5 per cent of sales are not paid until one month after they are made. For simplicity, we are assuming no bad debts. The second row is readily computed for months 1–4 from the first. Note that the value of sales for month 0 is required for this purpose. The next row gives the direct costs of sales, i.e. of the various raw material and other costs in manufacturing them. This is assumed to be 93 per cent of SALES.

The payments to suppliers associated with these costs are not all made immediately. More specifically, we assume that 11 per cent of them are paid in the month when the goods are sold and the remaining 89 per cent the following month. The fourth row of the table is calculated in this way. Note that to effect this calculation the value of DIRECT COSTS for month 0 is needed.

The fifth row of the table WAGES AND FIXED COSTS represents a pair of items that can rarely be forecast using ratios in a small business. For simplicity, they have been combined here. It is assumed that forecasts have been derived for this item as entered in that row. INTEREST PAYMENTS are given in the sixth row of the table. They are assumed to be charged at 2 per cent of the previous month's loan outstanding. TAX PAYMENTS (row 7) again can rarely be forecast with any accuracy in small new businesses. The actual timing of them within the year can also be very erratic. Here it is assumed that a payment of 28.30 is to be made in month 1 and nothing in the other months. The eighth row contains CAPITAL INVESTMENT. Again this item is not suited to forecasting by ratios in a small business. It is assumed that a forecast of the actual cash spent on capital investment is available. In fact, this is 25.00 in month 3. The ninth row represents the LOAN REPAYMENTS. The full amount outstanding (see row 10) of 212.00 is repaid at the end of month 4. The tenth row of the table is readily computed by: subtracting from the cash inflow in row 2 the various cash outflows in rows 4–9; and adding the corresponding net cash flow for the month to the CASH at the end of the previous month. For month 1, for instance, the net cash flow is found to be 45.78, which, when added to the month 0 CASH of 13.00 gives the month 1 value of CASH as 58.78. It will be noted, incidentally, that the forecast is that the loan can be repaid at the end of month 4 without difficulty. Finally, the eleventh row merely keeps track of the value of LOAN, which, of course, drops to zero at the end of month 4.

Though this example is a simple one, it illustrates the key features of such models. Many variables are computed by means of ratios. The computations can in some cases, e.g. CASH FROM SALES here, require that past values of variables be available, in this case month 0 SALES. Again, some variables cannot be forecast using ratios, e.g. TAX PAYMENTS. These must be forecast directly. Finally, the model requires the values of a number of ratios. Here their actual numerical values were used. Though convenient for manual calculation this is undesirable if calculations are to be carried out by computer, since an important question is how the forecasts are affected by changes to these ratios.

The computer model

Model equations. One of the key operations in the use of any financial planning language is the specification of the model. Even though the example just considered represents a simplified version of a very simple model, it would be somewhat tedious merely to extend the calculations to cover the next financial year. In practice, ratio models need to be recomputed many times under differing sets of assumptions. It is, therefore, essential to formulate them using some suitable modelling package. The first key step in using such a package is to specify the equations of the ratio model. Because our current model is a simple one, it is possible to specify them as a single block (Equations 4.2):

CASH FROM SALES = proportion sales paid same month ×
SALES
+ proportion sales paid following month
× SALES (−1)

DIRECT COSTS = direct costs:sales ratio × SALES

PAYMENTS TO
SUPPLIERS
= proportion direct costs paid same month
× DIRECT COSTS
+ proportion direct costs paid following
month × DIRECT COSTS (−1)

INTEREST = interest rate × LOAN (−1)

CASH = CASH (−1) + CASH FROM SALES
− PAYMENTS TO SUPPLIERS
− WAGES AND FIXED COSTS − TAX
PAYMENTS − INTEREST
PAYMENTS
− LOAN REPAYMENTS

LOAN = LOAN (−1) − LOAN REPAYMENTS
(4.2)

The equations merely describe algebraically the computations of Table 4.1 taking into account the variable definitions of Table 4.2. The notation CASH (−1), etc, is used to represent the previous period's value of the variable concerned. Thus in Month 1, CASH (−1) is the value of CASH at the end of month 0, i.e. 13.00. We shall need this notation frequently in what follows.

The model data. Another key operation in using a financial planning language is to supply the model with the data needed to run it. Data need to be supplied for all variables used in the computations but for which no rule to compute their value is available. Any financial model involves the use of time periods; those that we wish to forecast ahead for and, in most cases, certain past periods for which data are required. For our forecast periods it is necessary to supply values for those variables that appear in Table 4.2 but for which no equation appears in Equations 4.2. This includes the model ratios and period-by-period sales forecasts. For past periods it is only necessary to supply data implicitly referenced by the model equations. Thus the equation for the variable LOAN involves the previous period's value of LOAN. The value of the loan in month 0 must, therefore, be supplied. The data needed to run the model are shown in Table 4.4. The dashes (–) in the table indicate data values that are not required for the computation, a convention that will be adhered to hereafter.

Table 4.4
Data needed to run model

| | Month | | | | |
	0	1	2	3	4
SALES	801.00	865.00	930.00	1003.00	1075.00
DIRECT COSTS	744.93	–	–	–	–
WAGES AND FIXED COSTS	–	32.00	32.00	33.10	33.70
TAX PAYMENTS	–	28.30	0	0	0
CAPITAL INVESTMENT	–	0	0	25.00	0
LOAN REPAYMENTS	–	0	0	0	212.00
CASH	13.00	–	–	–	–
LOAN	212.00	–	–	–	–
proportion sales paid same month	–	0.95	0.95	0.95	0.95
proportion sales paid following month	–	0.05	0.05	0.05	0.05
direct costs:sales ratio	–	0.93	0.93	0.93	0.93
proportion direct costs paid same month	–	0.11	0.11	0.11	0.11
proportion direct costs paid following month	–	0.89	0.89	0.89	0.89
interest rate	–	0.02	0.02	0.02	0.02

Running the model. Having entered the data we are at last in a position to run the model and to print the results. Most sophisticated financial planning languages provide extensive facilities for report generation. Selected variables can be displayed in whatever format is required. Here, though, we shall not print the results of the computations since these would be identical to those in Table 4.4

Contingency planning. As we saw in Chapter 1, one reason forecasts are needed is for contingency planning. Ratio models are well suited to this purpose. The process can be illustrated by considering another of John Smith's problems. His business is in the rather unusual situation of requiring less working capital as sales increase, because most of his sales are for cash, whereas his major supplier extends him 30 days' credit. He has recently heard rumours, however, that his major supplier is considering tightening its credit terms and requiring cash payments from its smaller customers. He therefore wishes to evaluate the impact of such a change in his supplier's policy. This would have the effect of changing the model ratios: proportion direct costs paid in same month and proportion direct costs paid in following months to 1.0 and zero, respectively. If these changes are made to the data of Table 4.4, results are obtained as shown in Table 4.5. As can be seen, the loan cannot now be paid off at the end of month 4, as shown by the negative cash balance in month 4.

As a first stage in contingency planning John Smith examines what reduction in the direct costs:sales ratio would be necessary to allow the loan to be repaid in month 4. This clearly involves experimenting with different values of the ratio. He finds that if it is reduced to 0.89, the loan can now be repaid. Specifically, the month 1, month 2, month 3 and month 4 values of CASH are: 40.41, 103.22, 147.56 and 12.27, respectively.

Such a reduction in the direct costs:sales ratio would represent a discount of about 5 per cent from his major supplier for cash – by no means impossible. As a result of these investigations, John Smith decides to:

1 press his supplier's representative for such a discount for cash or alternatively to be allowed to retain his present credit terms, if the threatened policy change materializes;

2 look into the possibility of finding another supplier who will offer him lower prices if he pays cash.

Table 4.5
Result of changes made to Table 4.4

	Month				
	0	1	2	3	4
SALES	801.00	865.00	930.00	1003.00	1075.00
CASH FROM SALES	–	861.80	926.75	999.35	1071.40
DIRECT COSTS	744.93	804.45	864.90	932.79	999.75
PAYMENTS TO SUPPLIERS	–	804.45	864.90	932.79	999.75
WAGES AND FIXED COSTS	–	32.00	32.00	33.10	33.70
INTEREST PAYMENTS	–	4.24	4.24	4.24	4.24
TAX PAYMENTS	–	28.30	0	0	0
CAPITAL INVESTMENT	–	0	0	25.00	0
LOAN REPAYMENTS	–	0	0	0	212.00
CASH	13.00	5.81	31.42	35.64	– 142.65
LOAN	212.00	212.00	212.00	212.00	0

To use ratio models for contingency planning is essentially equivalent to carrying out a sensitivity analysis, i.e. examining the impact of changes to some of the forecasts and ratios used in the model. In general the process of sensitivity analysis will need to be applied to a variety of model data. There will usually be several ratios whose value is somewhat uncertain plus various forecasts that will also be subject to error. Because the need for sensitivity analysis is so great, any reasonable financial planning language will incorporate special facilities to make it easy to carry out.

ESTIMATING THE RATIOS

In our first example we passed over the question of how the ratios were estimated. It is convenient to focus on a particular ratio in the Payback Manufacturing model, the direct costs:sales turnover ratio, though the methods to be outlined are quite general.

The first approach that John Smith might have taken is to derive the estimates subjectively. Under those circumstances the value of 0.93 that was assumed for the ratio would represent his 'best guess' at its value. This approach is particularly suitable where substantial change has made past data misleading or where data are lacking, e.g. when the model is concerned with a new venture. The other approaches involve estimation from past data. The simplest, and probably the most common, such method is to average the ratios obtained over several months. Thus suppose John Smith actually had the following data for sales turnover and direct costs for the previous two months as given in Table 4.6. Averaging of the two ratios obtained by dividing direct costs by the corresponding sales turnover gives the value 0.93 to 2 decimal places.

Table 4.6
Data for sales turnover and direct costs

	Month −2	Month −1	Total
Direct costs	780	801	1581
Sales turnover	830	870	1700
Ratio	0.940	0.921	

The advantage of this approach is that it requires the calculation of the ratio for each month we have data, thus enabling any anomalous values of the ratio to be identified. Where the ratio is reasonably constant, however, a simpler approach can be adopted. We start by adding along each of the rows in Table 4.6. This gives a row total of 1,581 for the direct costs row and 1,700 for the sales turnover row. To obtain an estimate of the ratio we now divide one number by the other giving 0.93 to 2 decimal places. It should be emphasized that these two methods are different and can lead to different results. However, where the ratios are fairly constant there will be little practical difference between them.

Both these methods, as far as the statistician is concerned, might be criticized. From the statistical viewpoint a somewhat better procedure is the following:

1 create a third row of the table by multiplying the direct cost

(ratio numerator) value by the corresponding sales turnover value;
2 create a fourth row by multiplying the sales turnover (ratio denominator) value by itself;
3 total the rows;
4 estimate the ratio by dividing the row 3 total by the row 4 total.

In this case this leads to the situation shown in Table 4.7.

Table 4.7
Estimation of ratio

	Month -2	Month -1	Total
Direct costs	780	801	
Sales turnover	830	870	
Row 1 × Row 2	647400	696870	1344270
Row 2 × Row 2	688900	756900	1455800

This again gives an estimate of the ratio of 0.93 to 2 decimal places. The virtue of this approach is not that it is more respectable to a statistician but that it is equivalent to a regression approach. This means that estimates of ratios can be determined using the regression methods described in the next chapter. Where there are a number of ratios to be determined and we have a fairly large number of past periods for which there are data, this is usually more convenient, at least with the more powerful financial modelling languages. It is usual for them to offer the facility of applying a variety of forecasting methods including regression to the data. This allows the forecaster to derive his ratios during the modelling process without recourse to auxiliary manual calculations.

MORE COMPLEX FINANCIAL MODELS

The simple example just considered was built around a model of cash flows within the business. In many situations, however, we wish to introduce balance sheet and income statement variables into the model. There are two common reasons for this. First, many ratios involving balance sheet variables, e.g. current assets:sales turn-over are reasonably constant. Similarly many income statement ratios, e.g. fixed costs:sales turnover are also fairly constant. It is, therefore, convenient to base the model on them. Secondly, much of the assessment of companies by outsiders, e.g. investors, is done partly via the income statement and balance sheet. There is then an obvious need to forecast their evolution.

Such models are most naturally constructed using a flow of funds approach. The starting point for the construction of such a model is the selection of a number of balance sheet variables and a set of income statement variables. It is always a matter of judgement as to which variables should be selected. Rather than dealing with current assets, for example, we could split this down into the variables cash, stocks, etc. On the whole simplicity is to be preferred because the ratios associated with more highly aggregated variables are likely to be more stable and the models are cheaper to compute. For modell-ing several years ahead the items appearing in the company's pub-lished accounts often provide a reasonable basis on which to build the model. For shorter term models covering a year or so ahead the items appearing in the management accounts are likely to be a better choice.

A notion that will be useful in building up the model that follows is the standard equation for updating a balance sheet variable. This takes the form:

New value of balance sheet variable = previous value of the
variable
+ previous period's inflow
to variable
− previous period's outflow
from variable   (4.3)

By way of example consider the variable fixed assets. The correspond-ing inflow variable is investment (in fixed assets); the corresponding outflow variable is depreciation. Equation 4.3 applied to the balance sheet variable fixed assets accordingly reads:

This period's fixed assets = previous period's fixed assets
+ investment during period
− depreciation during period

THE HIGH TECH LEARNING COMPANY

As an example of this more complex type of financial model, let us consider the case of the High Tech Learning Company, a five-year-old company in a rapidly developing industry. Management are faced with the prospect of their present product line reaching its peak sales within a few years. Hitherto they have not been profitable, but they hope that, given expanding sales and declining production costs per unit they should become so in the next year or so. They wish to forecast their needs for external finance over the next three years. This is likely to take the form of relatively expensive short term debt and there are limits on the permissible ratio of short term debt to equity of about 50 per cent as far as their bankers are concerned. Because the time span of interest is longer here, we shall adopt an annual model, i.e. our time period will be a year.

The balance sheet variables we shall use are as follows:

ASSETS	LIABILITIES
Working capital	Short term debt
Fixed assets	Current taxation
	Equity

Our income statement variables for the model are:

Sales turnover
Cost of goods sold
Fixed costs
Profit before depreciation and interest
Depreciation
Interest on short term debt
Net profit before tax
Corporation tax payable
Profit after tax
Dividends
Retained earnings

The italicized variables are those that are forecast using ratios. With the exception of cost of goods sold, all the ratios are assumed constant. In the case of cost of goods sold, we assume that a trend curve has been fitted to the ratio to represent a decline in costs as efficiency increases (see Chapter 9). Sales turnover is assumed to follow an S-shaped market growth curve, which is again described in Chapter 9. Thus we note again the phenomenon encountered in the previous example of the dependence of ratio models on forecasts derived by other methods. We shall assume that the forecasts of future sales and the cost of goods:sales ratio are available as data for use in the model to be described.

Other balance sheet inflows and outflows

The retained earnings variable from the income statement defines the inflow into shareholders' equity. There are a number of other inflows and outflows to balance sheet variables that need to be defined, however. These are:

Investment
Tax paid
Exceptional write-offs

The italicized variable (investment) is again forecast using a ratio. The exceptional write-offs variable is the outflow to equity and represents the impact of exceptional profits or losses on shareholders' equity. In most cases these are small compared with retained earnings and are often ignored for the sake of simplicity. Here they will be assumed to be zero.

Other variables

It is usually convenient to introduce certain other variables in the model to make it clearer. Most will be discussed as we go. Two, however, are worthy of especial remark. Obviously, given the principles of double entry, the balance sheet totals of assets and liabilities should be equal at the end of each period. It is therefore a useful check to compute total assets and total liabilities.

The model

The variables appearing in this model are listed in Table 4.8. As before, variables whose values are determined using ratios are italicized. Ratios are as before shown in lower case and other model variables in upper case.

Table 4.8
Variables appearing in model

SALES
COST OF GOODS SOLD
GROSS MARGIN
FIXED COSTS
PROFIT BEFORE DEPRECIATION AND INTEREST
DEPRECIATION
INTEREST
PROFIT BEFORE TAX
TAX
PROFIT AFTER TAX
DIVIDENDS
RETAINED EARNINGS
INVESTMENT IN FIXED ASSETS
FIXED ASSETS
TAX PAID
TAXATION
EQUITY
EXCEPTIONAL WRITE-OFFS
CURRENT ASSETS
OTHER CURRENT LIABILITIES (EXCLUDING SHORT TERM DEBT)
WORKING CAPITAL INCREASE
INCREASE IN FIXED ASSETS
EQUITY INCREASE
SHORT TERM DEBT
TOTAL ASSETS
TOTAL LIABILITIES
cost of goods sold:sales ratio
fixed costs:sales ratio
interest rate
corporation tax rate
dividends:profit after tax ratio
marginal fixed assets:sales ratio
current assets:sales ratio
other current liabilities:sales ratio

The model is given in Equations 4.4a to 4.4g. It will now be discussed in detail in terms of groups of equations that fall naturally together.

1 Cost of goods sold

$$\text{COST OF GOODS SOLD} = \text{cost of goods sold:sales ratio} \times \text{SALES}$$

$$(4.4a)$$

The cost of goods sold is obtained by multiplying sales turnover by the current value of the ratio of cost of goods sold:sales. As stated earlier, this is assumed to be declining with time.

2 Profit computations.

The equations for the computation of profits and retained earnings are given in equations (4.4b). Given the calculation of the cost of goods sold, gross margin follows automatically. Fixed costs are computed by applying a ratio to sales.

A slight complication is involved in the computation of interest. In this case the value of the interest payments is computed by applying the interest rate to the average of the value of short term debt at the end of the previous period, SHORT TERM DEBT (-1), and its value at the end of the period, SHORT TERM DEBT. The remaining equations through to net profit before tax are straightforward. Corporation tax, for simplicity, is calculated at the standard rate and ignores the complications that may occur in practice in modelling tax. Dividends are modelled as being in a fixed ratio to profit after tax, an approximation that often works well. The retained earnings calculation then follows.

$$\text{GROSS MARGIN} = \text{SALES} - \text{COST OF GOODS SOLD}$$

$$\text{FIXED COSTS} = \text{fixed costs:sales ratio} \times \text{SALES}$$

$$\text{PROFIT BEFORE DEPRECIATION AND INTEREST} = \text{GROSS MARGIN} - \text{FIXED COSTS}$$

$$\text{DEPRECIATION} = \text{depreciation:fixed assets} \times \text{FIXED ASSETS}$$

$$\text{INTEREST} = \text{interest rate} \times [\text{SHORT TERM DEBT} (-1) + \text{SHORT TERM DEBT}]/2$$

$$\text{PROFIT BEFORE TAX} = \text{PROFIT BEFORE DEPRECIATION AND INTEREST} - \text{DEPRECIATION} - \text{INTEREST}$$

TAX = corporation tax rate × PROFIT BEFORE TAX

PROFIT AFTER TAX = PROFIT BEFORE TAX − TAX

DIVIDENDS = dividends:profit after tax ratio × PROFIT AFTER TAX

RETAINED EARNINGS = PROFIT AFTER TAX − DIVIDENDS (4.4b)

3 Fixed asset calculations. The calculation of depreciation has already been discussed. The other component of fixed assets, investment in fixed assets, is here calculated using the idea of a marginal capital:output ratio. It is often the case that the capital cost of fixed assets for an annual increase in sales of $1 (the marginal capital:output ratio) is fairly constant and this leads to a convenient ratio model for investment in fixed assets. The increase in sales over the year is: SALES − SALES (−1). Accordingly, the capital investment required to support that is obtained by multiplying that increase by the marginal capital:output ratio. The value of fixed assets then follows via the standard update equation. This block of equations is given in equations (4.4c).

INVESTMENT IN FIXED ASSETS = marginal capital:output ratio × [SALES − SALES (−1)]

FIXED ASSETS = FIXED ASSETS (−1) + INVESTMENT IN FIXED ASSETS − DEPRECIATION (4.4c)

4 Tax paid and taxation. The approach taken to determining tax payable has already been described. The determination of tax paid also poses problems in practice. Once again, since our purposes are illustrative only, we take the very simple rule that tax is paid one year in arrear, i.e. this year's tax paid is last year's tax payable. The value of TAXATION then follows from the standard update equation as shown in equations (4.4d).

TAX PAID = TAXATION (−1)

TAXATION = TAXATION (−1) + TAX − TAX PAID (4.4d)

5 Equity. The value of equity is determined straightforwardly from the computed value of retained earnings and the value supplied for

exceptional write-offs using the standard update equation as shown in equations (4.4e).

EQUITY = EQUITY (−1) + RETAINED EARNINGS −
    EXCEPTIONAL WRITE-OFFS   (4.4e)

6 Current assets and other current liabilities. Both current assets and other current liabilities are determined by simple ratio calculations as shown in equations (4.4f).

CURRENT ASSETS = current assets:sales ratio × SALES

OTHER CURRENT LIABILITIES = other current liabilities:
       sales × SALES   (4.4f)

7 Short term debt, total assets and liabilities. In any model which contains a balance sheet it is always necessary to determine one of the balance sheet variables in such a way that the basic principles of double entry are met, i.e. that asset totals are equal to corresponding liability totals. Such variables are often referred to as 'plug' variables, since they are 'plugged' into one or other side of the balance sheet to ensure the equality of total assets and total liabilities. Often, however, in the early stages of model construction one or more variables is omitted from the model. This usually shows itself in a difference between the value of total assets and the value of total liabilities. A check that they are equal should, therefore, always be carried out as a matter of good modelling practice. We are now in a position to determine the value of the 'plug' variable which in this case is short term debt. For completeness the computations of the check variables total assets and total liabilities are given, too. The calculations are shown in equations (4.4g).

WORKING CAPITAL INCREASE = CURRENT ASSETS −
CURRENT ASSETS (−1) − OTHER CURRENT
LIABILITIES + OTHER CURRENT LIABILITIES (−1) −
    TAXATION + TAXATION (−1)

FIXED ASSET INCREASE = INVESTMENT −
      DEPRECIATION

EQUITY INCREASE = RETAINED EARNINGS −
    EXCEPTIONAL WRITE-OFFS

SHORT TERM DEBT = SHORT TERM DEBT (-1) +
WORKING CAPITAL INCREASE + FIXED ASSET
INCREASE $-$ EQUITY INCREASE

TOTAL ASSETS = CURRENT ASSETS + FIXED ASSETS
TOTAL LIABILITIES = OTHER CURRENT LIABILITIES
+ SHORT TERM DEBT + TAXATION + EQUITY   (4.4g)

Following a flow of funds approach, it is convenient to compute the increase in short term debt during the period. The first step is to compute the increase in working capital excluding short term debt by subtracting from the increase in current assets, the increase in other current liabilities and the increase in current taxation. The increase in fixed assets is readily computed and the increase in equity similarly. The increase in short term debt is, in fact, the increase in working capital (exclusive of short term debt) plus the increase in fixed assets, minus the increase in equity. The equation for the new value of short term debt then follows.

Model data

As in the previous example, data must be supplied for variables whose previous values are used. Again for the forecast periods, data are needed for those variables that cannot be computed. The values of those variables for years 0–3 are shown in Table 4.9, as are the values of the various ratios in the model. By year 0 we understand the year before the start of the forecast period, years 1–3. As before dashes indicate data values that are not required to run the model.

Calculations and results

The results of calculating the model are given in Table 4.10. Because of the larger number of variables the printout has been restricted essentially to income statement and balance sheet variables. It will be noted that the ratio of short term debt to equity never reaches 50 per cent. In this respect the forecasts are more satisfactory than in the previous example. Nevertheless, High Tech Learning would, without doubt, wish to undertake a number of sensitivity analyses to establish that no plausible changes to the various ratios and

Table 4.9
Values of variables for years 0–3

	Year 0	Year 1	Year 2	Year 3
SALES	1400	1708	1978	2185
FIXED ASSETS	1700	–	–	–
EQUITY	1500	–	–	–
TAXATION	0	–	–	–
EXCEPTIONAL WRITE-OFFS	–	0	0	0
SHORT TERM DEBT	200	–	–	–
fixed costs:sales	–	0.37	0.37	0.37
cost of goods sold:sales	–	0.376	0.361	0.349
marginal capital:output ratio	–	1.30	1.30	1.30
depreciation:fixed assets	–	0.20	0.20	0.20
interest rate	–	0.16	0.16	0.16
corporation tax rate	–	0.50	0.50	0.50
dividends:profit after tax	–	0.55	0.55	0.55
current assets:sales	–	0.40	0.40	0.40
other current liabilities:sales	–	0.20	0.20	0.20

forecasts involved could cause that limit to be exceeded. We shall, therefore, now consider the question of sensitivity analysis in greater depth.

Sensitivity analysis

In principle, any forecasts derived by a ratio model can be affected by changes to the various data used by the model. Typically, these data are either 'driver series' for which forecasts are supplied, e.g. SALES in the present case, or the various ratios that are used in the model. In practice, there are usually only a few items of data that, if plausible changes are made to them, have a significant effect on the forecasts produced by any particular model. Since all these items may simultaneously be in error, however, the effort required to carry out a sensitivity analysis for a model of any size can be very considerable. To reduce the effort it is necessary to determine

133

Table 4.10
Results of calculating the model

	Year 1	Year 2	Year 3
SALES	1708.00	1978.00	2185.00
PROFIT BEFORE DEPRECIATION AND			
INTEREST	427.00	534.06	611.80
DEPRECIATION	340.00	352.08	351.86
INTEREST	62.75	93.58	83.66
NET PROFIT BEFORE TAX	24.25	88.40	176.27
TAX	12.12	44.20	88.14
PROFIT AFTER TAX	12.12	44.20	88.14
DIVIDENDS	6.67	24.31	48.47
RETAINED EARNINGS	5.46	19.89	39.66
Balance sheet			
CURRENT ASSETS	683.20	791.20	874.00
FIXED ASSETS	1760.40	1759.32	1676.56
TOTAL ASSETS	2443.60	2550.52	2550.56
SHORT TERM DEBT	584.42	585.38	460.41
OTHER CURRENT LIABILITIES	341.60	395.60	437.00
TAXATION	12.12	44.20	88.14
EQUITY	1505.46	1525.34	1565.01
TOTAL LIABILITIES	2443.60	2550.52	2550.56

which items of data will have a significant impact on the forecasts, if changed; and to provide approximate methods that enable the manager to gain some feel for the range of values possible for the variables of interest, i.e. to construct informal confidence intervals.

To reduce the effort required in the first stage of the analysis, it is usually best to estimate the maximum likely error in a particular data item in any period and apply this change to that variable in each period and examine its effects on the forecasts. This takes into account that errors in a particular data item may have a significant effect either because errors in that item are very large or because the model forecasts are very sensitive to changes in it. More sophisticated financial planning packages usually provide some mechanism to automate this procedure.

In the present example there are two 'driver series', SALES and EXCEPTIONAL WRITE-OFFS. Assume that after some thought it is decided that the maximum error that might occur in SALES is in year 3 and is about 23 per cent and that there is no reason to expect EXCEPTIONAL WRITE-OFFS to differ from zero. Of the eight ratios in the model the maximum errors that the manager is willing to contemplate are: cost of goods sold:sales 8 per cent (i.e. since this ratio varies from year to year the 8 per cent is applied to each year's value), corporation tax rate 10 per cent, current assets: sales 20 per cent, depreciation:fixed assets 10 per cent, fixed costs:sales 16 per cent, interest rate 25 per cent, marginal capital output ratio 19 per cent, other current liabilities:sales 8 per cent. Note that the percentages given are the maximum possible numerical percentage changes in the ratios concerned. If the manager expects a negative change in some item to have a larger impact than a positive change, he should, of course, make a negative change. Most often, however, practicality dictates that all the changes be made either positive or negative. Certainly this is likely to be the case if the financial planning package being used provides automatic sensitivity analysis features.

The estimates of maximum numerical percentage error may, of course, arise as a by-product of another forecasting process, e.g. the errors in SALES and cost of goods sold:sales here. Alternatively, they may represent the manager's own feelings as to what is conceivable, e.g. the error in corporation tax rate in this case.

In financial modelling it is rare that we are interested in forecasts of one variable only. Since, though, the same procedure needs to be repeated for each variable of interest, we shall focus on the ratio of short term debt to equity in this particular instance. The first stage is to apply the maximum changes listed above to the model one at a time and observe the effect on the model. These effects can then be ranked in descending numerical order. Usually only a few of the effects will turn out to be significant enough to warrant further detailed investigation. In this case, those effects are associated with changes to SALES, cost of goods sold:sales, current assets:sales, fixed costs:sales and the marginal capital output ratio. The next step is to apply the maximum changes in each of the variables considered in stage 1 in such a way as to maximize the change in the variable(s) of interest. If this maximum change is acceptable, there is no need for the manager to concern himself further with the impact of errors on the forecasts. In practice, this is rarely the case. Indeed it is not here, so it is now necessary to proceed to the second stage of sensitivity analysis.

Though the first stage of sensitivity analysis involves a fair amount of computation, the next stage involves much more. This is because it addresses two problems that were not dealt with in the first stage: the size of the errors in some of the variables may depend on the time period; and errors may occur in all the variables at once. Both these factors cause a substantial increase in the computation required. Therefore, the first stage of analysis is indispensable, if the manager is not to be swamped by the output from these sensitivity analyses. Furthermore, to deal with the second of our problems above it is necessary to adopt rather approximate methods. The aim should, in our view, be to obtain some 'feel' for the likely margin of error in the forecasts without being overwhelmed by impossible amounts of computation and output. The way this is done is to generate errors randomly in each of the variables selected for further study as a result of stage 1 and apply these errors to the model and observe the results. A number of such sets of errors is generated and applied to the model. In this way a picture can be built up of the likely range of errors in the ratio of short term debt:equity.

Some sophisticated financial planning languages provide the facilities to do this automatically. We shall illustrate the process assuming that the manager generates his random errors by dice throwing. The first step of the process is to determine what set of errors is of interest. Here we assume that these are: SALES in year 1, SALES in year 2, SALES in year 3, the current assets:sales ratio, the fixed costs:sales ratio, the marginal capital output ratio and the cost of goods sold:sales ratio. Next we consider the distribution of errors in each of these variables. We select seven points for each variable in such a way that they divide the range of possible errors into six equally likely 'chunks'. We then select the mid-point of each of these 'chunks'. The process is illustrated in Table 4.11, which gives the distributions of errors of interest here. The mid-points of the 'chunks' are in italics beneath the relevant row. For all variables save the cost of goods sold:sales ratio it is convenient to give the actual values that result from applying the various percentages. For the cost of goods sold:sales ratio, however, it is necessary to show the percentage changes that are applied to the value of the ratio originally assumed for each year.

The error distributions can be set up using the manager's own

Table 4.11
Application of random errors to the model

SALES 1	1488	*1558*	1628	*1653*	1678	*1693*	1708	*1723*	1738	*1763*	1788	*1858*	1928
SALES 2	1508	*1643*	1778	*2717*	1878	*1928*	1978	*2028*	2078	*2138*	2178	*2313*	2448
SALES 3	1665	*1785*	1885	*1975*	2065	*2125*	2185	*2245*	2305	*2395*	2485	*2585*	2685
current assets: sales	0.36	*.370*	0.38	*.385*	0.39	*.395*	0.40	*.405*	0.41	*.420*	0.43	*.455*	0.48
fixed costs: sales	0.34	*.345*	0.35	*.355*	0.36	*.365*	0.37	*.380*	0.39	*.400*	0.41	*.420*	0.43
marginal capital output ratio	1.25	*1.255*	1.26	*1.270*	1.28	*1.290*	1.30	*1.380*	1.46	*1.480*	1.50	*1.525*	1.55
cost of goods sold: sales	−2.00%	*−1.75%*	−1.50%	*−1.25%*	−1.00%	*−0.5%*	0%	*+1.00%*	+2.00%	*+3.00%*	+4.00%	*+6.00%*	+8.00%
Dice throw		*1*		*2*		*3*		*4*		*5*		*6*	

137

judgement or from confidence intervals produced by other forecasting methods where appropriate. Each distribution has the same intepretation. We shall illustrate it using the first variable SALES 1. For this variable there is a 50 per cent chance that the true value will be above the middle value in the row, i.e. 1,708 (the forecast value assumed in our first model run). There is a zero chance that SALES 1 will be less than the left hand value, i.e. 1,488, and a zero chance it will be greater than the extreme right hand value (1,928). There is a 1 in 6 chance it is between 1,488 and 1,628, a 1 in 6 chance of it lying between 1,628 and 1,678, etc. The mid-points of the six equally probable chunks are given on the row below and are associated with one of the six possible values from the throw of a dice. Thus the value 1,558 is associated with a throw of 1, 1,653 with a throw of 2, etc.

Before generating a number of sets of values of the seven variables in Table 4.11, one more issue needs to be addressed. Usually some of our variables will show a fairly strong tendency to move together and this needs to be taken into account. For our present purposes let us assume that SALES 2 is strongly linked to SALES 1, i.e. if SALES in year 1 are unusually high, they are also likely to be unusually high in year 2 and vice versa. Similarly, we assume SALES 3 and SALES 2 are strongly linked in the manager's opinion. We further suppose that in his judgement there is no particular link between SALES and the various ratios but that there is a strong, positive relationship between the current assets:sales ratio and the fixed costs:sales ratio and a fairly strong positive relationship between the fixed costs:sales ratio and the cost of goods sold:sales ratio. The underlying rationale for this might be that the manager judges that if fixed costs increase faster than he expects and therefore the fixed costs:sales ratio does not drop as low as expected, then the value of inventories will be higher than anticipated and thus the current assets:sales ratio will also tend to be higher. Similarly he judges that if fixed costs are higher than expected this also makes it somewhat more likely that direct costs will be higher than expected and so the cost of goods sold:sales ratio will also tend to be higher. These considerations will now be taken into account by using the following rules for generating a set of values for the variables of Table 4.11.

1 Throw the dice and select the value of SALES 1 corresponding to the value thrown.

2   Throw the dice a second time. Generate a new value as 60 per cent of this throw plus 40 per cent of the value obtained as a result of the previous step. Round the number thus obtained to the nearest whole number and select the value of SALES 2 corresponding to that number.

3   Throw the dice a third time. Take 60 per cent of the value thrown and 40 per cent of the value obtained as a result of the previous step. Round to the nearest whole number and thus select the value of SALES 3.

4   Throw the dice a fourth time. Use the number obtained to select the appropriate value of the current assets:sales ratio.

5   Throw the dice a fifth time. Take 60 per cent of the value thrown + 40 per cent of the value obtained at the previous step and round to the nearest whole number. Thus select the value of the fixed costs:sales ratio.

6   Throw the dice a sixth time. Take 80 per cent of the value thrown plus 20 per cent of the value obtained at the previous step, round to the nearest whole number, which is used to select the value of the cost of goods sold:sales ratio.

7   Throw the dice a seventh time. Use the number thrown to select the value of the marginal capital output ratio.

Note we have associated a 40 per cent previous value + 60 per cent this throw rule with a strong relationship and a 20 per cent previous value + 80 per cent this throw with a fairly strong relationship. Note also that if a relationship is strongly negative rather than strongly positive we need only reverse the lower row. So, if the manager feels that the higher year 2 sales are strongly associated with lower year 3 sales then all that would be necessary would be to reverse the order of row 3.

Let us now work through an example.

1   Throw = 4. SALES 1 value is fourth in row 2 of Table 4.11, i.e.1723.

2   Throw = 4. 40% previous value + 60% this throw = 40% × 4 + 60% × 4 = 4. Select fourth value in row 4 for SALES 2, i.e. 2028.

3   Throw = 6. 40% previous value + 60% this throw = 40% × 4 + 60% × 6 = 5.2. Nearest whole number 5. Select fifth value of row 6 for SALES 3, i.e. 2395.

4   Throw = 3. Select third value of row 8 for current assets:sales ratio, i.e. 0.395.

5 Throw = 4. 40% × previous value + 60% of this throw = 3.6. Nearest whole number = 4. Fixed costs:sales ratio is fourth value in row 10, i.e. 0.380.

6 Throw = 3. 20% × previous value + 80% × this throw = 20% × 4 + 80% × 3 = 3.2. Nearest whole number = 3. Select third value in row 14 as the value of cost of goods sold:sales, i.e. −0.5%.

7 Throw = 6. Select the sixth value in row 12 of the table for the marginal capital output ratio, i.e. 1.525.

This type of procedure can readily be used to generate around 20–30 different sets of values for the half a dozen or so variables whose errors have a significant effect on the variable(s) of interest. In this case we shall generate just four sets which are given in Table 4.12. The values of the ratio of short term debt to equity corresponding to those sets are also tabulated.

Table 4.12
Four sets of values

	Set 1	Set 2	Set 3	Set 4
SALES 1	1723	1693	1723	1858
SALES 2	2028	2028	2138	2028
SALES 3	2395	2245	2395	1975
current assets:sales	0.395	0.395	0.395	0.340
fixed cost:sales	0.380	0.400	0.355	0.365
cost of goods sold:sales	−0.50%	+6.00%	−0.50%	−1.75%
SHORT TERM DEBT:EQUITY RATIO year 1	0.46	0.47	0.38	0.49
SHORT TERM DEBT:EQUITY RATIO year 2	0.60	0.61	0.48	0.40
SHORT TERM DEBT:EQUITY RATIO year 3	0.57	0.60	0.42	0.05

In our first run of the model using our 'best guess' estimates of the various driver series and ratios, the short term debt to equity ratio remained below its ceiling of 0.5 over all three years. The more extensive sensitivity analysis in Table 4.12 shows that this is somewhat misleading. The ceiling is almost attained in year 1 and is exceeded in years 2 and 3 for two of the data sets. Obviously, this information could be of considerable use to the manager, either for contingency planning, i.e. deciding what might be done if the limit is exceeded; or as a basis for further experiments with the model to decide what variables to control more tightly to make sure the problem does not arise. In the latter case the information derived from the first stage of the sensitivity analysis, where each of the uncertain variables was altered individually, is likely to be particularly useful as a guide to where the manager should best direct his attention.

Clearly, the procedure that has just been outlined is very crude. It does, however, provide a way of assessing how sensitive the forecasts of interest are to errors in those variables that have a major impact on the variable(s) of interest without requiring infeasible amounts of computation and, more importantly, unreasonable amounts of the manager's time. It can, of course, be readily automated and some sophisticated financial planning languages incorporate such features. Consideration of the procedure outlined, however, should make it clear why, carelessly used, such procedures can use enormous amounts of computer time, if care is not taken to restrict the number of variables whose errors are considered to have a significant impact.

VEHICLE PARK MODELS

We turn now to a different, non-financial application of ratio models. The example that we shall consider is concerned with forecasting demand for spare parts. This problem occurs in a wide variety of industries. It will be presented in terms of the car spares industry.

RATIO SPORTS CAR SPARES

Ratio Sports Car Spares stocks spare parts for the Ratio brand of sports cars. Over the years good statistics have been kept of sales of spares and, in particular, a note has been kept of the year in which the car on which the spare is to be fitted was manufactured. Information is available from the manufacturers about the actual number of each car model produced in each year. For simplicity, we shall consider only one type of spare part that fits on a particular

Ratio Sports Car model, though the approach is easily generalized. Let us suppose Ratio Sports Car Spares constructs a table of the number of cars sold in any particular year and the number of the spare parts in question that it sells for fitting on cars manufactured in that year one year after the car was produced, two years, etc. (see Table 4.13). Note that all the spare part sales in a given row of the table relate to usage on cars manufactured in the same year. Thus the first column of row 1 gives the number of Ratio Sports Cars sold in year 1. The second column gives the number of spares sold 1 year after the year of manufacture, i.e. in year 2, for fitting on cars manufactured in year 1. Similarly, the last column of row 1 gives sales of spares in year 1+6, i.e. year 7, for fitting onto cars manufactured in year 1. At the opposite end of the table, the first column of row 6 gives the number of cars manufactured in year 6 and the second column the spares sold in year 6+1, i.e. year 7, for fitting to cars made in year 6.

Examination of the table shows that the figures along the diagonal all relate to year 7, which by implication is the last year for which we have data. We shall assume that Ratio Sports Car Spares wishes to derive forecasts for the next 3 years, i.e. years 8, 9 and 10. For greater generality, we shall refer in what follows to the 'car sales' as 'original equipment sales'.

Table 4.13
Number of cars and spare parts sold

Year		Sales of spares					
	Years after prodn	1	2	3	4	5	6
	Number cars made						
1	283098	116906	26100	17691	6644	3488	814
2	269440	110550	23768	14711	11635	4885	
3	268530	114927	20711	20192	6695		
4	289082	141000	26922	15036			
5	309577	137729	31267				
6	332544	138474					
7	355042						

Using any of the methods mentioned earlier, it is simple to derive a number of ratios that enable forecasts to be constructed. We shall use the regression method to derive the ratios. If we consider first the ratio of spare sales six years after manufacture to original equipment sales we find that only the first row of the table is relevant and the ratio is essentially between the element in the last column of that row and the one in the first column. In fact the regression method requires us to calculate it as follows:

spare sales six years after manufacture:original equipment sales
$$= \frac{814 \times 283098}{283098 \times 283098}$$

This gives the value 0.0029.

The ratio of spare sales five years after year of manufacture to original equipment sales is a slightly more complex calculation, since the first two rows of the table now contain relevant data. The regression calculation in this case is:

$$\frac{3488 \times 283098 + 4885 \times 269440}{283098 \times 283098 + 269440 \times 269440} = 0.0151$$

Clearly, as we progress down the table more and more calculation is involved in deriving the ratios. This illustrates our earlier point about the attractiveness of the regression approach for deriving ratios in situations like this. In fact, the complete set of ratios derived by regression is:

sales 1 year after manufacture:original equipment sales = 0.4335

sales 2 years after manufacture:original equipment sales = 0.0911

sales 3 years after manufacture:original equipment sales = 0.0608

sales 4 years after manufacture:original equipment sales = 0.0303

sales 5 years after manufacture:original equipment sales = 0.0151

sales 6 years after manufacture:original equipment sales = 0.0029

We are now in a position to construct a forecasting model for Ratio

Sports Car Spares sales of this particular part over the next three years provided we have forecasts of original equipment sales for the next two years. The model is given below. Note that, for example, SALES (-6) denotes original equipment sales six years ago in line with our previous notation. We assume that forecasts of original equipment sales have been obtained for the next two years.

FORECAST SPARE SALES = spare sales:original equipment sales 1 year ago $\times$ SALES (-1)

$+$ spare sales:original equipment sales 2 years ago $\times$ SALES (-2)
$+$ spare sales:original equipment sales 3 years ago $\times$ SALES (-3)
$+$ spare sales:original equipment sales 4 years ago $\times$ SALES (-4)
$+$ spare sales:original equipment sales 5 years ago $\times$ SALES (-5)
$+$ spare sales:original equipment sales 6 years ago $\times$ SALES (-6)

$$(4.5)$$

The forecasts of original equipment sales for years 1 and 2 that are needed to derive the spares sales forecast for years 1–3 are shown in Table 4.14 along with the resulting spare sales forecasts.

Table 4.14
Forecasts for original equipment and spares sales

	Year 1	Year 2	Year 3
ORIGINAL EQUIPMENT SALES	380000	405000	–
FORECAST SPARE SALES	216623	231817	247361

Sensitivity analysis

In an actual application it will normally be necesssary to examine the effects of uncertainties in the forecasts of the original equipment sales and in the various ratios involved on the forecasts of spares sales. Since the procedures used have been covered in the previous examples, no sensitivity analysis will be carried out here.

Uses of vehicle park models

The reason for the name often applied to this type of ratio model should by now be clear. Sales of spares are related to the total 'vehicle park', i.e. all vehicles using that type of spare part that were ever manufactured. Essentially, all such a model does is to recognize that some events cast long shadows and that, therefore, knowledge of past events can enable us to forecast a fair way into the future. Vehicle park models can often be successfully applied to forecasting spares markets, e.g. in the aerospace industry. In a somewhat different context, they can be used to forecast the output from a multistage production process where the yield from each stage is less than 100 per cent. Such situations occur, for example, in the pharmaceutical industry because drug manufacture often requires several intermediate processes that rarely give a 100 per cent yield, and in many types of manufacturing where batches of parts are subject to quality control inspection between manufacturing stages and there are a proportion of rejects at each stage. Another slightly different application is in forecasting failures of standard units such as street lights given the history of when they were installed. This is typical of a number of applications in forecasting plant reliability and maintenance requirements. Finally, the same type of model is used in the insurance industry for the forecasting of future claims and settlements. In many types of accident insurance, for example, a significant proportion of the claims arising from an accident are submitted one or more years after the accident occurred. This phenomenon is even more marked with settlements of claims where a significant proportion may take five years, or more, to settle.

INPUT/OUTPUT MODELS

We now turn to a very different application of ratio models in demand forecasting. Let us start with the problem of forecasting bulk chemical sales some time out into the future. Obviously, such products are mainly used by industry rather than the consumer. The growth in demand for them is, thus, very dependent on the growth of the non-consumer sectors of the economy. Input/output analysis enables us to forecast such growth by means of a ratio model.

For the moment, we shall divide the economy into five sectors: the agricultural industry, manufacturing industry, the services industry, the bulk chemicals industry and the consumption (final demand) sector. The last sector represents sales to consumers and is always needed in this type of model. The first three would probably occur in most models: indeed, a more detailed breakdown of sectors is often favoured. Here only one sector has been singled out for special treatment: bulk chemicals. To avoid double counting, we assume that manufacturing industry here excludes bulk chemicals.

The ratios needed for the model are the set of ratios giving the amount sold by industry B to industry A for each $ of sales of industry A. To take a more specific example that shows how the ratio can be calculated, let industry A be agriculture, and industry B services then the ratio services sales to agriculture per 1$ agriculture sales can be calculated simply as:

$$\frac{\text{Total sales of services to agriculture}}{\text{Total sales of agriculture industry}}$$

In practice, as mentioned in Chapter 2, estimates of these ratios are available from a number of different sources.

We now assume that such a table is available and takes the form given in Table 4.15, where two additional columns have been added for later use.

Table 4.15
Sales ratios between industries

Selling Industry	To industry per unit of sales			Bulk chemicals	Sales to consumers	Total sales
	Agriculture	Manuf'ing	Services			
Agriculture	0.2	0.05	0.08	0		
Manuf'ing	0.1	0.3	0.2	0.15		
Services	0.15	0.2	0.3	0.02		
Bulk chemicals	0.05	0.07	0.009	0.3		

The rows of the table represent the selling industries and the columns the buying industries. The table entries give the ratio of sales by the selling industry to the buying industry to sales of the buying industry. Thus the entry of zero in the first row indicates that bulk chemicals buys nothing from agriculture. Conversely, the value 0.05 in the fourth row of the table shows that for each $1 of its sales the agriculture industry purchases $0.05 of bulk chemicals. It will also be noticed that sectors buy from themselves. This arises because in most sectors much of the output of some firms is sold to others for further processing.

We are now in a position to build the input/output model. To see how the model is derived let us consider the total sales of the agriculture industry. These are made up of five components:

Sales to agriculture = 0.2 × total agriculture sales
Sales to manufacturing = 0.05 × total manufacturing sales
Sales to services = 0.08 × total services sales
Sales to bulk chemicals = 0 × total bulk chemical sales
Agriculture Sales to Consumers

where 0.2, for example, is the value given in Table 4.15 for the amount agricultural industry sells to itself for each unit of its sales; 0.05 is the amount it sells to manufacturing industry for each unit of manufacturing industry's sales; etc. The sum of these must be equal to total sales of the agricultural industry. Following the same arguments the complete model of Table 4.16 can be derived from Table 4.15. Essentially total sales of any sector are derived by totalling the sales across the rows of the table. The addition of the last two columns to Table 4.15 is a useful way of remembering this.

Table 4.16
The complete model

AGRICULTURE SALES = agriculture sales to agriculture per $ of agriculture sales × AGRICULTURE SALES
+ agriculture sales to manufacturing per $ of manufacturing sales × MANUFACTURING SALES
+ agriculture sales to services per $ of services sales × SERVICE INDUSTRY SALES
+ agriculture sales to bulk chemicals per $ of bulk chemicals sales × BULK CHEMICALS SALES
+ AGRICULTURE SALES TO CONSUMERS

MANUFACTURING SALES = manufacturing sales to agriculture per $ of agriculture sales × AGRICULTURE SALES
+ manufacturing sales to manufacturing per

$ of manufacturing sales × MANUFAC-TURING SALES

+ manufacturing sales to service industry per $ of service industry sales × SERVICE INDUSTRY SALES

+ manufacturing sales to bulk chemicals per $ of bulk chemicals sales × BULK CHEMICALS SALES

+ MANUFACTURING SALES TO CONSUMERS

SERVICE INDUSTRY SALES = service industry sales to agriculture per $ of ·agriculture sales × AGRICULTURE SALES

+ service industry sales to manufacturing per $ of manufacturing sales × MANUFAC-TURING SALES

+ service industry sales to service industry per $ of service industry sales × SERVICE INDUSTRY SALES

+ service industry sales to bulk chemicals per $ of bulk chemicals sales × BULK CHEMICALS SALES

+ SERVICE INDUSTRY SALES TO CONSUMERS

BULK CHEMICALS SALES = bulk chemicals sales to agriculture per $ of agriculture sales × AGRICULTURE SALES

+ bulk chemicals sales to manufacturing per $ of manufacturing sales × MANUFAC-TURING SALES

+ bulk chemicals sales to service industry per $ of service industry sales × SERVICE INDUSTRY SALES

+ bulk chemicals sales to bulk chemicals per $ of bulk chemicals sales × BULK CHEMICALS SALES

+ BULK CHEMICALS SALES TO CONSUMERS

Obviously the model of Table 4.16 involves the solution of a set of simultaneous equations for the sales of the four different industries. Not all financial planning packages are capable of doing this. More sophisticated packages can, however, and we assume that such a package is available to obtain the solution. The other thing we shall require before proceeding is the sales to consumers of the four different producing industries. We assume that we wish to forecast sales over a four-year period and that the sales to consumers are given as an estimate for year 1 plus a set of different, but constant, linear growth rates as in Table 4.17.

Table 4.17
Estimated sales and growth rates

	Year 1 value	Annual growth rate (%)
Agriculture	100	4
Manufacturing	200	2
Services	300	3.5
Bulk chemicals	10	0.2

The forecasts generated by the model are given in Table 4.18. Particularly noteworthy is that despite the low sales of the bulk chemical industry to the consumer industry and their sluggish growth, both the size of its total sales and their growth rate are much more respectable. This, of course, is because sales to the other sectors are far more important as far as the bulk chemicals industry is concerned.

Table 4.18
Forecasts generated by model

	Year 1	Year 2	Year 3	Year 4
AGRICULTURE SALES	221.4	229.3	237.2	245.1
MANUFACTURING SALES	530.6	544.2	557.8	571.4
SERVICES SALES	632.0	652.7	673.4	694.1
BULK CHEMICALS SALES	152.5	156.5	160.5	164.4

Deriving sales of an individual company

It is relatively straightforward to generate a forecast for the sales of an individual firm based on an input/output model of the economy. The firm needs to construct its own row of the input/output table, i.e. to determine its sales to each of the other producing sectors per $1 of their output and determine a forecast of its sales to final consumers. Suppose, for example, that the I/O Manufacturing Company wishes to use the results obtained above to produce forecasts of its own sales for the next four years. Suppose the relevant ratios are estimated by the firm to be as in Table 4.19.

Table 4.19
I/O Manufacturing's estimate of ratios

Purchasing industry	Agriculture	Manufactur- ing	Services	Bulk chemicals	Final demand Years 1 to 4
I/O Manufac- turing	0.003	0.002	0.001	0.005	0.5

To produce a sales forecast for I/O Manufacturing's total sales in years 1–4, assuming that the sales of the other sectors are as given in Table 4.18, requires only the addition of the following equation to the model:

$$
\begin{aligned}
\text{I/O SALES} = {} & \text{I/O sales to agriculture per \$ agriculture sales} \times \\
& \text{AGRICULTURE SALES} \\
+ {} & \text{I/O sales to manufacturing per \$ of manufacturing} \\
& \text{sales} \times \text{MANUFACTURING SALES} \\
+ {} & \text{I/O sales to services per \$ of services sales} \times \\
& \text{SERVICES SALES} \\
+ {} & \text{I/O sales to bulk chemicals per \$ of bulk chemicals} \\
& \text{sales} \times \text{BULK CHEMICAL SALES} \\
+ {} & \text{I/O SALES TO CONSUMERS} \qquad\qquad (4.6)
\end{aligned}
$$

The additional ratios needed by the model and the forecasts of I/O's SALES TO CONSUMERS are given in Table 4.20.

Table 4.20
I/O's sales to consumers and additional ratios

	Year 1	Year 2	Year 3	Year 4
I/O SALES TO CONSUMERS	0.5	0.5	0.5	0.5
I/O sales to agriculture per $ agriculture sales	0.003	0.003	0.003	0.003
I/O sales to manufacturing per $ manufacturing sales	0.002	0.002	0.002	0.002
I/O sales to service industry per $ services sales	0.001	0.001	0.001	0.001
I/O sales to bulk chemicals per $ bulk chemical sales	0.005	0.005	0.005	0.005

The forecasts of I/O Manufacturing's total sales generated by this model are:

Year 1 – 3.62
Year 2 – 3.71
Year 3 – 3.80
Year 4 – 3.89

Obviously, there is a slight amount of double counting in this forecast, since I/O Manufacturing's sales are also counted as part of those of the manufacturing sector. Save for the very largest firms, however, the approximation need not concern us. Here, for instance, I/O's sales make up somewhat under 0.6 per cent of total manufacturing sales. By contrast, if I/O Manufacturing's sales were a significant proportion of those of the manufacturing industry, it could be split off as a single industry, as was done for bulk chemicals from the outset.

Sensitivity analysis

A full input/output analysis would require exploration of the impact of uncertainties in the ratios used and the estimates of the various industries' sales to consumers. Again this has been omitted for reasons of space.

Uses of input/output models

Input/output models are of considerable use in medium to long term economic forecasting. It is usual to break the economy down into many more industries, perhaps 50–100, than was convenient here. They can, then, provide detailed industry-by-industry forecasts. These forecasts are consistent in that they do not involve mere extrapolation of past trends of growth in an industry's sales. Instead, the forecast for a specific industry is based on the sum of the sales to various different customer industries. These may well be moving in different directions. Some customer industries will be growing and others declining. Furthermore, provided we can supply forecasts of the future values of the input/output coefficients, the model can easily cope when some of these are changing. This enables companies to examine, for example, the impact of competitive imports, since these will reduce the input/output coefficients for its products; or the effects of technological change, which again will impact on those coefficients.

As well as applying input/output analysis to produce forecasts at the level of the national economy, a similar approach can be taken at the sub-national, i.e. regional level. Equally, such models can be used to forecast demand on an international basis. Input/output models can also be employed for forecasting resource needs in organizations with a number of operating units, each of which supplies products or services to other units or the outside world. Examples range from universities and hospitals through to large manufacturing organizations.

ADVANTAGES AND DISADVANTAGES OF RATIO MODELS

As has been demonstrated, ratio models can be applied to a large number of apparently different forecasting problems. This is because they provide a fairly detailed model of the processes underlying the evolution of the variables concerned. Again, given the widespread availability of purpose-built financial planning packages that can readily be adapted to the construction of other types of ratio model, they are probably one of the easiest types of forecasting model for the manager to come to grips with. They are by no means restricted to time series forecasting applications. Rather, they can be used for a wide range of strategic planning purposes including contingency planning.

The chief drawback of such models is the time needed for their construction. Save for the simplest examples they require much more time to build and a great deal more data analysis than other types of forecast model. Again, as we have seen, it is always necessary to supply a number of other forecasts to drive them. The scale of effort involved to use such models is clearly very different from that implied by the simpler time series or trend curve analysis techniques.

FURTHER READING

Brealey, R. A. and Myers, S., *Principles of Corporate Finance,* 2nd edn, chaps 26 and 27, McGraw-Hill, 1984.

Chow, G C., *The Demand for Automobiles in the United States,* North Holland, 1957.

Floyd, S. H. and Warkman, L. S., *Fundamental Mathematics of Life Insurance,* Richard D. Irwin, 1970.

Leontieff, W., *Input-Output Economics,* Oxford University Press, 1966.

Matulich, S. and Hutger, L. E., *Financial Accounting,* McGraw-Hill, 1980.

5 Regression analysis

Regression analysis involves studying relationships between variables. Regression is used to estimate the quantitative relationship between the variable to be forecast and those variables which appear likely to influence the forecast variable. The estimation is carried out using historic data, and future values of the forecast variable are obtained by using forecasts of the influencing variables in conjunction with the estimated relationship.

The process of forecasting by regression may be summarized as:

1 Select those variables which are expected to influence the forecast variable and specify the relationship in mathematical form.
2 Assemble data relevant to the model.
3 Use the data to estimate the quantitative effects of the influencing variables on the forecast variable in the past.
4 Carry out statistical tests on the estimated model to see if it is sufficiently realistic.
5 If the tests show that the model is satisfactory then it can be used for forecasting.

Econometrics is the application of statistical methods to attempt to establish quantitative relationships between economic variables. To the extent that business forecasting is concerned with economic relationships, regression analysis is used to estimate econometric forecasting models.

ADVANTAGES AND DISADVANTAGES

A major advantage of the regression technique is that it explicitly takes into account the impact on the variable to be forecast of changes in the determining forces, that is we are following a causal model approach. Furthermore, this approach to forecasting permits a company to link its forecasting with tactical and strategic plans for the future. Given an explicit forecast, the company may accept the change of trend as inevitable and adjust its operations accordingly. Alternatively, a forecasting system based on a regression model gives the company the ability to explore the consequences of alternative future policies. A third advantage of regression analysis is that it provides several statistical measures of the accuracy and significance of the forecasting equations and actual forecasts. Fourth, regression can handle a wide range of relationships including leads and lags.

Several disadvantages of the regression technique are evident. First, it requires a large amount of data. Second, considerable user understanding is necessary in order to develop the correct relationships. Third, substantial development time and costs are involved. A fourth disadvantage of regression is that the values of the determining variables need to be forecast in order to generate future values of the forecast variable.

TYPICAL APPLICATIONS

Regression analysis has many applications such as forecasts of sales, manpower, production, costs and interest rates. Regression models also permit decision makers to assess the likely impacts of alternative policies; for example, the effect on sales of a price change or alteration in the level of advertising may be estimated.

Sales forecasting

The most common application of regression analysis is in sales forecasting, which is therefore used for illustrative purposes in this chapter and also the next. The usual approach to forecasting the sales of a product by an individual firm is to consider a two-stage forecasting model. The first stage is a forecast of the total market demand for the product, that is a market size forecast. The second stage is a market share forecast – what share of the total market for the product the individual firm is likely to obtain. The company sales forecast is then given by

$$\frac{\text{company sales}}{\text{forecast}} = \frac{\text{market size}}{\text{forecast}} \times \frac{\text{market share}}{\text{forecast}}$$

(5.1)

Market size forecasting

If we consider the case of a product which is sold to the final consumer, then the micro-economic theory of consumers' behaviour may be used to construct a market size forecast. The first stage is to examine those variables which are likely to influence the market demand for the product. The standard market demand function is given from economic theory by

$$Y = f(X_1, X_2, \ldots, X_k)$$

(5.2)

where

Y is the market demand for the product;
X_1 is consumers' disposable income;
X_2 is the price of the product;
$X_3, \ldots, X_{k-3}$ are the prices of other products which may affect the demand for the product under consideration;
X_{k-2} is consumer tastes;
X_{k-1} is the size of the population;
X_k is the distribution of income; and
f   denotes some function.

Normally a change in income results in a change in the same direction in the demand for a commodity, that is a positive relationship is expected between X_1 and Y. Such goods are known as superior goods. There are, however, certain goods for which a negative relationship is expected between X_1 and Y (inferior goods); here an increase in income results in a decrease in demand because consumers substitute more desirable goods. For example, a rise in income increases the probability of substituting new tyres for remould tyres.

A change in price generally results in a change in the opposite direction in quantity demanded, that is a negative relationship is expected between X_2 and Y. It is possible that a positive relationship may hold, for example if consumers judge the quality of a good by its price (as may be the case with perfume), but such cases are likely to be extremely rare.

The prices of other products which are expected to have a marked impact on the demand for the commodity under consideration should be included in the demand function, and are denoted by $X_3, \ldots, X_{k-3}$. Changes in the prices of competing goods or substitutes are expected to cause changes in the same direction in the demand for the commodity, whereas changes in the prices of complementary goods are expected to cause changes in the opposite direction. Examples of substitutes are butter and margarine or gas and electricity; a rise in the price of margarine increases the demand for butter as the latter becomes relatively more price attractive. Examples of complements are cars and petrol or bread and butter; an increase in the price of petrol decreases the demand for cars on account of the higher running costs.

Changes in consumer tastes or preferences may have an important effect on the demand for certain products, although in the short term it is often assumed that tastes remain constant. One of the objectives of advertising is to bring about a change in tastes towards the product being advertised, and therefore X_{k-2} may be represented in the model by the level of advertising expenditure. As well as producer advertising, consumer 'advertising' may also be important; the decision to consume a given product may be the result of previous personal experience of that product or of contact with other people who have already consumed it. In this case X_{k-2} may appear in the model as consumption of the product in previous periods. There are many other reasons why tastes may change, and a common procedure is to incorporate a trend term in the analysis to represent movements in consumer preferences over time. This permits a steady change in tastes towards or away from the product.

Clearly the market demand for a product depends on the number of potential consumers, that is the size of the population, and a positive relationship is expected between X_{k-1} and Y. An alternative but more restrictive assumption about the form of the relationship between population and market demand is to remove population as a separate influencing variable and to consider demand (and also income) in per capita (divided by population) terms.

Not only the level but also the distribution of income is sometimes considered to have an influence on the demand for a good. A change in income distribution over time may be caused, for example, by changes in the tax structure; the distribution of incomes may become more equal if the tax system is altered so that the rich are taxed more heavily and the poor more lightly. The impact of such a change on the demand for a good depends upon the good under consideration. The demand for washing machines is likely to increase as the distribution of income becomes more equal, since some (relatively poor) people who previously could not afford one will now be able to, whereas those who previously were able to buy one will still be in that position. The demand for a commodity which is regarded very much as a luxury and is therefore only consumed by the wealthy, for example caviar, is likely to decrease as the distribution of incomes becomes more equal. Now, within a given country, changes in the distribution of income tend to be rather gradual and hence there is little effect on the demand for most consumer products unless a substantial time span is considered. In most applications of market size forecasting, income distribution is therefore ignored.

Although equation (5.2) gives the set of determining variables considered in the standard market demand function, this is by no means exhaustive, and it is essential that the forecaster is familiar with the market he is examining so that he can determine the forces operating in that particular market. For example, the demand for goods that are frequently purchased on credit may be influenced by interest rates; an increase in the rate of interest is likely to cause a decrease in the demand for such goods.

Market share forecasting

The construction of a market share forecast is very similar in principle to that of a market size forecast. It is necessary to specify those variables which are likely to affect the company's share of the market. Although these will vary considerably from market to market, certain variables have commonly been identified by marketing economists as important determinants of market share. A typical market share model is given by

$$S = g(V_1, V_2, V_3, V_4) \qquad (5.3)$$

where

S is the market share of firm A;

V_1 is the price of the product sold by firm A relative to the average price of products sold in the same market by competing firms;

V_2 is advertising expenditure by firm A relative to the average advertising expenditure of competing firms;

V_3 is the quality of the product sold by firm A relative to the average quality of competitive products;

V_4 is the quality of firm A's distribution system relative to the average quality of competitors' distribution systems; and

g denotes some function.

A change in relative price usually results in a change in the opposite direction in market share, so a negative relationship is expected between V_1 and S. If firm A reduces the price of its product compared to the average price of products sold in the same market by competing firms, then the market share of firm A should increase. A possible exception is if price is a primary indicator of quality in which case the impact of V_3 cannot be separated out from V_1; in such a situation a cut in relative price may cause the market share to decrease. Although theoretically relative price is an important determinant of market share, in practice price competition is unimportant in many markets – relative prices tend not to change over time.

Advertising is often considered to be a major influence on market share, and advertising competition is very prevalent in many markets for consumer goods. A change in relative advertising expenditure is expected to result in a change in the same direction in market share, so a positive relationship is expected between V_2 and S. A particular problem with advertising is that the impact on consumer demand may be distributed over time, so that advertising in a given period is likely to influence not only purchases in that period but also in subsequent periods, although the effect will diminish with the passage of time. Hence, firm A's market share depends on the relative advertising expenditure of firm A in the current period and previous periods.

An increase in relative product quality is expected to cause an increase in market share, that is a positive relationship is expected between V_3 and S. The likely scope for improving product quality will vary considerably from market to market; for relatively cheap consumer goods (such as washing powder) the opportunities are probably minimal, whereas for more expensive goods (such as cars) there are likely to be many opportunities. For example, product quality may be improved in the case of cars by increasing the maximum speed, reducing fuel consumption, including a radio, and so on.

A change in the relative quality of firm A's distribution system is expected to cause a change in the same direction in the firm's share of the market, so a positive relationship is expected between

V_4 and S. This factor will be particularly important in markets for reasonably homogeneous products (where there is little or no possibility of increasing relative product quality) with low brand loyalty which are purchased often. Here convenience is likely to play an important role, and therefore the number and siting of retail outlets may be crucial in determining the firm's market share. An obvious example is the market for petrol, where motorists are unlikely to make a detour to purchase fuel.

Equation (5.3) shows those variables which generally influence market share, but there are many other possible influences. It is important that the market share forecaster is familiar with the forces which determine market share in the particular market under consideration, and that these are incorporated in the regression model.

SIMPLE LINEAR REGRESSION MODEL

The simplest relationship between variables is linear, that is, such relationships can be described by straight lines or by generalizations of straight lines to many dimensions. If interest is focused on relationships between two variables only, then simple regression is under consideration. The simple linear regression model assumes that there is a theoretical relationship between two variables X and Y of the form

$$Y = a + bX \tag{5.4}$$

where Y is the variable to be forecast and is known as the dependent variable, X is the variable thought to influence Y and is known as the independent or explanatory variable, and a and b are unknown parameters indicating the intercept and slope of the function, that is the structure of the relationship.

Equation (5.4) postulates an exact functional relationship between the variables X and Y, but real economic data never fall exactly on a straight line (or other smooth function). Hence, formulations such as (5.4) are inadequate for estimation and testing purposes and need to be extended by the introduction of a stochastic (or random) error (or disturbance) term (u) into the model, giving

$$Y = a + bX + u \tag{5.5}$$

161

A diagrammatic representation of model (5.5) is given in Figure 5.1, where the scatter of points represents pairs of sample observations on X, Y and X_i, Y_i is the ith pair.

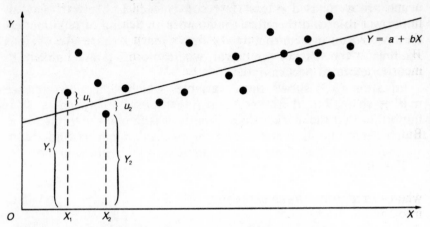

Figure 5.1 Theoretical simple linear regression model

Error term justification

The inclusion of the error term may be justified in several ways. First, equation (5.4) states that X is the only factor influencing the variable Y, whereas in reality there will be many forces affecting the dependent variable. Several of the influences will, however, not be quantifiable, and it will be impossible to obtain data on other determinants of Y. Furthermore, the number of potential explanatory variables is likely to exceed the feasible number of observations, so that the influence of all these variables cannot be estimated statistically. In addition, the impact of many variables will be marginal, so that even with a considerable amount of data meaningful estimation of these influences would be impossible. Equation (5.5) states that X is the single most important variable affecting the dependent variable Y, and that the net effect of the less important excluded variables is represented by the error term, u.

The insertion of the error term in equation (5.5) may also be rationalized by assuming that even if it were possible to list all relevant explanatory variables and overcome the data and estimation problems, there is still a basic and unpredictable element of randomness in human behaviour which can be captured only by the inclusion of such a stochastic term.

A third justification for the disturbance term relates to observation or measurement errors in the dependent variable. In general, quantitative variables cannot be measured with perfect accuracy. Even if there were an exact linear relationship between two variables X and W, the observed relationship may be between X and Y where Y incorporates measurement error. Hence

$$W = a + bX \tag{5.6}$$

But

$$Y = W + u \tag{5.7}$$

where u represents measurement error. Substituting equation (5.6) into equation (5.7) gives

$$Y = a + bX + u \tag{5.8}$$

Ordinary least squares

If we have n pairs of sample observations on the variables X and Y, then the simple linear model (5.5) may be written as

$$Y_i = a + bX_i + u_i; \, i = 1, 2, \ldots, n \tag{5.9}$$

The parameters a and b in equation (5.9) are unknown, but it is desired to estimate them statistically on the basis of the sample of observations on the variables X and Y. Since the true values of a and b are unknown, the disturbance values u_i cannot be observed.

The estimated line corresponding to model (5.9) is

$$\hat{Y}_i = \hat{a} + \hat{b}X_i; \, i = 1, 2, \ldots, n \tag{5.10}$$

where $\hat{a}$ and $\hat{b}$ are estimates of the unknown parameters a and b and $\hat{Y}_i$ is the predicted value of the dependent variable given by the fitted line. The observed values of the dependent variable do not, in general, lie on the estimated line, and the discrepancies between the observed and estimated values of the dependent variable are termed residuals (e), so

$$e_i = Y_i - \hat{Y}_i; \ i = 1,2,\ldots,n \tag{5.11}$$

Hence

$$\hat{Y}_i = Y_i - e_i \tag{5.12}$$

Substituting (5.12) into (5.10) yields

$$Y_i = \hat{a} + \hat{b}X_i + e_i \tag{5.13}$$

Comparing equations (5.9) and (5.13) it can be seen that the residuals may be regarded as estimates of the disturbance terms. A diagrammatic representation of equation (5.13) is given in Figure 5.2.

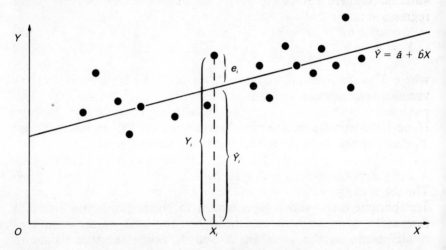

Figure 5.2   Estimated simple linear regression model

In order that the estimated line should pass closely through the observed points, it is necessary for the residuals to be small. The estimation method of ordinary least squares (OLS) selects that line which minimizes the sum of squared residuals. From equation (5.13)

$$e_i = Y_i - \hat{a} - \hat{b}X_i \tag{5.14}$$

Hence

$$\Sigma e_i^2 = \Sigma(Y_i - \hat{a} - \hat{b}X_i)^2 \qquad (5.15)$$

For a given set of data, the OLS estimates are those values $\hat{a}$ and $\hat{b}$ which minimize (5.15). This minimization problem may be solved using a least squares regression computer program.

MULTIPLE LINEAR REGRESSION MODEL

In a managerial forecasting context, any variable which we wish to forecast is unlikely to be related merely to a single explanatory variable. It is therefore necessary to generalize the simple linear regression model to the multiple regression case where several explanatory variables are permitted to have an impact on the dependent variable. If there are k explanatory variables then the multiple linear regression model may be written as

$$Y_i = a + b_1X_{1i} + b_2X_{2i} + \ldots + b_kX_{ki} + u_i; i = 1,2,\ldots,n \qquad (5.16)$$

where Y is the forecast variable, $X_1, X_2, \ldots, X_k$ are the explanatory variables, u is a disturbance term, $a, b_1, b_2, \ldots, b_k$ are unknown parameters and the subscript i represents the observation number. Hence Y_1 denotes the first period observation on the variable Y, Y_2 denotes the second period observation on this variable, and so on. Similarly, X_{11} denotes the first period observation on the variable X_1, X_{12} denotes the second period observation on X_1, and so on. The set of explanatory variables should include all those forces which are thought to have an important influence on the variable to be forecast.

The parameters in equation (5.16) are estimated from a sample of n observations on the variables $Y, X_1, X_2, \ldots, X_k$:

$$Y_i = \hat{a} + \hat{b}_1X_{1i} + \hat{b}_2X_{2i} + \ldots + \hat{b}_kX_{ki} + e_i \qquad (5.17)$$

where $\hat{a}, \hat{b}_1, \hat{b}_2, \ldots, \hat{b}_k$ are estimates of the parameters $a, b_1, b_2, \ldots, b_k$ and e is a residual. A computer program may be used to provide OLS estimates of the parameters, that is those values of $\hat{a}, \hat{b}_1, \hat{b}_2, \ldots, \hat{b}_k$ which minimize

$$\Sigma e_i^2 = \Sigma(Y_i - \hat{a} - \mathit{b}_1 X_{1i} - \mathit{b}_2 X_{2i} - \ldots - \mathit{b}_k X_{ki})^2 \qquad (5.18)$$

ASSUMPTIONS OF REGRESSION MODELS

Any model is an abstract simplification of reality and regression models therefore must incorporate various simplifying assumptions. Now the rule defining a particular estimation method is termed an estimator, whereas a given value of the estimator obtained from a set of observations on the variables is an estimate. An unknown parameter may be estimated in many different ways, but there are certain desirable properties that an estimator should possess in order to be acceptable. The OLS estimator does in fact satisfy these criteria, but only if various assumptions hold. The initial specification of the linear regression model (5.16) therefore includes the following set of assumptions (known as the classical assumptions):

1   The expected value of the error term is zero

$$E(u_i) = 0; \; i = 1,2,\ldots,n$$

where E denotes expected value
2   The variance of the error term is constant

$$\mathrm{var}(u_i) = \sigma^2; \; i = 1,2,\ldots,n$$

where var denotes variance and σ^2 is an unknown parameter
3   The various values of the error term are drawn independently of each other

$$\mathrm{cov}(u_i u_j) = 0; \; i,j = 1,2,\ldots,n, \; i \neq j$$

where cov denotes covariance
4   The explanatory variables are distributed independently of the error term

$$E(u_i X_{hj}) = 0; \; i,j = 1,2,\ldots,n: h = 1,2,\ldots,k$$

5   The explanatory variables are linearly independent of each other and $n > k + 1$

For the moment the set of assumptions 1–5 is taken to hold. The effect of relaxing some of these assumptions is considered in Chapter 6.

PROPERTIES OF LEAST SQUARES ESTIMATORS

Linearity

Least squares estimators are linear functions of the actual observations on Y, and attention is restricted to linear estimators because they are easy to analyse and compute.

Unbiasedness

Least squares estimators are unbiased:

$$E(\hat{a}) = a$$
$$E(\hat{b}_j) = b_j; j = 1, 2, \ldots, k$$

The expected value of the OLS estimator is equal to the true population parameter. For some sets of observations a parameter estimate would exceed the true value and for others it would be less, but on average there is no tendency to either overestimate or underestimate the true parameter value.

Minimum variance

Least squares estimators are best, that is within the class of linear unbiased estimators they have the smallest variance (Gauss–Markov Theorem). It is clearly desirable that the OLS estimator should have the minimum variance possible, because this indicates that it is distributed relatively closely about the expected value which, for an unbiased estimator, is equal to the true parameter value. This property provides the major justification for the choice of OLS as a method of estimation. The OLS estimator is therefore the best linear unbiased estimator (BLUE) when the classical assumptions hold.

INTERPRETATION AND EVALUATION OF PARAMETER ESTIMATES

The estimated simple linear relationship is

$$\hat{Y} = \hat{a} + \hat{b}X \tag{5.19}$$

where $\hat{a}$ is an estimate of the intercept and $\hat{b}$ is an estimate of the slope. The interpretation of $\hat{a}$ is as follows: if $X = 0$, then $\hat{Y} = \hat{a}$; so if the explanatory variable were equal to zero, the predicted value of the dependent variable would be given by the estimated value of a. The interpretation of $\hat{b}$ is of prime interest: if X rises by one unit, then $\hat{Y}$ rises by $\hat{b}$ units; $\hat{b}$ therefore represents the predicted change in the dependent variable resulting from a unit change in the explanatory variable.

If the market demand for a product (Y) is thought to depend only upon consumers' disposable income (X), and the appropriate simple regression is carried out, the following parameter estimates might be obtained:

$$\hat{Y} = 4.1 + 1.3X \tag{5.20}$$

In this case, if income were equal to zero, the predicted demand for the product would be 4.1 units, and if income increased by one unit then the predicted increase in demand would be 1.3 units.

The estimated multiple linear relationship is

$$\hat{Y} = \hat{a} + \hat{b}_1 X_1 + \hat{b}_2 X_2 + \ldots + \hat{b}_k X_k \tag{5.21}$$

Here the interpretation of $\hat{a}$ is similar to that in the simple linear model; if all the explanatory variables were equal to zero, the predicted value of the dependent variable would be equal to $\hat{a}$. The interpretation of $\hat{b}_j, j = 1, 2, \ldots, k$, is as follows: a unit change in a single explanatory variable X_j, with all the other explanatory variables held constant, results in a predicted change of b_j units in the dependent variable.

If it is now supposed that the market demand for a product (Y) depends upon consumers' disposable income (X_1) and the price of the product (X_2), the following multiple regression model might be estimated:

$$\hat{Y} = 3.6 + 2.1X_1 - 0.9X_2 \tag{5.22}$$

If income and price were equal to zero, the predicted demand for the product would be 3.6 units. A rise in income of one unit (with price held constant) would result in a predicted rise in demand of 2.1 units. An increase in price of one unit (with income held constant) would result in a predicted decrease in demand of 0.9 units.

It is necessary to evaluate the parameter estimates obtained in a regression model in terms of both sign and magnitude in order to determine whether these estimates are theoretically meaningful. Economic theory imposes restrictions on the signs and values of the parameters in economic relationships, and the estimates need to be examined to see whether they satisfy these constraints. For example, in the standard market demand function (5.2) considered earlier in the chapter it was stated that a positive relationship is normally expected between income and demand but a negative relationship is generally expected between the price of a good and the demand for that good. The signs of the estimated parameters in equation (5.22) thus conform to economic theory; they have the 'correct' signs. Knowledge of the market for the particular product under consideration may permit theoretical limits to be imposed on the sizes of the income and price parameters.

If an estimated parameter has an 'incorrect' sign or does not satisfy the restrictions on magnitude it should be rejected, as it is theoretically implausible. In general, an unexpected parameter sign or size is the result of deficiencies in the model: it may be incorrectly specified, or in the data used for estimation: for example, too few observations may be employed, the observations may be unrepresentative, or the data may violate some of the model assumptions.

The interpretation and evaluation of parameter estimates in practice may be illustrated using computer output from the ORION software package. A multiple linear regression market share model is constructed and estimated using 48 quarterly data points on the products of a number of competing manufacturing companies which together comprise a complete market. The typical market share model suggested earlier in this chapter is of the form

$$S = g(V_1, V_2, V_3, V_4) \qquad (5.23)$$

where

S is the market share of firm A;

V_1 is the price of the product sold by firm A relative to the average price of products sold in the same market by competing firms;

V_2 is advertising expenditure by firm A relative to the average advertising expenditure of competing firms;

V_3 is the quality of the product sold by firm A relative to the average quality of competitive products;

V_4 is the quality of firm A's distribution system relative to the average quality of competitors' distribution systems; and

g denotes some function.

If additional explanatory variables are included in the market share model, then, since we are considering linear regression, equation (5.23) may be rewritten as

$$S = a + b_1 V_1 + b_2 V_2 + \ldots + b_{12} V_{12} + u \tag{5.24}$$

where

S, V_1, V_2, V_3, V_4 are as defined in model (5.23);
u is an error term;
$a, b_1, b_2, \ldots, b_{12}$ are unknown parameters; and
$V_5, V_6, \ldots, V_{12}$ are defined as follows:

V_5 is the number of salesmen used by firm A relative to the average number of salesmen used by competing firms (the higher the relative number of salesmen, the higher the expected market share);

V_6 is sales promotion expenditure by firm A relative to the average sales promotion expenditure of competing firms (the higher relative sales promotion expenditure, the higher the expected market share);

V_7 is research and development expenditure by firm A relative to the average of competing firms (the higher relative research and development expenditure, the higher the expected market share);

V_8 is the number of product development breakthroughs by firm A relative to the average number of competing firms (the higher the relative number of breakthroughs, the higher the expected market share);

V_9 is market research expenditure by firm A relative to the average of competing firms (the higher relative market research expenditure, the higher the expected market share);

V_{10} is V_2 lagged one period, that is the previous period's relative advertising expenditure (this is justified in terms of advertising building up a stock of goodwill over time which depreciates – so the higher lagged relative advertising expenditure, the higher the expected market share);

V_{11} is S lagged one period, that is the lagged value of the dependent variable (this is justified in terms of consumers demonstrating brand loyalty – so the higher the lagged value of market share, the higher the expected market share);

V_{12} is a dummy variable which accounts for a change in the packaging of firm A's product that occurred part way through the period under consideration. (Dummy variables are considered in detail in Chapter 6.)

The empirical results corresponding to the ordinary least squares estimation of model (5.24) are given in Table 5.1, where the dependent and independent variables are denoted as follows:

S = ORDERS
V_1 = PRICE
V_2 = ADVERT
V_3 = QUAL
V_4 = DIST
V_5 = SMEN
V_6 = SP
V_7 = RD
V_8 = BTHROS
V_9 = MR
V_{10} = LAGADVERT
V_{11} = LAGORDERS
V_{12} = DUMMY

The estimated equation yields the following implications. If all the explanatory variables were equal to zero, the predicted market share would be 0.037 or 3.7 per cent. A one unit increase in firm A's relative price results in a predicted decrease of 0.262 in the market share of firm A. A 'correct' parameter sign has therefore been estimated for the price variable. A one unit increase in firm A's relative sales promotion expenditure results in a predicted increase of 0.004 in firm A's market share, so this variable has the expected estimated parameter sign. If relative advertising expenditure by firm A increases by one unit the market share of the firm is predicted to increase by 0.021, so this variable also has the expected estimated parameter

Table 5.1

Initial estimation of market share model

REG> JOB /ECONXX.FILE

REG> MULTIPLE ORDERS ON PRICE,SP,ADVERT, RD,&

    2: BTHROS,QUAL,SMEN,MR,DIST,DUMMY,&

    3: LAGADVERT,LAGORDERS &

    4: DISPLAY FULL

Equation

$$ORDERS = .037322 - .26228*PRICE + .0044374*SP$$
$$+ .020742*ADVERT + .0037288*RD - .0010669*BTHROS$$
$$+ .017262*QUAL - .069159*SMEN - .0031996*MR$$
$$+ .3856*DIST + .0090999*DUMMY + .019462*LAGADVERT$$
$$- .16086*LAGORDERS$$

R-squared = .96619

48 Observations, 12 Variables

Corrected R-Squared	= .9546	Residual Sum Squares	= .0003972
Standard Error	= .0033687	F-Ratio	= 83.35
Dependent Mean	= .16604	Degrees of Freedom	= 35
Durbin–Watson	= 2.3133		
Standard Error as % Mean ORDERS = 2.0289			

172

Coefficients Table

Variable	Coefficient	Standard Error	95.00% Confidence		Beta
			Lower	Upper	
PRICE	−.26228	.15729E-01	−.29421	−.23035	−1.0367
SP	.44374E-02	.28878E-02	−.14250E-02	.10300E-01	.88634E-01
ADVERT	.20742E-01	.29876E-02	.14676E-01	.26807E-01	.39707
RD	.37288E-02	.19136E-02	−.15604E-03	.76137E-02	.13133
BTHROS	−.10669E-02	.73442E-03	−.25578E-02	.42410E-03	−.77503E-01
QUAL	.17262E-01	.12506E-02	.14723E-01	.19801E-01	1.4594
SMEN	−.69159E-01	.55421E-01	−.18167	.43351E-01	−.33155
MR	−.31996E-02	.10911E-02	−.54146E-02	−.98461E-03	−.21040
DIST	.38560	.23332	−.88052E-01	.85926	.46375
DUMMY	.90999E-02	.10797E-02	.69080E-02	.11292E-01	.29083
LAGADVERT	.19462E-01	.44755E-02	.10377E-01	.28548E-01	.34938
LAGORDERS	−.16086	.52398E-01	−.26723	−.54486E-01	−.15961
Constant	.37322E-01	.18114	−.33041	.40506	Undefined

Variable	Elasticity	T-Statistic	Partial F
PRICE	−1.5776	−16.675	278.07
SP	.26719E-01	1.5366	2.3612
ADVERT	.12583	6.9425	48.198
RD	.22490E-01	1.9486	3.7969
BTHROS	−.64252E-02	−1.4526	2.1102
QUAL	.31192	13.803	190.53

Table 5.1 (continued)

SMEN	-.41651	-1.2479	1.5572
MR	-.19270E-01	-2.9325	8.5997
DIST	2.3233	1.6527	2.7315
DUMMY	.27402E-01	8.4284	71.039
LAGADVERT	.11807	4.3486	18.911
LAGORDERS	-.16066	-3.0699	9.4246
Constant	Undefined	.20604	.42452E-01

Coefficient Correlation Matrix

	C1	C2	C3	C4	C5	C6	C7
C1	1.0000						
C2	-.0490	1.0000					
C3	-.1879	-.0768	1.0000				
C4	-.2163	-.1449	-.1870	1.0000			
C5	-.0171	.3783	-.0102	-.4532	1.0000		
C6	-.4136	.4001	-.1505	.6349	-.2614	1.0000	
C7	-.2512	.3305	-.2107	.2438	.0147	.4067	1.000
C8	.1062	-.2293	-.0147	-.6713	.3948	-.7242	-.4034
C9	.2079	-.3671	.2047	-.1897	-.1659	-.2959	-.9636
C10	.1519	.0295	-.1067	-.0884	.0718	-.0344	-.0362
C11	-.1147	.1817	-.4323	.0601	.1971	-.0377	.3429
C12	-.2485	-.0916	.1928	.1971	-.1935	.0760	.0349

174

Table 5.1 (continued)

	C8	C9	C10	C11	C12
C8	1.0000				
C9	.3376	1.0000			
C10	.0780	-.0067	1.0000		
C11	-.0625	-.5021	.1471	1.0000	
C12	-.1582	.0852	-.4280	-.4506	1.0000

Variable Correlation Matrix

	PRICE	SP	ADVERT	RD	BTHROS	QUAL
PRICE	1.0000					
SP	-.4216	1.0000				
ADVERT	.6789	-.1661	1.0000			
RD	-.0848	.5905	.1986	1.0000		
BTHROS	.2638	-.2100	.3229	.2618	1.0000	
QUAL	.7003	-.6943	.4187	-.5247	.0086	1.0000
SMEN	.2269	.1983	.4774	.4764	.6110	-.2350
MR	.6135	-.1273	.5712	.1682	-.0624	.5953
DIST	.2189	.2087	.4705	.4690	.6235	-.2271
DUMMY	-.0135	.0007	.0285	.0004	-.0000	.0000
LAGADVERT	.6749	-.2379	.7526	.0534	.4001	.4359
LAGORDERS	.5350	-.3983	.2767	-.3564	-.0118	.6097
ORDERS	.2296	-.4212	.4575	-.3357	.0469	.6708

Table 5.1 (concluded)

	SMEN	MR	DIST	DUMMY	LAGADVERT	LAGORDERS
SMEN	1.0000					
MR	.0982	1.0000				
DIST	.9892	.0743	1.0000			
DUMMY	.0000	.0004	.0000	1.0000		
LAGADVERT	.5768	.4648	.6062	.0304	1.0000	
LAGORDERS	−.1879	.3912	−.1724	.2953	.4399	1.0000
ORDERS	−.0178	.3667	.0198	.2797	.4703	.3439

	ORDERS
ORDERS	1.0000

Analysis of Variance

Source	Sums of Squares	Degrees of Freedom	Mean Square
Regression	.11351E-01	12	.94589E-03
Residual	.39720E-03	35	.11348E-04
Total	.11748E-01	47	.24996E-03

F-Ratio of 83.350 Significant at the .05 Level

REG>

sign. A one-unit increase in relative research and development expenditure is predicted to cause an increase of 0.004 in market share, which gives the 'correct' sign for the estimated parameter. If the relative number of breakthroughs by firm A increases by one unit, the estimated parameter implies that the firm's market share will decrease by 0.001, which is not expected. Hence this estimated parameter must be rejected. Of the remaining explanatory variables, relative product quality, relative quality of the distribution system and lagged relative advertising expenditure all have the 'correct' estimated parameter signs, whereas those of the relative number of salesmen, relative market research expenditure and the lagged dependent variable are 'incorrect' and so must be rejected. The positive coefficient estimated for the dummy variable is expected, since it implies that an improvement in product packaging results in a predicted increase in market share.

STATISTICAL MEASURES OF ACCURACY AND SIGNIFICANCE OF FORECASTING EQUATIONS

Coefficient of determination, R^2

This measures the explanatory power of the model, that is the extent to which the independent variables explain the behaviour of the dependent variable. The estimated multiple regression line is given by

$$\hat{Y}_i = \hat{a} + \hat{b}_1 X_{1i} + \hat{b}_2 X_{2i} + \ldots + \hat{b}_k X_{ki}; \ i = 1,2,\ldots,n \qquad (5.25)$$

Now if $X_{1i}, X_{2i}, \ldots, X_{ki}$ were unknown, the best prediction of Y_i would simply be the average of the observed values, $\bar{Y} = \Sigma Y_i/n$. In general, although the regression equation (5.25) will not give perfect predictions the estimated value of Y_i is likely to be more accurate than that yielded by $\bar{Y}$. The total deviation of an observed value of the dependent variable from its mean may therefore be split into two parts: that which is 'explained' by the regression of Y on X_1, $X_2, \ldots, X_k$; and the 'unexplained' deviation:

$$Y_i - \bar{Y} = (\hat{Y}_i - \bar{Y}) + (Y_i - \hat{Y}_i) \qquad (5.26)$$

| total | explained | unexplained |
| deviation | deviation | deviation |

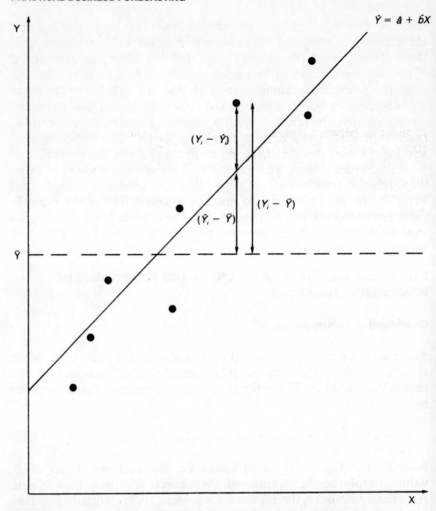

Figure 5.3 Split of total deviation into explained and unexplained

The split is illustrated for the simple regression case in Figure 5.3. If equation (5.26) is squared and summed over all observations $i = 1, 2, \ldots, n$, the following is obtained:

$$\Sigma(Y_i - \bar{Y})^2 = \Sigma(\hat{Y}_i - \bar{Y})^2 + \Sigma(Y_i - \hat{Y}_i)^2 \qquad (5.27)$$

total variation	explained variation	unexplained variation

where variation is the sum of squared deviations.

Now the coefficient of determination is defined as the proportion of the total variation in Y explained by the regression:

$$R^2 = \frac{\text{explained variation of } Y}{\text{total variation of } Y}$$

R^2 must lie between zero and unity. If $R^2 = 1$, the regression explains 100 per cent of the variation in Y and we have a perfect fit. If $R^2 = 0$, the regression explains none of the variation in Y. Clearly, the closer the value of R^2 to unity, the better is the fit of the least squares line. R^2 thus provides an overall measure of how well the dependent variable is explained by the independent variables.

The increase in R^2 resulting from the inclusion of additional explanatory variables in the model indicates how helpful this extra set of variables is in explaining the variation in the dependent variable. However, the addition of any explanatory variable to the model will always increase R^2, and hence R^2 may be scaled down to correct for the number of independent variables, which gives rise to corrected or adjusted R^2, denoted $\bar{R}^2$.

R^2 and $\bar{R}^2$ values appear in the computer printout of standard regression programs. What is considered a 'reasonable' value for R^2 depends on the particular application under consideration, and reference should be made to values obtained in similar previous studies. Thus, whereas in certain circumstances an R^2 value of 0.9 may be considered unsatisfactory, in others a value of 0.4 may be regarded as acceptable.

The interpretation of R^2 and $\bar{R}^2$ may be illustrated by reference to the estimated market share model given in Table 5.1. The R^2 value of 0.966 indicates that 96.6 per cent of the variation in firm A's market share is explained by the regression. When this value is adjusted for the number of explanatory variables a corrected R^2 value of 95.5 per cent is obtained. The values show that the market share model fits the data well.

Significance tests – additional assumption

In order to derive significance tests it is necessary to add a further assumption to the list of five specified for the classical linear regression model:

6 The error terms are normally distributed

u_i has a normal distribution; $i = 1, 2, \ldots, n$

F test

The multiple linear regression model

$$Y_i = a + b_1 X_{1i} + b_2 X_{2i} + \ldots + b_k X_{ki} + u_i; \, i = 1, 2, \ldots, n \quad (5.28)$$

suggests that the dependent variable Y is influenced by a set of k explanatory variables $X_1, X_2, \ldots, X_k$. The F statistic may be used to test the overall significance of the regression, that is to ascertain whether the explanatory variables taken together do actually have any significant influence on the dependent variable. The null hypothesis being tested (H_0) is that all the explanatory variable parameters are simultaneously equal to zero:

$$H_0: b_1 = b_2 = \ldots = b_k = 0 \quad (5.29)$$

The alternative hypothesis (H_1) is:

$$H_1: \text{not all the } b_i \text{s are zero} \quad (5.30)$$

If the null hypothesis is true, then there is no linear relationship between the dependent and independent variables, and so the model offers no explanation of the behaviour of the dependent variable.

The calculated F statistic is given by

$$F = \frac{\text{explained variation of } Y/k}{\text{unexplained variation of } Y/(n-k-1)} \quad (5.31)$$

This ratio is compared with the theoretical F value with $k, \, n-k-1$ degrees of freedom which may be obtained from tables of the F distribution. A significance level of 5 or 1 per cent is usually chosen. If the calculated F value is greater than the theoretical value the null hypothesis is rejected, that is not all the b_is are zero. If the calculated F value is less than the theoretical value the null hypothesis cannot be rejected, that is the regression is not significant and the empirical results may simply be generated by random factors; in such a case the model must be rejected and alternative models examined. In general, the higher the calculated F ratio the more likely it is that a significant relationship exists between the dependent and independent variables.

The F statistic may also be regarded as a test of the significance of R^2, since equation (5.31) may be rewritten as

$$F = (R_2^2/k)/[(1 - R^2)/(n - k - 1)] \qquad (5.32)$$

R^2 is generally non-zero, but when the null hypothesis (5.29) is true any apparent explanation of the variation of Y is due entirely to random causes – there is no genuine explanation. If the calculated F statistic results in rejection of the null hypothesis, then R^2 is significantly different from zero, which implies that the model provides some real explanation of the behaviour of the dependent variable.

The computer output of regression programs usually generates the calculated F value for testing the overall significance of the regression. For the estimated market share model given in Table 5.1, the calculated F statistic is equal to 83.35. The theoretical F value with k ($=12$), $n - k - 1$ ($=35$) degrees of freedom at the 5 per cent significance level is 2.04. Since the calculated value exceeds the theoretical value the regression is significant and the hypothesis that the explanatory variable coefficients are all equal to zero is rejected.

Standard error or t test

Rejection of the null hypothesis in an F test gives no indication of which individual parameters are non-zero, so an additional test is required. The t test may be used to examine the hypothesis that a particular explanatory variable coefficient is significantly different from zero, or whether the estimated value may simply have been generated by chance. The null hypothesis being tested (H_0) is

$$H_0 : b_i = 0 \qquad (5.33)$$

The alternative hypothesis (H_1) is

$$H_1 : b_i \neq 0 \qquad (5.34)$$

If the null hypothesis is true, then the explanatory variable X_i does not influence the dependent variable – there is no relationship between

Y and X_i.

The calculated t statistic is given by

$$t = \hat{b}_i / SE(\hat{b}_i) \tag{5.35}$$

where $SE(\hat{b}_i)$ is the standard error of $\hat{b}_i$, which is equal to the square root of the estimated variance of $\hat{b}_i$. The absolute value of the t ratio (5.35) is compared with the theoretical t value with $n - k - 1$ degrees of freedom which may be obtained from tables of the t distribution. A significance level of 5 per cent is generally chosen. If the calculated absolute t value exceeds the theoretical value the null hypothesis is rejected, that is the population parameter b_i is significantly different from zero at the 5 per cent level. If the calculated absolute t ratio is less than the theoretical value the null hypothesis cannot be rejected, that is b_i is not significantly different from zero at the 5 per cent level. The hypothesis under consideration is a two-tail test, so the appropriate tabled t value is that which cuts off 2.5 per cent of the area of the t distribution at the upper end.

When the number of degrees of freedom is at least 20, the theoretical t value is approximately equal to 2 (2.09 for 20 reducing eventually to 1.96 for an infinite number). Hence if the absolute value of the calculated t ratio is greater than 2, the parameter is significantly different from zero at the 5 per cent level, whereas if it is less than 2 the parameter is not statistically significant. However, from equation (5.35) we can see that if the absolute value of the t statistic exceeds 2, then the absolute value of $\hat{b}_i$, $|\hat{b}_i| > 2SE(\hat{b}_i)$, and if the value is less than 2 then $|\hat{b}_i| < 2SE(\hat{b}_i)$. The t test may therefore equivalently be stated in terms of standard errors: if the absolute value of the estimated parameter exceeds twice its standard error, then the parameter is significantly different from zero at the 5 per cent level, but if the absolute value of the parameter estimate is less than twice the standard error, then the parameter is not statistically significant.

The calculated t values and/or standard errors corresponding to each parameter appear in the printout of standard computer regression programs. If the empirical results for the market share model depicted in Table 5.1 are examined, the significance of the individual parameters may be deduced. As the theoretical t value has $n - k - 1 = 35$ degrees of freedom, it is approximately equal to 2 at the 5 per cent significance level. The absolute values of the calculated t statistics exceed 2 for the following set of independent variables: PRICE, ADVERT, QUAL, MR, DUMMY, LAGADVERT, LAGORDERS; hence the parameters of these variables are significantly different from zero at the 5 per cent level. Equivalently the absolute values of the estimated coefficients of these variables are greater than twice the corresponding standard errors. The parameters of the remaining explanatory variables – SP, RD, BTHROS, SMEN, DIST and the constant – are not statistically significant.

When a calculated t value or standard error shows that a parameter is not statistically significant at the 5 per cent level, this does not prove that there is no relationship between the corresponding explanatory variable and the dependent variable. For example, the following regression relationship may be estimated from a sample of 25 observations, where there are strong theoretical grounds for believing that Y is positively related to the explanatory variable X_1:

$$\hat{Y} = 3.9 + 1.2X_1 + 0.8X_2 - 4.7X_3 \qquad (5.36)$$
$$\phantom{\hat{Y} = }(2.6) \quad (1.8) \quad (3.4) \quad (-3.1)$$

Here the figures in brackets are calculated t values. Equation (5.36) provides support for the hypothesis in that Y is related to X_1 by a positive coefficient; the statistical evidence is consistent with prior belief and provides weak support for the hypothesis, so X_1 should not be eliminated from the equation. (The insignificance of the parameter may be a result of statistical problems.) As the absolute value of the t ratio becomes smaller the statistical support lessens, but it is only if the ratio is zero or negative that the statistical results provide no support for the hypothesis. Prior belief therefore plays a vital role in the decision about which explanatory variables should be retained in the equation in view of the statistical evidence. If the 'correct' sign is estimated for a parameter and it is statistically significant, this provides strong support for the hypothesis that the variable has an impact on the dependent variable.

The results which appear in Table 5.1 show that although the sales promotion variable (SP) has the expected estimated parameter sign, the parameter is not significantly different from zero at the 5 per cent level, and therefore only weak support is provided for the hypothesis that relative sales promotion expenditure should be included as an explanatory variable in the model. If prior belief does not clearly indicate that this variable should be included in the model – relative sales promotion expenditure may or may not be expected to have a noticeable impact on market share – the variable should not be retained in the equation.

FINAL MODEL FORM

The empirical results given in Table 5.1 indicate that the following explanatory variables should be excluded from the market share model because their estimated parameters have 'incorrect' signs: relative number of breakthroughs, relative number of salesmen, relative market research expenditure, lagged dependent variable. Of the remaining explanatory variables, the following have statistically insignificant parameters at the 5 per cent level: relative sales promotion expenditure, relative research and development expenditure, relative quality of distribution system. As there are no very strong grounds for including these latter three independent variables and only weak statistical support has been obtained for their retention, they should be excluded from the model. However, as explanatory variables are removed from the model it may be the case that the parameters of certain remaining variables become significantly different from zero. In particular, it was found that when the variables with 'incorrect' parameter signs were removed and also the sales promotion expenditure and research and development expenditure variables, then the parameter of the quality of the distribution system variable achieved statistical significance. The relative quality of the distribution system was therefore re-introduced as an explanatory variable, so the final model contains the following set of explanatory variables: relative price, relative advertising expenditure, lagged relative advertising expenditure, relative product quality, relative quality of distribution system, packaging dummy. The empirical results corresponding to this final model are given in Table 5.2. Inspection of the table shows that the estimated parameters of all the explanatory variables have the expected signs, and that each of the explanatory variables has a statistically significant impact on market share.

PRODUCING FORECASTS

Once a model has been estimated in its final form it may be used for forecasting purposes. The estimated multiple linear regression relationship is

Table 5.2
Final estimation of market share model

REG> MULTIPLE ORDERS ON PRICE,ADVERT,QUAL,DIST,DUMMY,LAGADVERT DISPLAY FULL

Equation
ORDERS = .22059 − .27943*PRICE + .021772*ADVERT
+ .014066*QUAL + .1418*DIST + .0076523*DUMMY
+ .015224*LAGADVERT

R-Squared = .93511

48 Observations, 6 Variables

Corrected R-Squared	= .92562	Residual Sum Squares	= .00076231
Standard Error	= .0043119	F-Ratio	= 98.475
Dependent Mean	= .16604	Degrees of Freedom	= 41
Durbin–Watson	= 2.2934		
Standard Error as % Mean ORDERS = 2.5969			

Table 5.2 (continued)

Coefficients Table

| Variable | Coefficient | Standard Error | 95.00% Confidence | | Beta |
			Lower	Upper	
PRICE	-.27943	.18405E-01	-.31660	-.24226	-1.1044
ADVERT	.21772E-01	.34185E-02	.14868E-01	.28676E-01	.41680
QUAL	.14066E-01	.87209E-03	.12305E-01	.15828E-01	1.1892
DIST	.14118	.58618E-01	.22798E-01	.25956	.16979
DUMMY	.76523E-02	.12485E-02	.51309E-02	.10174E-01	.24457
LAGADVERT	.15224E-01	.45806E-02	.59729E-02	.24474E-01	.27328
Constant	.22059	.57016E-01	.10544	.33574	Undefined

Table 5.2 (continued)

Variable	Elasticity	T-Statistic	Partial F
PRICE	-1.6808	-15.182	230.51
ADVERT	.13208	6.3689	40.563
QUAL	.25418	16.130	260.16
DIST	.85062	2.4085	5.8007
DUMMY	.23043E-01	6.1293	37.568
LAGADVERT	.92354E-01	3.3235	11.046
Constant	Undefined	3.8689	14.968

Coefficient Correlation Matrix

	C1	C2	C3	C4	C5	C6
C1	1.0000					
C2	-.3103	1.0000				
C3	-.5280	-.0272	1.0000			
C4	-.1114	-.1398	.6493	1.0000		
C5	.0483	-.0337	.0132	.0429	1.0000	
C6	-.1476	-.3300	-.3969	-.6239	-.0509	1.0000

187

Table 5.2 (concluded)

Variable Correlation Matrix

	PRICE	ADVERT	QUAL	DIST	DUMMY	LAGADVERT
PRICE	1.0000					
ADVERT	.6789	1.0000				
QUAL	.7003	.4187	1.0000			
DIST	.2189	.4705	−.2271	1.0000		
DUMMY	−.0135	.0285	.0000	.0000	1.0000	
LAGADVERT	.6749	.7526	.4359	.6062	.0304	1.0000
ORDERS	.2296	.4575	.6708	.0198	.2797	.4703

	ORDERS
ORDERS	1.0000

Analysis of Variance

Source	Sums of Squares	Degrees of Freedom	Mean Square
Regression	.10986E-01	6	.18309E-02
Residual	.76231E-03	41	.18593E-04
Total	.11748E-01	47	.24996E-03

F-Ratio of 98.475 Significant at the .05 Level

REG> ORI

188

$$\hat{Y}_i = \hat{a} + \hat{b}_1 X_{1i} + \hat{b}_2 X_{2i} + \ldots + \hat{b}_k X_{ki} \tag{5.37}$$

Forecasts of the dependent variable, $\hat{Y}_F$, are generated by multiplying future values of the explanatory variables, $X_{1F}, X_{2F}, \ldots, X_{kF}$, by their respective estimated parameters and then summing. This yields a point estimate of the forecasted dependent variable – the expected value of the forecast variable. In the context of the classical linear regression model, the OLS parameter estimates will yield the best linear unbiased forecast.

Inaccurate forecasts may occur for various reasons. First, poor parameter estimates are likely to give rise to poor forecasts, so considerable attention to estimation is necessary. Second, in order to produce forecasts of the dependent variable, the values of the explanatory variables must be forecast for the period over which forecasts of the dependent variable are required, and these may contain errors. Third, the structure of relationships may change over time, so that parameter values applicable to the estimation period may not apply strictly to the forecast period. Fourth, an incorrectly specified model (for example, omitting a relevant variable) may have a substantial effect on forecasts as the values of the variables move outside the range used for estimation. It is therefore often necessary to adjust forecasts generated by regression models in view of information concerning such factors. This modification is usually carried out on the basis of qualitative information and the forecaster's experience.

For the standard market size forecasting model considered at the beginning of this chapter, forecasts of population size, income, prices and possibly advertising expenditure are normally required to generate forecasts of market demand for a product. Population projections may be obtained from published sources (see the Sources of data section of Chapter 2). Forecasts of consumers' disposable income can be derived from the framework of national income analysis, and several macro-economic forecasts are published (see Chapter 2). Price forecasts are required for the product under consideration as well as substitutes and complements. These forecasts are likely to be more problematical, but it should be possible to make reasonable estimates from market intelligence work and the knowledge of marketing staff. Advertising expenditure forecasts may be obtained in a similar manner to price forecasts or from published sources (see Chapter 2).

For the typical market share forecasting model considered earlier in this chapter, it is necessary to forecast own and competitors' prices, advertising expenditures, product qualities and distribution system qualities. Forecasts of the variables which are under the control of the firm should present no problem, and forecasts of the variables relating to competing firms should again be possible from market intelligence work and the knowledge of marketing staff.

STATISTICAL MEASURE OF ACCURACY OF ACTUAL FORECASTS – PREDICTION INTERVAL

In the general managerial forecasting situation, the decision maker is often not merely interested in a point forecast, but also requires some information regarding the accuracy of the forecast. It is possible to construct a range around the expected value of the forecast variable so that we may be, say, 95 per cent certain that the observed value will lie within these limits, that is we can construct a 95 per cent prediction interval (conditional upon known values of the explanatory variables in the forecast period). We would wish our model to generate as narrow a prediction interval as possible, to minimize the risk of decision taking; if the classical assumptions hold for the linear regression model, then the OLS parameter estimates will produce a prediction interval which is narrower than that generated by any other linear unbiased forecast. The two sources of imprecision allowed for in the forecasts are first that estimates are used instead of known parameter values, and second that the value of the disturbance term is unknown (but assumed equal to zero).

This confidence interval for a forecast is narrowest at the point of sample means and widens as we diverge from these means. Hence forecasting with a regression model becomes increasingly uncertain as the values assumed by the explanatory variables for the period of the forecast depart from the mean of the sample which was used to estimate the relationship.

If the OLS point forecast of the dependent variable is denoted $\hat{Y}_F$ and the actual value is Y_F, then the forecast error is equal to $Y_F - \hat{Y}_F$. The approximate 95 per cent prediction interval for Y_F is given by

$$\hat{Y}_F - 2S_F \leqslant Y_F \leqslant \hat{Y}_F + 2S_F \qquad (5.38)$$

if there are at least 20 degrees of freedom (so that the theoretical t value may be taken as 2), where S_F is the estimated standard deviation of the forecast error.

Many computer regression packages provide facilities to output both point and interval forecasts of the dependent variable for given values of the explanatory variables in the forecast period.

FURTHER READING

Johnston, J. *Econometric Methods,* McGraw-Hill, New York, 1984, 568 pp.

Koutsoyiannis, A., *Theory of Econometrics,* Macmillan, London and Basingstoke, 1981, 681 pp.

Robinson, C., *Business Forecasting: An Economic Approach,* Nelson, London, 1971, 199 pp.

Wonnacott, R. J. and Wonnacott, T. H., *Econometrics,* Wiley, New York, 1979, 580 pp.

Wood, D. and Fildes, R., *Forecasting for Business: Methods and Applications,* Longman, London and New York, 1976, 280 pp.

6 Extensions of regression

The multiple linear regression model developed in Chapter 5 is given by

$$Y_i = a + b_1 X_{1i} + b_2 X_{2i} + \ldots + b_k X_{ki} + u_i;\ i = 1, 2, \ldots, n \quad (6.1)$$

where Y is the dependent variable, $X_1, X_2, \ldots, X_k$ are the explanatory variables, u is a disturbance term, $a, b_1, b_2, \ldots, b_k$ are unknown parameters and the subscript i represents the observation number. For many business forecasting applications the linear relationship between the dependent and explanatory variables assumed in equation (6.1) may be inappropriate. In such cases an attempt may be made to fit a non-linear relationship directly to the data, but this usually requires a computer search procedure which involves highly complex calculations. Alternatively, it may be possible to find a suitable transformation of the data such that the relationship between the transformed data becomes linear; the estimation method of ordinary least squares may then be used on the transformed data.

LOG-LINEAR REGRESSION MODELS

The most commonly used transformation in sales forecasting regression models is the log-linear. Here we have a multiplicative relationship between the dependent and explanatory variables of the form

$$Y = a X_1^{b_1} X_2^{b_2} \ldots X_k^{b_k} e^u \quad (6.2)$$

where $e \cong 2.718$ is the base of natural logarithms. It should be noted that the error term must also be treated as multiplicative rather than additive. In order to render equation (6.2) amenable to estimation using OLS, it is necessary to take logarithms of the variables (to the base e) which yields an equation which is linear in the natural logs of the variables:

$$\log Y = \log a + b_1 \log X_1 +$$
$$b_2 \log X_2 + \ldots + b_k \log X_k + u \tag{6.3}$$

An OLS regression of $\log Y$ on $\log X_1$, $\log X_2, \ldots, \log X_k$ yields estimates $\widehat{\log a}$, $\hat{b}_1$, $\hat{b}_2, \ldots, \hat{b}_k$ of the parameters $\log a$, b_1, $b_2, \ldots, b_k$. If the classical assumptions of the linear regression model hold for equation (6.3), then these least squares estimators are best linear unbiased estimators (BLUE). However, although the estimators of the parameters b_1, $b_2, \ldots, b_k$ in equation (6.2) are therefore also BLUE, if we wish to obtain an estimate of a in equation (6.2) it is necessary to take antilogs of $\widehat{\log a}$ which gives a biased estimator.

The log-linear transformation is often employed because the multiplicative model (6.2) corresponds to the assumption of constant elasticity. The derivative of Y with respect to X_1 in equation (6.2) yields:

$$\partial Y / \partial X_1 = ab_1 X_1^{b_1-1} X_2^{b_2} \ldots X_k^{b_k} e^u$$
$$= b_1 Y / X_1 \tag{6.4}$$

The elasticity of Y with respect to X_1 is defined as

$$q_{YX_1} = \partial Y / \partial X_1 \cdot (X_1) / Y \tag{6.5}$$

Substitution of equation (6.4) into equation (6.5) gives

$$q_{YX_1} = b_1 \tag{6.6}$$

Hence b_1 is the constant elasticity of Y with respect to X_1, and in general b_j is the constant elasticity of Y with respect to X_j, $j = 1, 2, \ldots, k$. Consider the following market size forecasting model:

$$Y = aX_1^{b_1} X_2^{b_2} X_3^{b_3} e^u \tag{6.7}$$

where

Y is the market demand for the product;
X_1 is consumers' disposable income;
X_2 is the price of the product, and
X_3 is the price of a substitute product.

In equation (6.7) the parameters b_1, b_2 and b_3 may be interpreted as elasticities; hence b_1 is the income elasticity of demand, b_2 is the own-price elasticity of demand and b_3 is a cross-price elasticity of demand.

Most of the computer programs for regression analysis have facilities for performing simple transformations of the data such as taking logs, so the data may be input in the usual form. All the regression calculations, however, refer to the transformed relationship, and care must therefore be exercised in interpreting results. For example, estimation of equation (6.3) yields a value for R^2 which shows the proportion of the variation in the dependent variable that is explained by the regression, but the dependent variable is now log Y and not Y as in the standard linear model. Thus, the R^2 values which appear in computer output may not be used directly to compare the goodness of fit of linear and log-linear models since the dependent variables are different.

The interpretation of regression results for log-linear models may be illustrated using a model developed by Witt and Pass (1981 and 1983) to forecast the size of the UK cigarette market. The dependent variable is the number of cigarettes consumed and the explanatory variables include the following which were discussed when considering the standard market demand function in Chapter 5 – consumers' disposable income, price of cigarettes and advertising. The influence of population size is incorporated by considering demand, income and advertising in per capita terms. In addition, the impact of anti-smoking publicity on cigarette demand is examined by inserting dummy variables in the model to represent the effects of health scares (dummy variables are considered in detail in the next section of this chapter). The log-linear relationship postulated by Witt and Pass is as follows:

$$\log(Y_t/P_t) = \log a + b_1 \log (X_{1t}/P_t) + b_2 \log X_{2t}$$
$$+ b_3 \log (X_{3t}/P_t) + \text{health scare variables} + u_t$$

$$\text{(6.8)}$$

$$t = 1,2,\ldots,21 \ (1 = 1955,\ldots,21 = 1975)$$

where

Y_t is the number of (manufactured) cigarettes consumed in year t;

P_t is the UK de facto population over 15 years of age in year t;

X_{1t} is UK real personal disposable income in year t;

X_{2t} is the real price of cigarettes in year t;

X_{3t} is real (press and television) advertising expenditure in year t;

u_t is a random disturbance term; and

a, b_1, b_2, b_3 are parameters.

Under inflationary conditions when price levels in general are changing, it is usual to eliminate the effects of inflation by measuring all variables expressed in money values in real terms, that is after dividing money prices by an appropriate price index. This adjustment assumes that consumers react to changes in real values rather than money values. The income, price and advertising variables therefore enter model (6.8) in real terms.

Table 6.1
Estimation of cigarette demand model (ignoring results for dummy variables)

Dependent variable: log (Y/P); $\bar{R}^2 = 0.957$; $F = 74.92$

Explanatory variables	Estimated coefficients	t values
log (X_{1t}/P_t)	0.126	2.88
log X_{2t}	−0.321	−4.59
log (X_{3t}/P_t)	0.068	2.68
intercept	7.268	21.98
dummy variables (3)		

The empirical results corresponding to the ordinary least squares estimation of equation (6.8) are given in Table 6.1. If log (X_1/P), log X_2, log (X_3/P) and the health scare variables were all equal to zero, then the predicted value of the logarithm of cigarette demand per capita would be 7.268. The estimated income elasticity of demand is 0.126, that is, a 1 per cent increase in real personal disposable income per capita results in a predicted increase of 0.126 per cent in the demand for cigarettes per capita. The sign of the estimated income elasticity is therefore 'correct', and the magnitude implies that although cigarettes are superior goods they are regarded very much as necessities (elasticity < 1) rather than luxuries (elasticity > 1). The estimated own-price elasticity of demand is -0.321, that is a 1 per cent increase in the real price of cigarettes is predicted to cause a decrease of 0.321 per cent in cigarette demand per capita. The estimated price elasticity has the expected sign and shows that the demand for cigarettes is price inelastic which is not surprising given the habit forming nature of cigarettes. The estimated advertising elasticity is 0.068, so a 1 per cent increase in real advertising expenditure per capita results in a predicted increase of 0.068 per cent in the demand for cigarettes per capita. Again the sign of the estimated advertising elasticity is 'correct', but the magnitude implies that advertising only has a very small effect on the overall size of the cigarette market. The t values given in Table 6.1 show that each of the parameters is significantly different from zero at the 5 per cent level, and the corrected R^2 value indicates that 95.7 per cent of the variation in log (Y/P) is explained by the regression.

The choice of functional form, for example whether a model should be specified as linear or log-linear, may be apparent on grounds of prior knowledge – the evidence may be generated by theory or earlier empirical studies, but in many situations the choice must be determined as part of the data analysis. Where the choice is made on empirical grounds, the alternative functional forms must be estimated and the results evaluated and compared on the basis of criteria which include expected parameter signs, expected parameter magnitudes, significance of the parameters, goodness of fit of the models, and non-violation of the classical assumptions.

DUMMY VARIABLES

The usefulness of the linear regression model can often be extended by the inclusion of dummy (or indicator) variables as explanatory variables in the model. These are qualitative variables which generally take the value 0 or 1 and may be used to represent factors which include the following:

1 Temporal effects – a behavioural relationship may shift between

one period and another. For example, if we are using quarterly data to estimate a demand function, a seasonal pattern may be expected.

2   Spatial effects – a behavioural relationship may shift between one area and another. For example, a market demand function estimated jointly for the UK and West German data may well generate a higher income elasticity for the UK (where the good is likely to be regarded as more of a luxury) than for Germany (where the good is likely to be regarded as more of a necessity).

3   Qualitative factors – the non-quantifiable characteristics of a good may be important determinants of consumer demand.

4   Broad bands of quantitative variables – although numerical values of a variable are available, only broad groupings may be required. For example, the demand for sports cars may not be taken to depend on a person's precise age, but rather merely whether he or she is aged over 35 or less than or equal to 35.

The use of dummy variables may be clarified by considering a market demand function for foreign holidays. It is supposed that the demand for foreign holidays (Y) depends upon consumers' disposable income (X_1) and the price of foreign holidays (X_2). In addition, part way through the estimation period the government introduced foreign currency restrictions on holidaymakers, which are assumed to cause a reduction in foreign holiday sales. The following demand functions are postulated:

$$Y = a + b_1 X_1 + b_2 X_2 + u \text{ (no currency restrictions)} \qquad (6.9)$$
$$Y = a^1 + b_1 X_1 + b_2 X_2 + u \text{ (currency restrictions)} \qquad (6.10)$$

where $a > a^1$. It is assumed that the coefficients of X_1 and X_2 are common to both periods. If none of the parameters was common to both periods, then nothing would be gained by using dummy variables – equation (6.9) would be fitted to the period without currency restrictions and equation (6.10) to the period when currency restrictions were in force. However, provided that at least one parameter is assumed to be common to both periods, equations (6.9) and (6.10) should be combined into a single equation in order to obtain as efficient an estimate as possible (that is, with minimum variance) of the common coefficient(s). The equations may be combined as follows:

$$Y = a + a_0R + b_1X_1 + b_2X_2 + u \tag{6.11}$$

where R is a dummy variable such that

R = 1 if the observation relates to the period of currency restrictions
       = 0 otherwise; and
a_0 is a parameter.

Hence during the period when there were no currency restrictions equation (6.11) reduces to

$$Y = a + b_1X_1 + b_2X_2 + u \tag{6.12}$$

which corresponds to equation (6.9). When the period of foreign currency restrictions is under consideration, equation (6.11) reduces to

$$Y = (a + a_0) + b_1X_1 + b_2X_2 + u \tag{6.13}$$

A comparison of equations (6.10) and (6.13) shows that

$$a^1 = a + a_0 \tag{6.14}$$

Since $a^1 < a$, a_0 is negative, and it represents the difference between the 'currency restrictions' and 'no currency restrictions' intercepts.

Dummy variables can accommodate different slopes as well as different intercepts. For example, if it is supposed that the price coefficient also changes when currency restrictions are introduced, but that the income coefficient is still common to the periods with and without currency restrictions, then equation (6.10) is replaced by

$$Y = a^1 + b_1X_1 + b_2^1X_2 + u \tag{6.15}$$

where $b_2^1 > b_2$ since the imposition of foreign currency restrictions is assumed to result in consumers being more sensitive to price changes. Equations (6.9) and (6.15) may be combined to give

$$Y = a + a_0R + b_1X_1 + b_2X_2 + b_0X_2R + u \tag{6.16}$$

When there are no currency restrictions $R = 0$, and so equation (6.16) reduces to

$$Y = a + b_1X_1 + b_2X_2 + u \tag{6.17}$$

which corresponds to equation (6.9). When the currency restrictions are in force $R = 1$, and so equation (6.16) may be rewritten as

$$Y = (a + a_0) + b_1X_1 + (b_2 + b_0)X_2 + u \tag{6.18}$$

A comparison of equations (6.15) and (6.18) shows that as before $a^1 = a + a_0$, but also that

$$b_2^1 = b_2 + b_0 \tag{6.19}$$

Since $b_2^1 > b_2$, b_0 is positive, and it represents the difference between the parameters of the price variable in the 'currency restrictions' and 'no currency restrictions' periods.

It is possible to include several sets of dummy variables in a regression model. For example, if quarterly foreign holiday data are available, then seasonal effects may be incorporated by extending model (6.11) as follows:

$$Y = a + a_0R + c_2Q_2 + c_3Q_3 + c_4Q_4 + b_1X_1 + b_2X_2 + u \tag{6.20}$$

where Q_2, Q_3 and Q_4 are seasonal dummy variables such that

$Q_i = 1$ if the observation relates to quarter i; $i = 2, 3, 4$

    $= 0$ otherwise

The dummy variable coefficients simply affect the size of the intercept term. If an observation falls in the first quarter during the period when there were no currency restrictions the intercept term is a. For the second quarter during the period of currency restrictions the intercept term is $(a + a_0 + c_2)$, and so on. c_2, c_3 and c_4 represent the differences in the seasonal effects compared with the first quarter.

It should be noted that one alternative (the reference category) must be dropped from each set of dummy variables in order to avoid the dummy variable trap. Thus when considering the two alternative periods of 'currency restrictions' and 'no currency restrictions' only one dummy variable is incorporated in model (6.20) to represent the differential effect. Similarly, although there are four quarters, only three seasonal dummy variables are included in the model. If a dummy variable were included for every alternative in a given set then one of the classical assumptions of the linear regression model – that the explanatory variables are linearly independent of each other – is violated, and the estimation procedure breaks down.

The use of dummy variables in practice and the interpretation of parameter estimates may be illustrated by further examination of the market demand model for cigarettes developed by Witt and Pass (1981 and 1983) which was considered earlier in this chapter. Here the demand for cigarettes is assumed to depend upon income, own price, advertising expenditure and smoking-related health scares. The major health scares which occurred during the period of the study (1955–75) are as follows:

A   First Report by Royal College of Physicians (1962)
B   Report by US Surgeon-General's Advisory Committee (1964)
C   Second Report by Royal College of Physicians (1971).

Casual inspection of the data suggested that the effects of health scares are of limited duration, and initial regression runs indicated that the impact was limited to the year of the scare and the subsequent year. The dummy variables corresponding to the health scares A, B and C are therefore given by:

HSA = 0 for 1955–61 and 1964–75
      = 1 for 1962–63
HSB = 0 for 1955–63 and 1966–75
      = 1 for 1964–65
HSC = 0 for 1955–70 and 1973–75
      = 1 for 1971–72

As the health scares are expected to cause a fall in cigarette consumption, the estimated coefficient signs for all the dummy variables are expected to be negative. The full specification of the cigarette demand model is

$$\log (Y_t/P_t) = \log a + b_1 \log (X_{1t}/P_t)$$
$$+ b_2 \log X_{2t} + b_3 \log (X_{3t}/P_t)$$
$$+ b_4 \text{HSA} + b_5 \text{HSB} + b_6 \text{HSC} + u_t \qquad (6.21)$$
$$t = 1, 2, \ldots, 21 \ (1 = 1955, \ldots, 21 = 1975)$$

where

Y_t is the number of (manufactured) cigarettes consumed in year t;

P_t is the UK de facto population over 15 years of age in year t;

X_{1t} is the UK real personal disposable income in year t;
X_{2t} is the real price of cigarettes in year t;
X_{3t} is real (press and television) advertising expenditure in year t;
u_t is a random disturbance term;
$a, b_1, b_2, \ldots, b_6$ are parameters

and HSA, HSB and HSC are as defined above.

Table 6.2
Full set of estimated coefficients and t values for cigarette demand model

Dependent variable: log (Y/P)

Explanatory variables	Estimated coefficients	t values
log (X_{1t}/P_t)	0.126	2.88
log X_{2t}	-0.321	-4.59
log (X_{3t}/P_t)	0.068	2.68
HSA	-0.042	-3.08
HSB	-0.071	-4.90
HSC	-0.034	-2.70
intercept	7.268	21.98

Table 6.1 shows the estimated cigarette demand model ignoring the empirical results for the dummy variables. The full set of estimated coefficients and t values corresponding to model (6.21) is given in Table 6.2. It can be seen that the expected negative sign is obtained for each of the estimated dummy variable coefficients, and that they are all significantly different from zero at the 5 per cent level. The interpretation of the dummy variable coefficients may be seen clearly by focusing attention solely on the variable of interest; for example, if we wish to assess the impact of the 1962 health scare on the demand for cigarettes we obtain

$$\log (Y_t/P_t) = \ldots - 0.042 \, \text{HSA} + \ldots \tag{6.22}$$

In 1962 equation (6.22) becomes

$$\log (Y_8/P_8) = \ldots - 0.042 + \ldots \tag{6.23}$$

For a year when the 1962 health scare did not apply, say 1961, the appropriate equation is

$$\log (Y_7/P_7) = \ldots + 0 + \ldots \tag{6.24}$$

Subtracting equation (6.23) from (6.24) yields

$$\log (Y_7/P_7) - \log (Y_8/P_8) = \ldots + 0.042 + \ldots \tag{6.25}$$

The effect of the 1962 health scare is thus given by

$$\log (Y_7/P_7)/(Y_8/P_8) = 0.042 \tag{6.26}$$

Hence by taking antilogs to the base e we see that

$$(Y_8/P_8)/(Y_7/P_7) = 0.959 \tag{6.27}$$

Thus the 1962 health scare resulted in a 4.1 per cent fall in cigarette consumption per capita during 1962 and 1963. Similar calculations for the later health scares show that the 1964 scare depressed cigarette demand in 1964 and 1965 by 6.9 per cent, and the 1971 scare led to a 3.3 per cent decline in consumption throughout that year and the next year.

LAGGED VARIABLES

Realistic formulations of business forecasting models often require the inclusion of lagged values of one or more independent variables and/or the dependent variable as explanatory variables. Such models are termed distributed lag models since the influence of a variable is distributed over several time periods. The insertion of lagged variables in a regression model may be justified in various ways; for example, sales of a good may depend upon sales in previous periods due to habit persistence, and also upon past levels of income as well as current income. The standard market demand function

$$Y = f(X_1, X_2, \ldots, X_k) \tag{6.28}$$

where

Y is the market demand for the product;
X_1 is consumers' disposable income;
X_2 is the price of the product;

.

.

.

and f denotes some function

must be modified in such cases to incorporate lagged values of the variables, giving

$$Y_t = g(Y_{t-1}, Y_{t-2}, \ldots, X_{1t}, X_{1(t-1)}, X_{1(t-2)}, \ldots, X_{2t}, X_{3t}, \ldots, X_{kt})$$
(6.29)

where g denotes some function.

Clearly lags are involved in all economic behaviour and a process of continuous adjustment is always taking place. Usually it is assumed that adjustments are instantaneous, but by including lagged variables in the set of explanatory variables it is possible to take into account the time involved in adjustment processes. Knowledge of the lag patterns associated with changes in, say, advertising expenditure is of crucial importance for managerial decisions.

Theory gives little indication regarding the length of time involved in economic adjustment processes, and so it is not obvious how many lags should be included in a function. If, however, the pattern of lags is examined using the sample observations to estimate a model of the form (6.29) including fairly long lags, certain problems are likely to arise. First, if the number of lags is large relative to the sample size, the number of degrees of freedom (= number of observations – number of parameters to be estimated) may be too low to obtain meaningful results. Second, it is very likely that successive values of the same variable will be highly correlated, which violates the classical assumption that the explanatory variables should be linearly independent of each other. To overcome these difficulties several procedures have been developed to reduce the number of lagged variables present in an equation.

Initially attention focuses on models containing lagged values of the explanatory variables. In market demand functions, the demand for a product (for example, an expensive consumer durable) is likely to depend on income in previous periods as well as current income.

In market share models, the impact of advertising is likely to be distributed over several periods, so that a firm's market share in a particular period will depend on its relative advertising levels in this and previous periods. If it is assumed that there is only one independent variable, in the presence of lags the simple linear regression model is modified to become

$$Y_t = a + b_0 X_t + b_1 X_{t-1} + \ldots + u_t \tag{6.30}$$

Almon distributed lag

The (simplified) Almon lag scheme assumes that the bs may be expressed approximately as polynomials of degree n with $n + 1$ parameters:

$$b_j = z_0 + z_1 j + z_2 j^2 + \ldots + z_n j^n \tag{6.31}$$

It is usually assumed that a polynomial of fairly low degree (3 or 4) is a sufficiently accurate approximation, and rewriting equation (6.31) for $n = 3$ gives

$$b_j = z_0 + z_1 j + z_2 j^2 + z_3 j^3 \tag{6.32}$$

If it is thought that Y is influenced by the current value of X and the previous five values, say, then equation (6.30) becomes

$$Y_t = a + b_0 X_t + b_1 X_{t-1} + \ldots + b_5 X_{t-5} + u_t \tag{6.33}$$

The b coefficients in equation (6.33) may now be expressed in terms of the z coefficients using equation (6.32):

$$
\begin{aligned}
b_0 &= z_0 \\
b_1 &= z_0 + z_1 + z_2 + z_3 \\
b_2 &= z_0 + 2z_1 + 4z_2 + 8z_3
\end{aligned}
\tag{6.34}
$$

.

.

.

$$b_5 = z_0 + 5z_1 + 25z_2 + 125z_3$$

These b values are substituted into equation (6.33) which gives (after rearrangement)

$$
\begin{aligned}
Y_t = a &+ z_0(X_t + X_{t-1} + \ldots + X_{t-5}) \\
&+ z_1(X_{t-1} + 2X_{t-2} + \ldots + 5X_{t-5}) \\
&+ z_2(X_{t-1} + 4X_{t-2} + \ldots + 25X_{t-5}) \\
&+ z_3(X_{t-1} + 8X_{t-2} + \ldots + 125X_{t-5}) + u_t
\end{aligned} \tag{6.35}
$$

Y_t is regressed on the explanatory variables in equation (6.35) to give estimates of the parameters a, z_0, z_1, z_2, z_3. The estimated z values are then substituted into equations (6.34) to generate estimates of $b_0, b_1, \ldots, b_5$. Thus the Almon scheme permits an equation such as (6.33) containing six unknown bs to be reduced to one such as (6.35) containing only four unknown zs.

The assumptions regarding the degree of the polynomial and length of the lag may both be varied, so the Almon polynomial formulation (6.31) provides a very flexible specification. The choice of the degree of polynomial may be determined empirically by examining the statistical significance of the z coefficients in the regression equation. The Almon model may easily be extended to accommodate additional explanatory variables with varying lengths of lags.

Standard regression programs such as ORION incorporate the facility for constructing polynomial distributed lags. For each explanatory variable to which this applies, the length of lag and degree of polynomial must be specified.

Koyck distributed lag

An alternative simplification of model (6.30) containing lagged independent variables is suggested by Koyck, and assumes that the bs decrease exponentially over time, so that more recent observations are given greater weight than earlier observations:

$$
b_j = bh^j; 0 < h < 1 \tag{6.36}
$$

Thus if equation (6.30) relates to a market share function where X denotes advertising, then equation (6.36) assumes that the current value of advertising has the greatest impact on demand and that the effect declines steadily with the passage of time. On substitution of equation (6.36) into equation (6.30) the following results:

$$Y_t = a + bX_t + bhX_{t-1} + bh^2X_{t-2} + \ldots + u_t \tag{6.37}$$

If equation (6.37) is lagged one period and multiplied by h we obtain

$$hY_{t-1} = ha + h(bX_{t-1} + bhX_{t-2} + \ldots + u_{t-1}) \tag{6.38}$$

Subtracting (6.38) from (6.37) yields

$$Y_t = hY_{t-1} + a(1 - h) + b_0X_t + (u_t - hu_{t-1}) \tag{6.39}$$

The Koyck scheme makes a strong assumption regarding the form of the lag coefficients, but a considerable simplification of equation (6.30) is achieved. Now, instead of having to estimate a large number of parameters $b_0, b_1, \ldots$, only two parameters, h and b_0, need be estimated in their place, and equation (6.36) may then be used to calculate the individual weights. If lagged values of the independent variable are permitted to influence the dependent variable according to a Koyck lag process, it is merely necessary to include one additional explanatory variable, the lagged dependent variable, in the linear regression model. The interpretation of the coefficients is as follows: the short run effect of X (advertising) on Y (market share) is given from equation (6.30) by b_0; the long term influence of X on Y is given from equation (6.37) by

$$b + bh + \ldots = b/(1 - h) = b_0/(1 - h) \tag{6.40}$$

The Koyck model may easily be extended to the case where more than one independent variable is present provided that each of the independent variables is assumed to possess the same Koyck lag structure. Thus the model

$$Y_t = a + b_0X_{1t} + b_1X_{1(t-1)} + \ldots + \\ c_0X_{2t} + c_1X_{2(t-1)} + \ldots + u_t \tag{6.41}$$

where $c_0, c_1, \ldots$ are unknown parameters and $c_j = ch^j$ as well as $b_j = bh^j$, may be rewritten as

$$Y_t = hY_{t-1} + a(1 - h) + b_0X_{1t} + c_0X_{2t} + (u_t - hu_{t-1}) \tag{6.42}$$

If not all the independent variables are assumed to exhibit the same Koyck lag structure, then the equation to be estimated becomes considerably more complicated.

Partial adjustment model

The application of the Koyck scheme to lagged values of the independent variable results in the appearance of a lagged dependent variable as an explanatory variable in the model. Other models can also give rise to a lagged dependent variable, and one such important model is the partial adjustment model. Suppose that we wish to estimate a market demand function for a good or service where supply constraints are present. It takes time for supply to adjust to demand, and so the actual level of sales only adjusts partially to the desired level within a given period. The following adjustment function is postulated:

$$Y_t - Y_{t-1} = p(Y^*_t - Y_{t-1}); 0 < p < 1 \qquad (6.43)$$

where * denotes the desired value and p is the adjustment coefficient. $0 < p < 1$ since there is some movement from the starting position (Y_{t-1}) to the desired position (Y^*_t), but it is incomplete.

If $p = 0$, then $Y_t = Y_{t-1}$ and there is no adjustment. If $p = 1$, then $Y_t = Y^*_t$ and there is full adjustment so that Y_t may merely be considered a function of income, price, and so on.

Equation (6.43) may be rewritten as

$$Y_t = (1 - p)Y_{t-1} + pY^*_t \qquad (6.44)$$

Y^*_t, the desired market demand in year t, is a function of the usual set of variables present in a demand function, so the only difference between this model and the linear form of equation (6.28) is that a lagged dependent variable has to be added as an extra explanatory variable. Equation (6.44) becomes

$$Y_t = (1 - p)Y_{t-1} + p\{a + b_1X_{1t} + b_2X_{2t} + \ldots + b_kX_{kt} + u_t\} \qquad (6.45)$$

where X_1 is consumers' disposable income, X_2 is the price of the product, and so on. The coefficients of $X_1, X_2, \ldots, X_k$ are pb_1, $pb_2, \ldots, pb_k$ and these relate to the short term. Dividing by p gives the parameters $b_1, b_2, \ldots, b_k$ which show the long term effects of the explanatory variables on the dependent variable, after complete adjustment of the actual level of sales to the desired level has taken place. The only difference between the Koyck model (6.42) and the partial adjustment model (6.45) is that the disturbance term is more complicated in the former.

The inclusion of a lagged dependent variable in a multiple regression model may be illustrated by considering a demand function for foreign holidays developed by Witt (1980a and b). The dependent variable is the number of foreign holiday trips per capita, and the independent variables include real personal disposable income per capita, foreign holiday prices, travel time to the destination country, and various sets of dummy variables. In addition, the demand function is rendered dynamic by including a lagged dependent variable. This may be justified in terms of habit persistence. Once people have visited a country, there is much less uncertainty associated with holidaying again in that country compared with travelling to a previously unvisited foreign country. Moreover, when people return from a foreign holiday they tell their friends about the trip, so that knowledge about the holiday is further disseminated. A type of learning process is therefore in operation, and as people are, in general, risk (that is, uncertainty) averters, the number of people choosing a given alternative in any year depends on the numbers who chose it in previous years. A second justification for the inclusion of a lagged dependent variable in holiday demand models comes from the supply side. Once the tourist industry to a country has become highly developed, it is unlikely to dwindle rapidly. The hotel industry will have invested large sums of money in the country, and tour operators will have built up contacts there. Similarly, there are physical constraints on the speed with which the tourist industry to a country can grow – hotels can only be built after a certain lapse of time, increases in hotel staff are limited in the short run, and growth in entertainment facilities is constrained. There exists, therefore, a certain amount of rigidity in the tourism market – it takes time for supply to adjust to demand, and so there is only a partial adjustment process. A log-linear functional form is postulated, so the model is

$$\log(Y_{jt}/P_t) - \log(Y_{j(t-1)}/P_{t-1}) = p\{\log(Y^*_{jt}/P_t) - \log(Y_{jt-1}/P_{t-1})\}$$
(6.46)

where Y_{jt} is the number of foreign holiday trips by UK residents to destination country j in year t and P_t is the UK population in year t. Thus the log of the number of foreign holiday trips per capita is a function of the lagged value of the dependent variable in addition to log income, log price and so on.

Lagged dependent variable problems

The appearance of lagged values of the dependent variable on the right-hand side of a regression model causes certain estimation problems. For a model where a lagged dependent variable is justified on account of, say, habit persistence or the partial adjustment hypothesis, so that the error term enters the model in the usual form, we may make the standard assumptions that the disturbance terms are normally and independently distributed with zero mean and constant variance. Thus the only complication is the presence of a lagged dependent variable as an explanatory variable, but this violates the classical assumption that the explanatory variables are distributed independently of the error term. If the lagged dependent variable model

$$Y_t = a + b_1 Y_{t-1} + b_2 X_t + u_t \qquad (6.47)$$

is lagged one period this yields

$$Y_{t-1} = a + b_1 Y_{t-2} + b_2 X_{t-1} + u_{t-1} \qquad (6.48)$$

Hence Y_{t-1} in equation (6.47) is a function of $u_{t-1}, u_{t-2} \ldots$, that is a function of all previous values of the error term. The consequence of the violation of this assumption is that the ordinary least squares property of unbiasedness no longer holds – OLS will give biased estimates in small samples, although the OLS estimators are consistent, that is as the number of observations approaches infinity the bias tends to zero. Empirical evidence suggests, however, that even in small samples OLS is likely still to be the best estimating technique.

For a model with a more complicated (non-random) disturbance term, such as the Koyck lagged dependent variable specification, the OLS estimators are not even consistent. The Koyck model is of the form

$$Y_t = h Y_{t-1} + a(1 - h) + b_0 X_t + \\ (u_t - h u_{t-1}); \ 0 < h < 1 \qquad (6.49)$$

If we make the usual assumptions about the us, in equation (6.49) the error term is $(u_t - h u_{t-1})$ and clearly the various values of the error term are now not drawn independently of each other, thus violating a second classical assumption. The consequence of the joint violation of the assumptions that each explanatory variable is distributed independently of the error term and that the values of the error term are drawn independently of each other is that the OLS estimators are both biased and inconsistent.

AUTOCORRELATION

If the classical assumption that the various values of the error term are drawn independently of each other is not satisfied, that is the value in any particular period is correlated with the preceding value(s), this gives rise to the problem of autocorrelation or serial correlation of the disturbance term. (Although autocorrelation can arise in cross-section applications, this is not common. Hence, the discussion centres on time series data.)

Autocorrelation may arise for several reasons. One of the functions of the error term is that it represents the influence of omitted variables, and some of these may be serially correlated; any given value may not be independent of previous values owing to the presence of time trends in the variables. For example, current income depends on past levels of income. If there are serially correlated omitted variables which do not cancel each other out in their effects, then the error term will be autocorrelated. Similarly, mis-specification of the mathematical form of the relationship (say linear, when the true form is quadratic) may give rise to a serially correlated disturbance term. The error term also accommodates measurement errors in the dependent variable, and any serial correlation in these measurement errors can give rise to autocorrelation.

Various consequences follow if autocorrelated disturbances are present in a model. First, if the estimation method of OLS is used the variances of the parameter estimates are likely to be larger than those achievable using a different method of estimation. Hence, the OLS estimators no longer exhibit the minimum variance (best) property – they are inefficient. Second, the variance of the error term is likely to be underestimated, and this is particularly serious in a situation involving a positively serially correlated disturbance in conjunction with positively serially correlated explanatory variables (which is the usual case). If the standard OLS formulae are used, the variances of the regression coefficients are likely to be seriously underestimated, the t and F tests are no longer strictly valid, and R^2 is likely to be overestimated. Third, the predictions obtained using

OLS estimators will be inefficient – a different estimation technique may be used to yield predictions with smaller variances. Fourth, if serially correlated errors are present in a model including lagged values of the dependent variable, the OLS estimators will be both biased and inconsistent.

Durbin–Watson test

The most common test for autocorrelation is the Durbin–Watson test. This is applicable to small samples, but is only appropriate for a first-order autoregressive scheme, that is, where the value of the error term in a particular period depends on its own value in the preceding period only. Such a scheme represents the simplest possible case of serial correlation in the disturbance term, and is usually a reasonable approximation. The autoregressive structure of a first-order scheme is

$$u_t = ru_{t-1} + v_t; \; |r| < 1 \tag{6.50}$$

where r is the autocorrelation coefficient, and v_t is a random error term satisfying the usual assumptions required by the classical model – in particular, the various values of v are assumed to be drawn independently of each other. The Durbin–Watson test is used to test the null hypothesis that the autocorrelation coefficient is equal to zero against the alternative that it is non-zero. This is accomplished using the Durbin–Watson statistic:

$$d = \sum_{t=2}^{n} (e_t - e_{t-1})^2 \; / \; \sum_{t=1}^{n} e_t^2$$

where n is the number of observations and the es are the computed residuals from the OLS regression. The values of d lie between 0 and 4 and when there is no autocorrelation ($r = 0$) $d = 2$. Furthermore, for d values below 2 the possibility of positively autocorrelated series arises and for d values above 2 there is a possibility of negatively autocorrelated series. The problem with the Durbin–Watson test is that the exact distribution of d is not known since it depends on the values of the explanatory variables. However, upper (d_U) and lower (d_L) limits for the significance levels of d have been established and these may be compared with the calculated d statistic. For sample values of d below 2:

If $d < d_L$ reject the hypothesis of no autocorrelation in favour of the hypothesis of positive autocorrelation.
If $d > d_U$ accept the hypothesis of no autocorrelation.
If $d_L < d < d_U$ the test is inconclusive.

The Durbin–Watson test is symmetric around the value 2, so for sample values of d above 2:

If $d > (4 - d_L)$ reject the hypothesis of no autcorrelation in favour of the hypothesis of negative autocorrelation.
If $d < (4 - d_U)$ accept the hypothesis of no autocorrelation.
If $(4 - d_U) < d < (4 - d_L)$ the test is inconclusive.

These decisions can be summarized as in Figure 6.1.

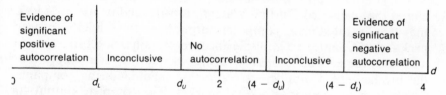

Figure 6.1   Durbin–Watson test for autocorrelation

A drawback with the Durbin–Watson test is the range of values of d over which the test is inconclusive. By making stronger assumptions about the explanatory variables it is possible to eliminate the inconclusive regions – the outcome is that the critical value of d generally tends to lie much closer to d_U than d_L. A very approximate procedure is therefore to add the inconclusive regions to the critical regions for autocorrelation, so that the hypothesis of no autocorrelation is rejected if either $d < d_U$ or $d > (4 - d_U)$. Given the seriousness of the consequences of autocorrelation, it may be better to reject the null hypothesis in cases of uncertainty. A further problem with the Durbin–Watson test is that it is not applicable when a lagged dependent variable is present in the model. In such cases the d statistic is biased towards the value 2 and thus may indicate serially independent disturbances when autocorrelation may in fact be present. Clearly, however, if the Durbin–Watson test suggests rejection of the null hypothesis of no autocorrelation in spite of the presence of a lagged dependent variable, the decision is unaffected. Finally, it should be noted that the tabulated upper and lower limits for d are only appropriate for a model which contains an intercept term.

Durbin–Watson tables give the d_U and d_L values for the 5, 2.5 and 1 per cent levels of significance. The values depend upon the sample size (n) and the number of independent variables (k). For example, if $n = 20$ and $k = 2$, then at the 5 per cent significance level $d_L = 1.10$ and $d_U = 1.54$. Hence, for calculated d values between 1.54 and 2.46 there is no evidence of autocorrelation, for values below 1.10 there is evidence of positive autocorrelation, for values above 2.90 there is evidence of negative autocorrelation, and for values falling between 1.10 and 1.54 or 2.46 and 2.90 the test is inconclusive. A simplified procedure that is often used is to assume that the range of values of d consistent with the hypothesis of no autocorrelation is (very) approximately 1.5 to 2.5.

The computer output of standard regression programs usually includes the calculated Durbin–Watson statistic, and its use in practice may be illustrated using computer output from the ORION software package. In Chapter 5 a multiple linear regression market share model was constructed and estimated using 48 quarterly data points on the products of a number of competing manufacturing companies which together comprise a total market. The complete output for the final estimated version of the model is given in Table 5.2, but the first page of the computer output showing the Durbin–Watson statistic is reproduced in Table 6.3. As the calculated d statistic exceeds 2, negative autocorrelation may be suspected, but since the value of 2.29 lies between 1.5 and 2.5 it appears unlikely to be a problem. Furthermore, the critical points of the Durbin–Watson test at the 5 per cent significance level with $n = 48$ and $k = 6$ are $d_L = 1.27$ and $d_U = 1.83$, so $4 - d_U = 2.17$ and $4 - d_L = 2.73$. The calculated d value therefore lies within the inconclusive region but close to the area showing no evidence of autocorrelation. Hence it is reasonable to proceed on the assumption that the disturbance term is not serially correlated.

Cochrane–Orcutt iterative technique

The corrective action if autocorrelation is found to be present is as follows. If the source of serially correlated disturbances is omitted variables, these variables should be included in the set of explanatory variables. Similarly, if serial correlation arises as a result of mis-

Table 6.3
Market share model showing Durbin–Watson statistic

REG > MULTIPLE ORDERS ON PRICE,ADVERT,QUAL,DIST,DUMMY,LAGADVERT DISPLAY FULL

Equation

ORDERS = .22059 − .27943*PRICE + .021772*ADVERT
+ .014066*QUAL + .14118*DIST + .0076523*DUMMY
+ .015224*LAGADVERT

R-Squared = .93511

48 Observations, 6 Variables

Corrected R-Squared	= .92562	Residual Sum Squares	= .00076231
Standard Error	= .0043119	F-Ratio	= 98.475
Dependent Mean	= .16604	Degrees of Freedom	= 41
Durbin–Watson	= 2.2934		
Standard Error as % Mean ORDERS	= 2.5969		

specification of the mathematical form of the relationship, alternative function forms should be investigated. If it is not possible to remove autocorrelation either by including additional explanatory variables or selecting a different mathematical form, the original data should be transformed to yield a model where the error term satisfies the classical assumptions so that OLS can optimally be applied to these data.

The multiple linear regression model is given by

$$Y_t = a + b_1X_{1t} + b_2X_{2t} + \ldots + b_kX_{kt} + u_t; t = 1,2,\ldots,n \tag{6.51}$$

If the error term in this model follows a first-order autoregressive scheme, then

$$u_t = ru_{t-1} + v_t \tag{6.52}$$

where v is a random error term satisfying the classical assumptions. If equation (6.51) is lagged one period and multiplied throughout by r we obtain

$$rY_{t-1} = ra + rb_1X_{1(t-1)} + \ldots + rb_kX_{k(t-1)} + ru_{t-1}; t = 2,3,\ldots,n \tag{6.53}$$

Subtracting equation (6.53) from equation (6.51) yields

$$Y_t - rY_{t-1} = a(1 - r) + b_1(X_{1t} - rX_{1(t-1)}) + \ldots + b_k(X_{kt} - rX_{k(t-1)}) + (u_t - ru_{t-1}); t = 2,3,\ldots,n \tag{6.54}$$

Equation (6.54) is the generalized differences specification of the relationship. The new error term in this equation is $u_t - ru_{t-1} = v_t$ (from equation (6.52)). Hence if we apply OLS to model (6.54) incorporating the transformed data autocorrelation should no longer be present.

In order to carry out the transformation shown in equation (6.54) it is necessary to estimate the autocorrelation parameter, r. The most commonly used estimation procedure is the Cochrane–Orcutt iterative technique, which involves a gradual convergence towards the estimate. (Given that r is unknown and also that model (6.54) implies the loss of one observation, the Cochrane–Orcutt estimation method is only approximately optimal – in general, however, it is more efficient than OLS.) Initially equation (6.51) is estimated by OLS and the residuals are calculated. The unobservable error term u in equation (6.52) is then replaced by its estimate, the residual, and OLS is used to calculate an estimate, $\hat{r}$, of the autocorrelation coefficient, r. This estimated value is used to obtain the transformed variables, $Y_t - \hat{r}Y_{t-1}$, $X_{1t} - \hat{r}X_{1(t-1)}, \ldots, X_{kt} - \hat{r}X_{k(t-1)}$ in equation (6.54), and this equation is then estimated by OLS; direct estimates of the parameters $b_1, b_2, \ldots, b_k$ are obtained, but the intercept is an estimate of $a(1 - r)$, so a is estimated from $\overline{a(1 - r)}/(1 - \hat{r})$. These revised estimates of the parameters $a, b_1, b_2, \ldots, b_k$ are then substituted into the original equation (6.51) in order to obtain revised values for the residuals. The new residuals are used to calculate a revised estimate, $\hat{r}$, of the autocorrelation coefficient, which is then employed to construct new transformed variables $Y_t - \hat{r}Y_{t-1}$, $X_{1t} - \hat{r}X_{1(t-1)}, \ldots, X_{kt} - \hat{r}X_{k(t-1)}$ in equation (6.54). This equation is again estimated by OLS, and so on. The procedure continues until the value of the estimated autocorrelation parameter converges, that is until it changes by less than some stated (small) number in successive iterations.

Computer programs for regression analysis such as ORION usually incorporate the Cochrane–Orcutt iterative technique. The computer output relates to the estimated generalized differences model, and the estimated value of the autocorrelation parameter is also shown.

Prediction

The procedure described in Chapter 5 for obtaining forecasts should be modified in the presence of autocorrelation in order to obtain the most efficient prediction. In Chapter 5 the estimated multiple linear regression relationship is used to generate forecasts of the dependent variable, $\hat{Y}_F$, as follows:

$$\hat{Y}_F = \hat{a} + \hat{b}_1 X_{1F} + \hat{b}_2 X_{2F} + \ldots + \hat{b}_k X_{kF} \tag{6.55}$$

Here the unknown random error term u_F is set equal to zero, but when autocorrelation is present additional information should be taken into account. If we have sample data for periods, $1, 2, \ldots, n$ and wish to predict for period $n + 1$, then the appropriate forecasting equation is

$$\hat{Y}_{n+1} = \hat{a} + \hat{b}_1 X_{1(n+1)} + \hat{b}_2 X_{2(n+1)} + \ldots + \hat{b}_k X_{k(n+1)} + u_{n+1}$$
$$(6.56)$$

If the error term follows a first order autoregressive scheme, then

$$u_{n+1} = r u_n + v_{n+1} \qquad (6.57)$$

Hence the error term in equation (6.56) may be estimated by

$$e_{n+1} = \hat{r} e_n \qquad (6.58)$$

since the unknown random error v_{n+1} is set equal to zero. Substituting into equation (6.58) yields

$$\hat{Y}_{n+1} = \hat{a} + \hat{b}_1 X_{1(n+1)} + \hat{b}_2 X_{2(n+1)} + \ldots + \hat{b}_k X_{k(n+1)} + \hat{r} e_n$$
$$(6.59)$$

where $\hat{a}, \hat{b}_1, \hat{b}_2, \ldots, \hat{b}_k$ are estimated using the Cochrane–Orcutt iterative procedure and e_n is the residual corresponding to the nth observation in the original model specification.

If predictions are required for more than one period ahead, the appropriate forecasting equation is

$$\hat{Y}_{n+s} = \hat{a} + \hat{b}_1 X_{1(n+s)} + \hat{b}_2 X_{2(n+s)} + \ldots$$
$$+ \hat{b}_k X_{k(n+s)} + \hat{r}^s e_n; \, s = 1,2,\ldots \qquad (6.60)$$

By including the additional information regarding the error term when predicting from autocorrelated functions, improved forecasts are obtained.

MULTICOLLINEARITY

If the classical assumption that the explanatory variables are linearly independent of each other is not satisfied, this gives rise to the problem of multicollinearity. The existence of an exact linear relationship among the independent variables (perfect multicollinearity) is extremely rare, but its occurrence results in a complete breakdown of the estimation procedure, that is it is impossible to calculate the OLS estimates. It is quite common, however, for there to be an approximate linear relationship among the independent variables.

This phenomenon (imperfect multicollinearity or simply multicollinearity) does not result in a complete breakdown of the estimation procedure, but does cause severe estimation problems. (Although multicollinearity does occur in cross-section data, it is more common in time series.)

Multicollinearity can arise for several reasons. First, the independent variables may share a common time trend – in general, there is a tendency for economic variables to move together over time. Second, multicollinearity can be caused by the use of lagged values of an explanatory variable as a separate explanatory variable. If this independent variable is subject to a trend, then there is likely to be an approximate linear relationship between the current and lagged values of the variable. Third, an approximate linear relationship may in fact exist among some of the explanatory variables.

There are several consequences of multicollinearity. The precision of estimation falls so that it becomes very difficult to establish the individual influence of each explanatory variable on the dependent variable. The parameter estimates may be seriously imprecise – the large errors present may even result in an unexpected sign for a parameter estimate. In addition, the coefficient estimates tend to be very unstable, so that the addition of just a few observations to the data set can cause substantial changes in the estimates. Furthermore, the variances of the coefficient estimates of the multicollinear variables are likely to be abnormally large, which can lead to model mis-specification in that a variable may be dropped from a model because its coefficient is not significantly different from zero, when in fact the variable is an important determinant of the dependent variable but this is not apparent on account of the particular set of sample data used. It should be noted that in the presence of multicollinearity the OLS estimator is still the best linear unbiased estimator and that the R^2 statistic is unaffected.

Tests

There are various methods which may be used to test for multicollinearity. First, if a high R^2 value is obtained together with insignificant coefficients, this is suggestive of multicollinearity.

Second, the simple correlation coefficient between each pair of explanatory variables should be examined, and if a value over about 0.8 is obtained this indicates multicollinearity between the two vari-

Table 6.4
Market share model showing variable correlation matrix

Variable Correlation Matrix

	PRICE	ADVERT	QUAL	DIST	DUMMY	LAGADVERT	ORDERS
PRICE	1.0000						
ADVERT	.6789	1.0000					
QUAL	.7003	.4187	1.0000				
DIST	.2189	.4705	−.2271	1.0000			
DUMMY	−.0135	.0285	.0000	.0000	1.0000		
LAGADVERT	.6749	.7526	.4359	.6062	.0304	1.0000	
ORDERS	.2296	.4575	.6708	.0198	.2797	.4703	1.0000

Analysis of Variance

Source	Sums of Squares	Degrees of Freedom	Mean Square
Regression	.10986E-01	6	.18309E-02
Residual	.76231E-03	41	.18593E-04
Total	.11748E-01	47	.24996E-03

F-Ratio of 98.475 Significant at the .05 Level

ables to which the correlation coefficient refers. These correlation coefficients appear in the printout of standard computer regression packages such as ORION. The complete empirical results for the final estimated version of the multiple linear regression market share model considered in Chapter 5 are given in Table 5.2, but the second page of the computer output showing the variable correlation matrix is reproduced in Table 6.4. Examination of this matrix shows that no simple correlation coefficient value exceeds 0.8, so multi-collinearity is not present in the model in terms of pairwise relationships between explanatory variables.

Consideration of the simple correlation coefficients is not always sufficient to detect multicollinearity when there are more than two explanatory variables, since one independent variable may be an approximate linear function of a set of several explanatory variables, so a third test for multicollinearity may be undertaken. This consists of regressing each explanatory variable in turn on the remaining set of explanatory variables and examining the coefficient of determination, R^2, and the F statistic. Clearly an R^2 value close to unity suggests the existence of multicollinearity, as does a high F value. Inspection of the R^2 and F values for each regression should indicate which variables are most affected by multicollinearity.

Corrective action

If multicollinearity is found to be present various courses of corrective action are possible. First, an increase in the size of the sample may reduce or eliminate the multicollinearity problem, so one possible solution is to try to collect additional observations, say by extending the time period covered or using quarterly rather than annual data.

A second possible approach is to incorporate further information in the model by imposing parameter estimates obtained from cross-section data on a time series equation. For example, we may wish to estimate the following market demand function:

$$Y_t = a + b_1 X_{1t} + b_2 X_{2t} + \ldots$$
$$+ b_k X_{kt} + u_t; \, t = 1, 2, \ldots, n \qquad (6.61)$$

where

Y is the market demand for the product;
X_1 is consumers' disposable income;

X_2 is the price of the product;

$X_3, \ldots, X_k$ are other factors affecting the market demand for the product under consideration.

It is likely that time series data on income and price will be highly correlated, resulting in multicollinearity problems. If cross-section expenditure survey data are also available, however, then since prices may be assumed to be approximately constant across households at a given point in time, the impact of income on demand may be investigated in the absence of price effects. The following household demand function is therefore estimated:

$$Z_i = p + c_1 V_{1i} + c_2 V_{2i} + \ldots$$
$$+ c_j V_{ji} + u_i; \, i = 1, 2, \ldots, m \qquad (6.62)$$

where

Z is the household demand for the product;

V_1 is the household's disposable income;

$V_2, \ldots, V_j$ are other factors affecting the household demand for the product under consideration such as household size and composition.

Estimation of model (6.62) yields a cross-section estimate, $\hat{c}_1$, of the income parameter, c_1. This value may then be substituted into equation (6.61) in place of the income parameter, b_1. Thus the new time series equation to be estimated becomes

$$Y_t - \hat{c}_1 X_{1t} = a + b_2 X_{2t} + \ldots$$
$$+ b_k X_{kt} + u^*_t; \, t = 1, 2, \ldots, n \qquad (6.63)$$

where u^*_t is the new disturbance term. The dependent variable $(Y_t - \hat{c}_1 X_{1t})$ is now regressed on a set of explanatory variables which includes the product price but excludes income. The main problem associated with this method of avoiding multicollinearity is that the cross-section coefficient c_1 may not be strictly equal to the time series coefficient b_1. In particular, cross-section estimates usually relate to long term parameters whereas time series studies are generally concerned with short term parameters.

If multicollinearity results from the presence of lagged values of the independent variables as explanatory variables in the model, it may be possible to avoid the problem by using the Koyck distributed lag scheme (see the Lagged variables section earlier in this chapter). Here the various lagged values of the independent variables X_{jt} $(j = 1, 2, \ldots, k) - X_{j(t-1)}, X_{j(t-2)}, \ldots$ – are replaced by a single lagged value of the dependent variable. Hence, by imposing restrictions on the parameters of the lagged independent variables in accordance with the Koyck scheme, it is possible to overcome the multi-collinearity problem.

Other prior restrictions can be imposed on models in order to avoid problems of multicollinearity. For example, the population and income data to be used to estimate the following log-linear demand function may be highly correlated:

$$\log Y_t = \log a + b_1 \log X_{1t} + b_2 \log X_{2t} + \ldots$$
$$+ b_k \log X_{kt} + u_t; \ t = 1, 2, \ldots, n \tag{6.64}$$

where

Y is the market demand for the product;
X_1 is the size of the population;
X_2 is consumers' disposable income;
$X_3, \ldots, X_k$ are other factors affecting the market demand for the product under consideration.

By removing the population variable as a separate explanatory variable and expressing the dependent variable in per capita terms, equation (6.64) reduces to

$$\log(Y_t/X_{1t}) = \log a + b_2 \log X_{2t} + \ldots + b_k \log X_{kt} + u_t; \ t = 1, 2, \ldots, n \tag{6.65}$$

In equation (6.65) there is no longer a problem of multicollinearity between population and income, but clearly this model is a more restrictive specification than (6.64). In equation (6.64) b_1, the population elasticity of demand, is to be estimated from the set of data, whereas in equation (6.65) the value $b_1 = 1$ is imposed on the model.

If multicollinearity is found to be present in a model, it may be that there is no appropriate course of corrective action. However, a multicollinear function may still yield good forecasts, even though the separate influences of the explanatory variables on the dependent variable cannot be disentangled. Provided that the multicollinearity pattern of the estimation period is expected to hold through the prediction period, the problems of multicollinearity may be ignored.

If, however, the pattern of intercorrelation of the explanatory variables is expected to change in the forecast period, then accurate knowledge of the individual influences of the explanatory variables on the dependent variable is required in order to obtain accurate forecasts.

FURTHER READING

Johnston, J., *Econometric Methods,* McGraw-Hill, New York, 1984, 568 pp.

Koutsoyiannis, A., *Theory of Econometrics,* Macmillan, London and Basingstoke, 1981, 681 pp.

Stewart, M. B. and Wallis, K. F., *Introductory Econometrics,* Basil Blackwell, Oxford, 1981, 337 pp.

Witt, S. F., 'An Abstract Mode–Abstract (Destination) Node Model of Foreign Holiday Demand', *Applied Economics,* 1980a, vol. 12, no. 2, pp. 163–80.

Witt, S. F., 'An Econometric Comparison of U.K. and German Foreign Holiday Behaviour', *Managerial and Decision Economics,* 1980b, vol. 1, no. 3, pp. 123–31.

Witt, S. F. and Pass, C. L., 'The Effects of Health Warnings and Advertising on the Demand for Cigarettes', *Scottish Journal of Political Economy,* 1981, vol. 28, no. 1, February, pp. 86–91.

Witt, S. F. and Pass, C. L., 'Forecasting Cigarette Consumption: the Causal Model Approach', *International Journal of Social Economics,* 1983, vol. 10, no. 3, pp. 18–33.

Wonnacott, R. J. and Wonnacott, T. H., *Econometrics,* Wiley, New York, 1979, 580 pp.

7 Subjective estimation

Subjective estimation is used for interactive managerial forecasting. The models do not produce sales projections but answer 'what if?' questions such as 'What would sales be next year if prices were reduced by 10 per cent?' The approach was championed by Little (1970) of MIT whose term 'decision calculus' is often used to describe it. His advertising decision model (ADBUDG) was not the first use of subjective estimation but it pioneered ideas that many other model builders have followed. Systems now extend through a wide range of marketing applications: e.g. competitive bidding (Edelman, 1965), MEDIAC (Little and Lodish, 1969) for media planning, CALLPLAN (Lodish, 1975) for sales force management, BRANDAID (Little, 1975) for brand management, retail management (Lodish, 1981) and STRATPORT (Larreche and Srinivasan, 1981) for strategic marketing.

Regression analysis can use past records of sales, marketing and competitive activity to produce a model for managerial forecasting. When no model is available managers have to use their experience and judgement to guess what sales will be. Subjective estimation is a method of making the most out of their experience and the judgemental information that is available. It includes methods of gathering experts' estimates and using the estimates to build models. The aim is to help decision makers make the most of the knowledge they have.

There is a difference between subjective forecasting and subjective estimation. Subjective forecasting asks experts to make direct estimates of what the future will be. For example they may be asked; 'What will be the sales rate of compact disk players in five years time?' or 'By what date will "lean burn" engines gain a 10 per cent share of the family saloon market?' This form of questioning is often used in strategic forecasting which will be discussed in a later chapter. Subjective estimation takes a less direct approach to incorporating judgement in forecasts. For example, a marketing manager may be asked a series of indirect questions which allows the relationship between advertising and sales to be defined. The information is then used to build a forecasting model for evaluating alternative marketing strategies.

ADVANTAGES AND DISADVANTAGES

There are two main advantages of subjective estimation. First, it allows models to be built when there are insufficient data available to use empirical methods. Also, because it does not depend upon the quality of data, and the limitations of statistical techniques, it can be used to build far more complex models than empirical methods allow. Its second major advantage is operational. Subjective estimation forces decision makers and forecasters to interact. Managers are helped to use their experience in designing 'their' model. It is thought that decision aids built in this way are more likely to be used by managers.

The major limitation of subjective estimation is the reliability of information on which it is based. It takes intuition and dresses it in the trappings of an analytical technique. GI–GO (Garbage in – Garbage out) obviously applies; if the subjective estimates are poor, so will be the forecasts. There is clearly a need for great care in validating subjectively estimated models.

A final limitation of subjective estimation is the demands they impose on decision makers and analysts. Analysts have to learn personal skills beyond those usually demanded of a 'back room boy'. Similarly, decision makers are forced to express their beliefs. However, many would say these are advantages rather than disadvantages.

LIMITATIONS OF EMPIRICAL METHODS

The primary aim of subjective estimation is to allow model building when empirical methods, like regression analysis, are inappropriate. This could occur because good data are not available, the environment has changed, linear specifications are inappropriate or there are too many variables for regression analysis to handle (Naert and Wenerbergh, 1981).

Good data are not available

To be good enough for regression analysis data must meet certain standards of quantity, quality and variability. As a rough rule of thumb forecasters need time series data that go back five times the distance they hope to forecast forward. If complex decision models with several decision variables (e.g. price, advertising, competition) are to be used the data series will have to be even longer. Often subjective estimation has to be used because such long data streams are not available. Records may not have been kept or the forecast is for a new product with no sales history.

The quality of data is as important as quantity. To relate advertising to sales a company will have to have records of sales at the consumer level and the date of transmission of publication of advertising material. Frequently firms only have records of shipments of goods from warehouses and the dates when advertising expenditure was budgeted.

Often the data available are not variable enough to use regression analysis. For example, to measure the impact of sales effort the number of salesmen will have to have been changed significantly. Most businesses base their decisions on previous years' figures so, in most cases, there is little variation from year to year. Another problem can be caused by businesses varying expenditures in unison rather than independently. If this has been done regression analysis may not be able to discriminate between the effect of, say, advertising and sales promotions. A danger of regression analysis is its ability always to produce results. Poor data give unreliable results but they can look convincing.

Environmental changes

Estimation using regression requires a long data stream with relationships that have not changed. Dummy variables can be used to represent some changes such as new legislation or crises, but it is difficult to accommodate more complex variations. For example, companies alter their adverising copy frequently because they believe that old copy wears out, or that they have found a more effective image. Marketers are always trying out new methods of sales promotion because they believe some are more effective than others. Forecasters need the impact of advertising and other effects to remain the same so they can model them. Unfortunately, managers are often paid to change relationships in an effort to spend limited resources effectively.

Robust specifications

Regression analysis is only able to assume a limited number of relationships between dependent and independent variables. The most commonly used regression equations give either a straight line or diminishing returns (if a log-log transformation is used). As a later section of this chapter will explain, these 'shapes' are not what common knowledge leads one to expect. They are also not robust, that is, they can give unrealistic answers. For example, the log-log transformation shows sales are zero if advertising is zero. The alternative linear model gives a particularly unhelpful result; when used to represent a sales advertising relationship it shows the optimal strategy is either to spend nothing or an infinite amount on advertising.

Too many variables

Reliable regression analysis depends on having a large surplus of observations over the number of parameters to be estimated. Data are often scarce, so limiting the number of variables that a regression model can accommodate.

The structure of the data can also limit the number of variables that can be meaningfully included in a regression model. Time series variables are often strongly correlated. As more variables are added the problem can become acute, reducing the reliability of all the estimates.

Some of the problems with ordinary regression analysis can be overcome by using more advanced forms of regression or other, more sophisticated, estimation techniques. These can remove some of the difficulties but these still retain the need for large quantities of historic data and are often not available to forecasters.

Subjective estimation makes other demands. It requires experts with the experience and judgement to estimate responses, and forecasters with the ability to question the experts and incorporate the results into acceptable models.

THE SHAPE OF RESPONSE

Subjective estimation requires experts to use their judgement in defining the 'shape' of market relationships. According to Little, 'shape' is of secondary importance: 'Actually I am willing to use anything. The curve could go down or up or loop the loop for all I care' (Little, 1975). This view can be dangerous. If left unguided managers can grossly mis-specify relationships by following myths about the shape of relationships, e.g. threshold levels and supersaturation. A safer approach is to educate managers about the shapes that are likely to exist. Researchers have accumulated a mass of evidence so guidance can be given with some confidence; Figure 7.1 gives a full set of curves that could be realistically expected to occur. Their characteristics, and the associated myths, will be described.

Characteristics of realistic shape are a positive relationship between cause and effect, sales not zero when effort is zero, decreasing returns to scale of effort, saturation level, and an S-shaped relationship. By expressing price as (1/price) the same characteristics can be applied to all marketing instruments.

A positive relationship

Evidence indicates that there is always a positive relationship between sales and marketing effort but the magnitude of the return is often much lower than one would expect. For example, advertising can be useful in doing the sort of task for which it is suited. When used skilfully to publicize a good new brand it can rapidly increase a manufacturer's market share and profits. On the other hand, it is very difficult to expand large mature markets. The evidence available strongly suggests that the total level of advertising plays no part in determining the total size of mature markets. Similarly, advertising to gain market share can have no effect if competitors retaliate by increasing their promotional activity. So, when considering the strength of relationships between effort and results the reality of

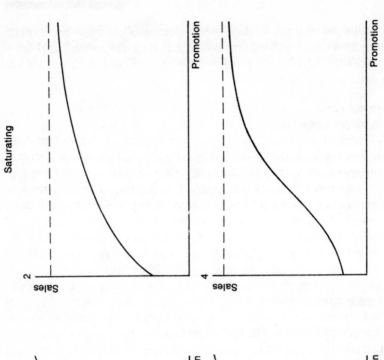

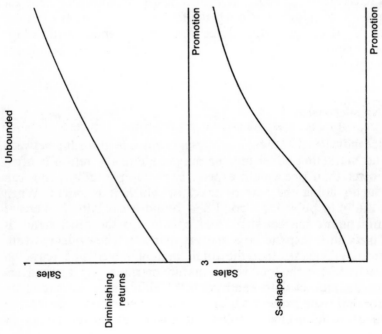

Figure 7.1 Plausible shapes

230

the likely effects should be borne in mind. Promotion can achieve awareness and trial of new products but it is very difficult to obtain repeat purchases or long term market share gains.

Sales are not zero

This is an important consideration because the log-log transformation often used in regression analysis gives zero for the dependent variable if any independent variables are zero. All the evidence suggests the zero-zero relationship does not exist. The highly successful retailer Marks and Spencer uses almost no advertising. Other 'square deal' brands sell well without offering consumer deals.

An exception to the zero-sales argument may be new products. If the consumer is not made aware then they may never buy them.

Decreasing returns to scale

There is strong argument for decreasing returns to scale:

1 As effort is increased new sales prospects become progressively difficult to find.
2 Increased effort often means more contact with the same customers when increased frequency beyond a few has minimal effect.
3 As expenditure is increased it is spent in an increasingly less cost effective way.

Whether or not these arguments are true, all the empirical evidence suggests decreasing returns.

Saturation levels

Saturation levels are a logical extension of diminishing returns. It seems likely that there is a point past which, whatever is done, no more sales will materialize. Never mind how cheap wine became, all of us would have a limited capacity to consume it (although for some the limit may be death). Empirical evidence for saturation levels for individual brands is less strong. They may exist but at levels that are beyond the limits that businesses can economically achieve. Most businesses limit promotions or price reduction, not because an increase would achieve no more sales, but because the sales would not be profitable.

S-shaped curve

S-shaped curves are rational and popular but they are supported by very little evidence. Virtually all attempts to locate S-shaped curves have resulted in the conclusion that there are only diminishing returns to scale. The idea is close to being a myth.

Forecasters who wish to use relationships that are supported by evidence should restrict themselves to diminishing returns. However, if they are faced with experts who want to believe in S-shaped curves they should be aware of problems that are likely to occur. In the region showing increasing returns to scale the curves will show rapidly increasing returns as more is spent. A company with limited budgets will also find it better to pulse promotional expenditure while they have increasing returns to scale, while those with diminishing returns will find it best to hold a steady level. The problem may not be critical if a company does not have a limited budget because companies using either diminishing returns or S-curves will both reach diminishing returns, or an optimal strategy, at similar high spending levels.

Re-examining the plausible response shapes available evidence suggests which should be preferred. Diminishing returns should be preferred over S-shaped curves, and unbounded curves over saturating ones. However, it will be shown later that there are operational reasons why saturating curves may be chosen.

Mythical shapes

Whereas S-shaped responses may exist but have not been found, 'threshold effects' and 'supersaturation' are complete myths (Figure 7.2). Both appear in marketing literature but there is no evidence to support them. Anyone who cares to trace the sources of the myths will find they originated from naive advertising research.

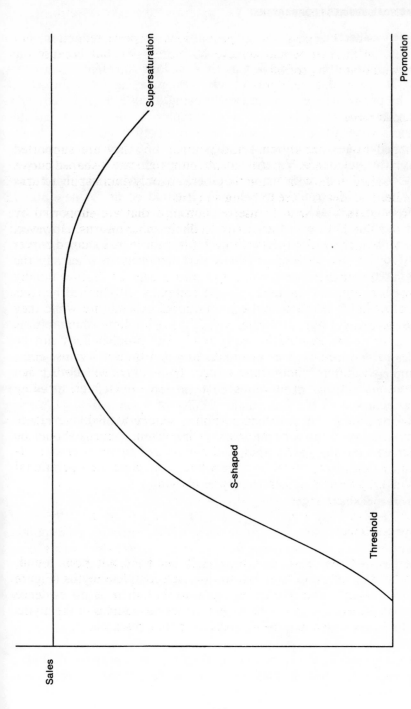

Figure 7.2 A mythical shape

New trier effects

Another belief that could be a myth is the long run effect of advertising. It is popular to represent advertising having maximum effect in the period it is used then slowly dying away after it is removed. In reality the effect is much more complex. Under certain circumstances advertising can have a very strong effect but rarely do the gains continue once advertising stops. Figure 7.3 shows an advertising response that has been reported. A campaign can increase sales to a new peak but once the campaign is over sales drop back to a new but higher equilibrium level. This could occur for new brands where the increased advertising gains trials from customers who like the product. Mature brands are unlikely to show such a violent increase in sales when advertising is increased. They do, however, tend to show an amazing ability to hold market share when advertising is removed.

Stocking effect

Sales promotions such as price cuts and games produce a response completely different from advertising. It is generally believed that, unlike advertising, promotions have no long run effect. Sales are only achieved in the immediate vicinity of a campaign. However, stocking effects sometimes occur. While a product is promoted regular customers stock up so that sales trough when campaigns end and customers use their extra holdings.

How responses change

A problem with using regression analysis is the variation of responses over time. As a product group follows its life cycle changes in response can be expected. Early in a product's life advertising can have a very strong effect as new triers are attracted. Innovators may be little concerned about price but as competition increases, and the product matures, price could become a critical variable.

There are other variations that mean that the sales responses of brands should be carefully examined. It is known that brands at the same time in the same market respond differently to marketing activity. Some brands may be highly price sensitive while others

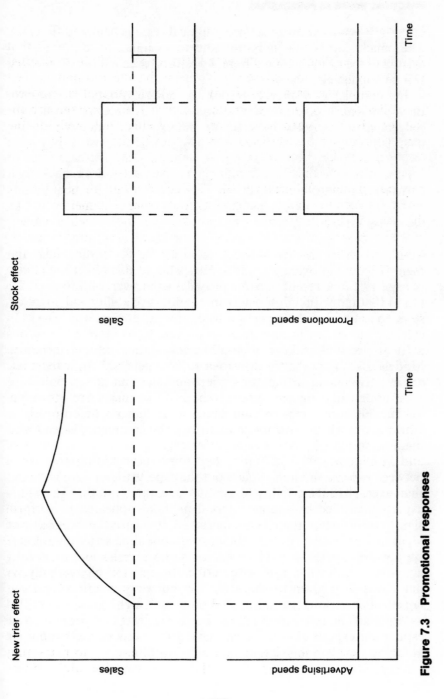

Figure 7.3 Promotional responses

are not. It is also known that geographical regions behave differently. The conclusion is that it is not safe to assume the responses that existed in the past, or for a different product, or in a different market, can be applied elsewhere.

The complexity of market responses and the variation across products and markets is a major reason why it is necessary to use the judgement of experts to estimate many managerial forecasting models.

OBTAINING EXPERT ESTIMATES

Identifying experts

Managers differ in their attitude towards the forecasting task and their ability to provide estimates. How should this affect the choice of experts? Some recent research provides an answer. McIntyre (1982) found that individual differences in quantitative ability and cognitive style do not negate the expectations of any category of user. Decision calculus models encourage decision makers to be more adventurous in their decision making as confidence in 'their' model increases. Models also allow better decisions to be made although their use did not give managers a better understanding of market response.

Although all managers appear to benefit from using decision calculus models some 'experts' are better than others; the problem is working out which ones are good. Self-rating confidence is a popular method borrowed from subjective forecasting. In a test by Larreche and Moinpour (1983) self-rating had some success in differentiating between experts and non-experts but the experts found were no better than average in their ability to estimate accurately. In the same study experts identified by simple external methods appeared to perform significantly better than non-experts. In this case the experts were identified according to their ability to decode time series data. Quite simply the experts were given a time series of sales and marketing activities and then asked to describe the relationship verbally. A mark was then given to characteristics correctly described, such as lag effect or seasonal variation, and those with highest score identified as experts. The research is limited but it suggests that for subjective estimation experts should be chosen on the basis of their cognitive ability rather than their experience or self-rating.

Questioning experts

People are generally unable to express sales responses as an equation so the necessary expressions have to be obtained by indirect means. Usually experts are asked to sketch a curve or asked a series of questions which define a shape. Questioning is the more popular approach but the choice should depend upon the bent of the experts.

In his decision calculus model (ADBUDG) Little (1970) derived a set of equations and an expression that has become the most influential in subjective estimation. Short term responses to marketing activity are estimated using five questions:

1 What is your market share percentage now? S_1
2 What level of advertising is necessary to maintain market share? A_1
3 What would the market share be next period if advertising were reduced to zero (A_0)? S_0
4 What would the market share be next period if advertising were increased to saturation (A_m)? S_m
5 What would the market share be next period if advertising were increased to 50 per cent above maintenance rate (A_n)? S_n

The questions look at the effect on market share if advertising were changed for one period. Figure 7.4 shows how the answers can be used to sketch a response shape. Question 4 dictates that the shape saturates but, depending on the other questions, it can be either S-shaped or show just diminishing returns.

ADBUDG uses a rather intractable looking equation to convert the experts' answers into a response equation:

$$S = S_0 + (S_m - S_0)A^d/(a + A^d) \tag{7.1}$$

where

$$a = A_1^d(S_m - S_1)/(S_1 - S_0)$$
$$d = 1/ln(1.50) \cdot ln[(S_m - S_1)/(S_1 - S_0) \cdot (S_n - S_1)/(S_m - S_n)]$$

A_1, S_0, S_1, S_n, S_m = the answers to the decision calculus questions.
S = sales after one period if advertising at level A.

The equation is non-linear, so could not be estimated using linear

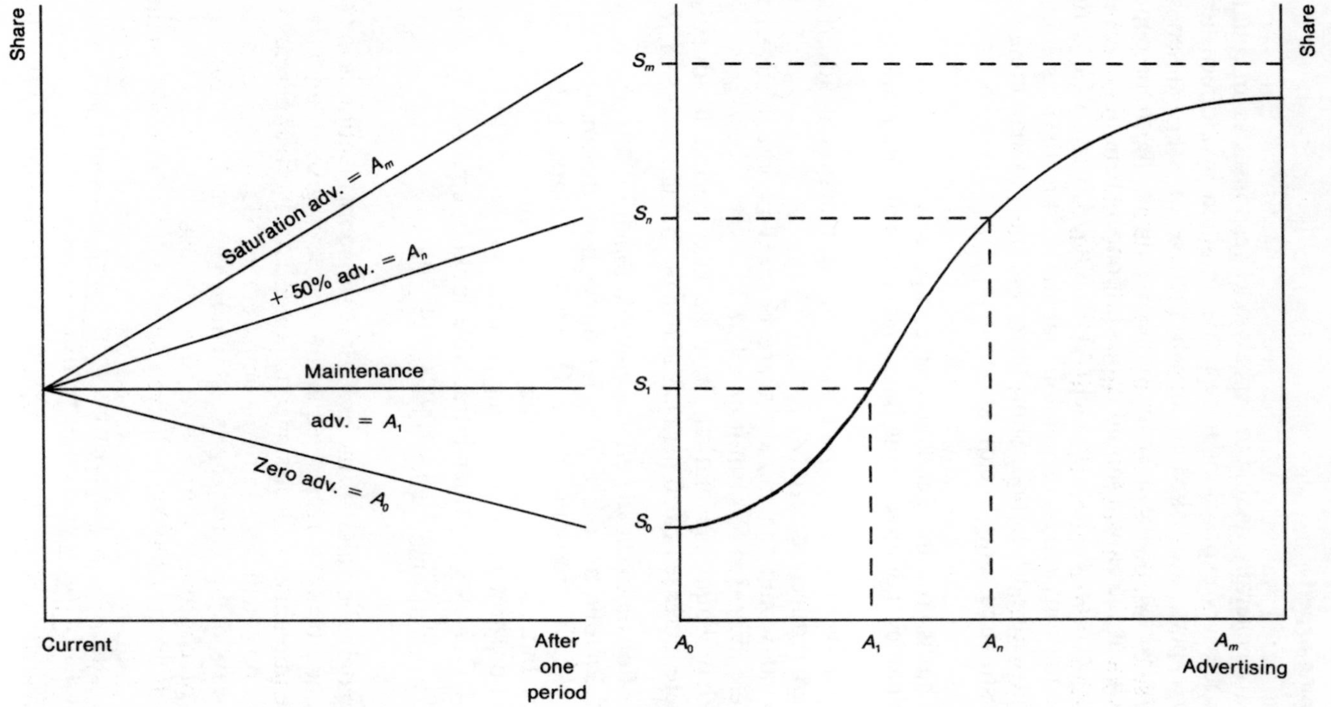

Figure 7.4 Decision calculus response

regression, but it is flexible and, although it looks daunting, it is easily estimated subjectively. By asking for four estimates the equation can be used to express a robust range of shapes.

Deriving a complex response function from four point estimates may seem courageous but it is doubtful that we can confidently specify a sales response curve in any greater detail than represented by a smooth curve through four 'appropriately' chosen points. Subjective estimation is after approximate estimates rather than fine detail.

Little's questions and equations are a neat answer to a complex problem but the 'appropriateness' of the chosen points can be questioned. Two of the estimates requested are for extreme values – zero and saturation levels – that are likely to be beyond those experienced. Experts are poor at estimating outside familiar regions so the reliability of their responses is questionable.

By adding one extra question a modification of (7.1) can be used to show the lag effect of advertising with diminishing returns.

6   What would the market share decline to if there was no advertising for a long time (A_{00})? S_{00}

The expression (7.1) then becomes:

$$S_t = S_{00} + p(S_0 - S_{00}) + (S_m - S_o) \cdot (A_t^d)/(a + At^d) \qquad (7.2)$$

where

$p = (S_0 - S_{00})/(S_1 - S_{00})$
S_t = market at time t when advertising held at A_t

Unfortunately the value of the extra level of sophistication is limited by (7.2) not being a robust equation – it can give poor answers – and the unreality of the assumed exponential advertising decay.

An example will be used to compare the ADBUDG approach to other ways of deriving experts' estimates. The results are for manufacturer of consumer durables with a 200,000 unit sales (S_1) for an expenditure of £200,000 on advertising (A_1). A consultant familiar with the industry was interviewed and estimated sales would be 100,000 units (S_0) if advertising were zero (A_0), a saturation level of sales of 350,000 (S_m), and sales of 270,000 ($S_{1.5}$) if advertising were increased by 50 per cent ($A_{1.5}$). The estimates specify an S-shaped equation with the shape illustrated in Figure 7.5:

$$S = 100,000 + 250,000 \, [A^{2.859}/(5,706,200 + A^{2.859})] \qquad (7.3)$$

In an alternative to the ADBUDG approach experts are asked a series of incremental questions about expenditure levels close to those they have experienced, for example:

What is current market share? $\qquad S_1$

What level of advertising is necesary to maintain market share? $\quad A_1$

What would market share be if advertising were changed by the following percentages:
Increased by 20 per cent $(A_{1.20})$? $\qquad S_{1.20}$
Increased by 40 per cent $(A_{1.40})$? $\qquad S_{1.40}$
.
.
.
Decreased by 20 per cent $(A_{0.80})$? $\qquad S_{0.80}$
Decreased by 40 per cent $(A_{0.60})$? $\qquad S_{0.60}$
.
.
.

Forecasters can convert the answers to a response shape by plotting results or using a curve fitting routine to estimate an equation.

To compare the decision calculus and incremental approaches the consultant was again asked to specify response but using incremental questions. The consultant felt confident about his estimates with advertising between 50 per cent and 200 per cent of regular levels so the questions were limited to that region. The answers were $S_{0.50} = 150,000$, $S_{0.75} = 170,000$, $S_{1.25} = 235,000$, $S_{1.50} = 270,000$, $S_{1.75} = 290,000$, and $S_{2.00} = 300,000$.

ORION's curve fitting routine was used to find an equation best able to represent the incremental estimate. The routine tries to fit ten equations with a variety of shapes to the data. The equations are summarized in Table 7.1 where their characteristics are compared. Although the expressions display a wide range of shapes most are linearizable so can be estimated using regression analysis. It will be noted, however, that none of the linearizable expressions have all the characteristics necessary to produce a realistic curve; this is one of the basic problems of estimation.

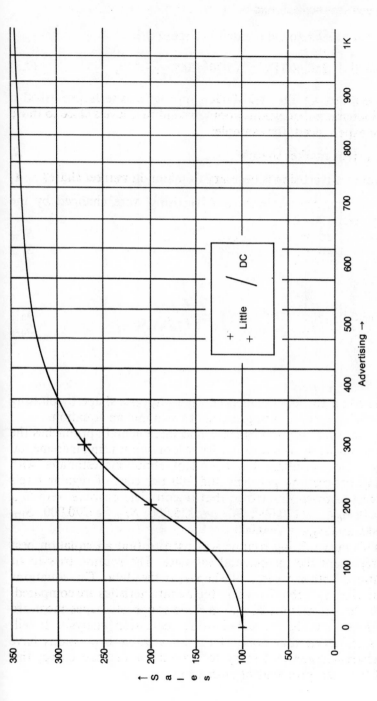

Figure 7.5　A decision calculus shape

Table 7.1
Curve fit expressions and shapes

Linearizable expressions

No	Name	Equations	Positive	$A=0$, $S>0$	Decreasing	Saturation	S-shaped	Threshold	Supersaturation
			Good characteristics					Bad characteristics	
1	Linear	$S = a + bA$	✓	✓					
2	Constrained hyperbola	$S = A/(a + bA)$	✓			✓			
3	Exponential	$S = ae^{bA}$	✓	✓	✓	✓			
4	Log-log	$S = aA^b$	✓		✓				
5	Semi-log	$S = a + b\log(A)$	✓	*	✓			×	
6	Modified exponential	$S = ae^{b/A}$	✓	*	✓	✓		×	
7	Hyperbola	$S = a + b/A$	✓	*	✓	✓		×	
8	Modified hyperbola	$S = 1/(a + bA)$	✓	✓	✓				
9	Quadratic	$S = a + bA + cA^2$	✓	✓	✓				×
10	Log quadratic	$\log(S) = a + bA + cA^2$	✓	✓	✓		✓		×

Not linearizable expressions

	Name	Equations	Positive	$A=0$, $S>0$	Decreasing	Saturation	S-shaped	Threshold	Supersaturation
	Decision calculus	$S = a + b[A^c/(d + A^c)]$	✓	✓	✓	✓	✓		
	Gompertz	$S = a*b^{cA}$	✓	✓	✓	✓	✓		

* S cannot be computed when $A = 0$
√ Good characteristics
× Bad characteristics

Table 7.2
The fit of ten expressions

Curve no.	R-squared	Equation
10	.992	SALES = EXP(4.5561 + .00474*AD − 4.5546E-06*AD↑2)
9	.987	SALES = 70 + .78095*AD − .00047619*AD↑2
1	.981	SALES = 95 + .54286*AD
4	.981	SALES = 11.698 * AD↑(.54386)
3	.967	SALES = 120.94 * EXP(.0024627*AD)
5	.962	SALES = −408.88 + 117.86*LOG(AD)
2	.947	SALES = AD / (.0022998*AD + .47125)
8	.940	SALES = 1 / (.0074993 − .000011546*AD)
6	.908	SALES = 360.38 * EXP(−97.033/AD)
7	.860	SALES = 332.12 − 20,662/AD

Regression analysis allows the ability of each of the expressions to fit the data to be compared using the coefficient of determination (R^2) (Table 7.2). The results show the danger of accepting goodness of fit as a reliable measure. The two quadratic equations have the highest R^2 yet they are curves that supersaturate – a characteristic that does not appear in the data used. This is a frequent occurrence that needs explaining. The quadratic equations are very flexible expressions with three parameters (a, b, c) that can be changed to fit almost any smooth curve – the other expressions only have two parameters. This allows the curve to fit the data and also causes the relative coefficients of determination to be exaggerated because a degree of freedom is lost. It is an unfortunate feature of these very flexible curves that they always supersaturate. Figure 7.6 shows the extent of the problem. The log quadratic curve (E10) steers close to the estimates (points) but overshoots and supersaturates soon after the range of the data. This can be compared with the simple curve (E2) and the decision calculus curve (DC) that tend to saturate after the data. Figure 7.7 shows the managerial consequences of these different specifications. It is a plot of the contribution after advertising if the gross margin per unit sold was £15.

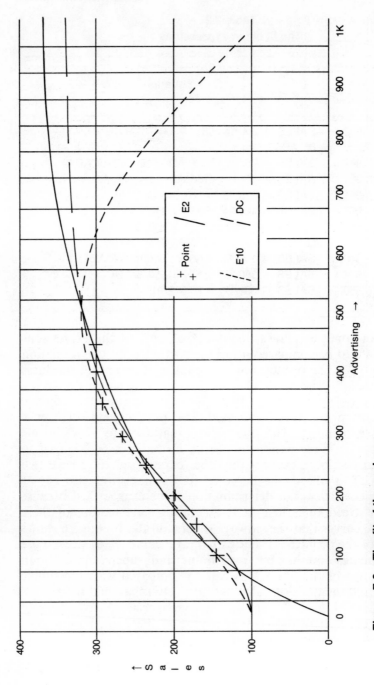

Figure 7.6 The fit of three shapes

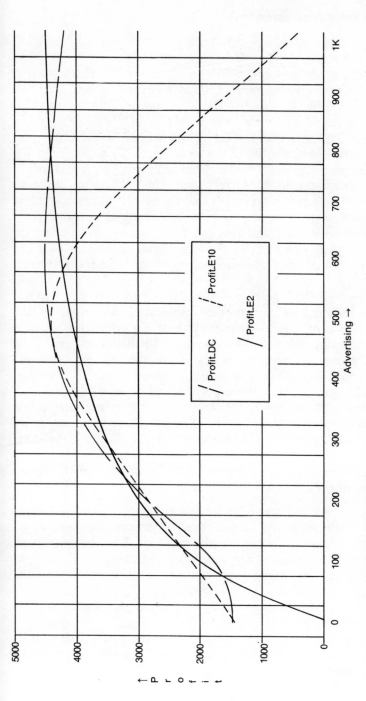

Figure 7.7 The implications of three shapes

245

$$\text{Profit} = \text{margin} \times \text{sales} - \text{advertising} \qquad (7.4)$$

The quadratic specification (profit $-$ E10) shows a distinct peak in the returns from advertising at £500,000 beyond which spending more reduces profit. In contrast the other two shapes suggest that a firm could spend anything over £500,000 and still achieve the same profits. This is an important result because it indicates that, above a certain limit, profits are insensitive to advertising. In the short term a company could choose either to keep promotional spending low or increase sales by advertising, while achieving the same contribution. This result is typical of that found with many marketing models – there is a wide range over which changing marketing expenditure increases sales and revenue while having little effect on short term profits. However, in the long term, there may be gains as higher expenditure and sales achieve experience which can convert to cost savings.

It will be noted that the two equations in Table 7.1 that are not linearizable have all of the good characteristics, and none of the bad ones. However, they also provide only an approximate fit to any series of point estimates. An exception to this occurs when the number of points is equal to, or less than, the number of points in the equation. Equations 1–8 will pass through any two points; 9, 10 and 12 through any three points; and the decision calculus equations through any four. In other cases the parameters allow the expression a limited amount of flexibility. There are many more expressions and shapes than those described but all retain the same difficulties.

Several conclusions can be drawn from the inability of regression equations to fit the subjective estimates:

1 All curves are a crude fit to the desired shape.
2 There is no curve with all the desired characteristics.
3 Do not choose a curve on the basis of R^2. The ones with the best fit often have the wrong characteristics.
4 Choose a curve among those that are realistic in terms of the characteristics essential to the model.
5 Ask if any results are a result of the data or the curve that has been used to fit it.
6 Don't worry a lot about the choice between the curves with the essential characteristics. Results are usually not sensitive to the details of a curve.

Probability estimate

Competitive bidding was an early application of subjective estimating (Edelman, 1965). This typically occurs in industrial markets when firms are asked to bid for a contract which is awarded to the company with the best combination of price and non-price features. If a company estimates the relationship between a price and the probability of winning a contract at that price, it can forecast the price that is likely to give it the highest expected return. Expert companies keep good records of competitors' bidding strategies to aid bidding decisions. Such data bases can be used to build analytical models but usually all competitive bidding models contain a high degree of subjectivity.

Table 7.3
Competitive bidding expected payoff

Price P (£000)	Probability of a win Q	Margin $M = (P - C^\dagger)$ (£000)	Expected payoff $X = M^*Q$ (£000)
10	1.0	2	2.00
12	0.99	4	3.96
14	0.87	6	5.22
16	0.35	8	2.80
18	0.03	10	0.30
20	0.00	12	0.00

$^\dagger C$ = Cost of completing contract = £8,000

Table 7.3 gives typical results of a subjective probability analysis. Higher prices increase margins but reduce the probability of making a sale. Somewhere there is a best strategy where the expected payoff peaks. In this case it is £14,000, although it is likely there is a bid between £12,000 and £14,000 that gives a better return.

A simple set of questions can be used to obtain probability estimates:

1 At what price would there be a 97.5 per cent chance of getting an order $(Q_{0.975})$? $P_{0.975}$
2 At what price would there be a 50 per cent chance of getting

an order ($Q_{0.5}$)? $\qquad$ $P_{0.5}$

3   At what price would there be a 2.5 per cent chance of getting
an order ($Q_{0.025}$)? $\qquad$ $P_{0.025}$

If the low ($P_{0.025}$) and high ($P_{0.975}$) estimates average close to the
middle estimate ($P_{0.5}$) a normal distribution may be assumed. The
mean ($\bar{P}$) and standard deviations (σ) can therefore be approximated
as:

$$\bar{P} = (P_{0.025} + P_{0.975})/2 \tag{7.5}$$
$$\sigma = (P_{0.025} - P_{0.975})/4 \tag{7.6}$$

Figure 7.8 shows normally distributed probabilities derived for
$P_{0.975} = £13{,}000$, $P_{0.5} = £15{,}500$ and $P_{0.025} = £18{,}000$.

A modified beta distribution allows means and standard deviations
to be estimated if the high and low estimates are asymmetrically
distributed about the modal value.

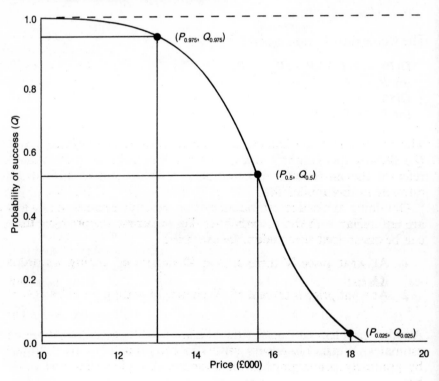

Figure 7.8   Normally distributed probabilities

In this case the usual questions are:

1 What is the lowest price at which there is no chance of making a sale (Q_H)? $\hspace{2cm} P_H$
2 What is the price at which there is a 0.5 probability of making a sale (Q_M)? $\hspace{2cm} P_M$
3 What is the highest price at which there is a certainty of making a sale (Q_L)? $\hspace{2cm} P_L$

The means of the beta distribution is arbitrarily assumed to be one-third of the way between the average of the extremes and the middle value:

$$\bar{P} = (Q_L + 4Q_M + Q_H)/6 \tag{7.7}$$

The standard deviation is similarly arbitrarily set at one-sixth of the range:

$$\sigma = (P_H - P_L)/6 \tag{7.8}$$

The whole distribution is given by:

$$Q(P) = k(P - P_L)^a(P_H - P)^b \tag{7.9}$$
for $P_L < P < P_H$ or
$$Q(P) = 0 \tag{7.10}$$
for $P_L > P > P_H$

where k, a and b are calculated from the estimates of Q_L, Q_M and Q_H. Strictly speaking it is not a beta distibution because P_M should refer to the mode of a distribution – a value that is difficult to estimate in this application.

Obtaining subjective estimates can be difficult because managers are unfamiliar with the probabilities. To overcome the problem they can be questioned using odds, for example:

1 At what price is there a 1 in 40 chance of getting an order $(Q_{0.025})$? $\hspace{2cm} P_{0.025}$
2 At what price is there a 50/50 chance of getting an order $(Q_{0.5})$? $\hspace{2cm} P_{0.5}$

Another problem can be the unwillingness of 'experts' to give their estimates. When this occurs estimates can sometimes be obtained by gradually converging on an estimate. A typical dialogue could be:

Analyst:	At what price is there a 1 in 40 chance of getting an order?
Expert:	I've no idea.
Analyst:	OK. Do you think there is any chance of getting an order if we price at £25,000?
Expert:	No, we would never get that price.
Analyst:	How about £20,000?
Expert:	No.
Analyst:	What about £15,000?
Expert:	A very good price, we would have a very good chance if we went in at that.
Analyst:	(Notes: $P_M \cong$ £15,000?) Let's go up a bit. How about £18,000?
Expert:	Maybe, but very slight.
Analyst:	(Notes: $P_M \cong$ £18,000?) And £19,000?
Expert:	No way.
Analyst:	(Notes: $P_M =$ £18,000) Let's talk about a price where we would be sure to get an order. Would we certainly get an order if we went in at £12,000?
Expert:	Certainly.

Usually after a series of questions an analyst will have the estimates required to build a probability distribution. The process may seem crude but tests show most estimates to be robust. Usually optimal strategies are far more dependent upon the cost assumptions (as in Table 7.3) than the probability estimates. Once again results are usually robust in the region of the optimal strategy where various strategies produce only a slight change in expected payoffs.

COMBINING ESTIMATES

There are two modes of combining estimates: the combining of estimates from several experts; and combining judgemental and empirical estimates.

Combining subjective estimates

It is generally accepted that forecasts improve if results from more than one source are combined. This is particularly true of subjective forecasting where more information is captured by employing several experts. Simmonds and Slatter (1978) have shown how similar gains are achieved by combining experts' estimates. Their competitive bidding results also showed that firms had a marked tendency to employ too few estimators.

A central issue is how to combine the divergent opinions. On the rare occasion that all estimates are the same there is no problem because any one forecast will do; the others act as confirmation. When experts have opinions that diverge a pooling scheme can combine opinions to produce a single forecast. Four basic pooling methods are available (Winkler, 1968):

1 Assign equal weight to each estimate.
2 Assign weightings that are proportional to the expert self-rating.
3 Assign weights that are proportional to someone's subjective ranking or rating of the expert's competence.
4 Assign weightings that are proportional to the past predictive accuracy of the experts.

Our earlier discussion suggests little benefit to be derived from experts' self-rating. It appears to discriminate, on average, between experts and non-experts but experts identified in this fashion are not likely to produce better results than non-experts. Conversely, experts identified by simple external measures can provide significantly better estimates than non-experts. There are also few gains to be had by using complex weighting schemes such as those based on past predictive accuracy. Many have been proposed but they give little improvement over a simple average of group opinions.

Analysts can avoid the pooling problem by using group methods of combining estimates. These have the advantage of converging to a response shape agreed by everyone and allow experts to adjust their estimates in response to feedback from others.

BRANDAID (Little, 1975) uses a simple group method where experts sketch their own response curves and then discuss them as a group. Although very common, this method is viewed with some misgivings because the actual confrontation of experts is likely to create certain psychological effects that may spoil the independence of experts' estimation processes; for example senior or particularly dominant managers, who are not really experts, may dominate a discussion.

It was in response to the problems of the simple group approach that the RAND Corporation developed the Delphi method. This has experts responding anonymously to requests for estimates. The results are compared by a co-ordinator who sends a summary of the first round back to the experts and asks them to make a second estimate. Any outliers are also asked to explain the reason for their deviance. The second estimates and their explanation are then circulated with a request for a third estimate. The process is continued until the participants agree, or the estimates are stable – usually it is not necessary to use more than three cycles.

The RAND Corporation's hopes for the Delphi method appear to be fulfilled. While the simple group method produces no significant gain over the average of experts' initial judgements, the Delphi process appears to provide significantly better estimates than other methods.

Although the Delphi method provides superior results there may be other reasons why, in practice, simple group methods are better. Personal interaction and arriving at a group consensus can be important for model building and implementation. The simple group methods provide an opportunity for this whereas the Delphi process keeps participants isolated. In addition, the simple group approach can be much quicker than the Delphi method.

To summarize, estimates can be improved by combining the opinions of experts. Many ways of doing this have been proposed but only a few are efficient. First, an average of opinions can be taken. More complex pooling methods have been proposed but they deliver little improvement over simple averages. Second, estimates can be improved if experts are correctly identified, that is, by external measures of expertise that focus on their ability to appreciate the task in hand rather than their self-rating or status. Finally, the Delphi approach can be used to allow an exchange of ideas without introducing the bias of personal interaction.

Combining subjective and empirical estimates

Theoretically subjective and empirical estimates can be combined using Bayesian analysis but in practice ad hoc processes are used. Is it correct to reject the theoretically sound Bayesian approach? Many proficient model builders would say 'Yes'. First, although it is theoretically possible to combine sample and prior information, in real cases the mathematics involved is far from trivial. Second,

Bayesian analysis involves eliciting many probability distributions from experts. The difficulty of doing this, in very simple cases, has been discussed earlier; it is operationally demanding and, in many cases, it is not at all clear that man is capable of probability assessment. Finally, and most important for implementation, the informal procedures permit decision makers to be more involved.

Having rejected the Bayesian approach model builders are not in agreement about the best way of combining estimates. In his marketing mix model, Lambin (1972) starts by using regression analysis to obtain objective estimates. The expert is then allowed to adjust the empirically determined coefficients by multiplying them by subjectively estimated indices whose reference value is 1. The judgemental input is minimal, the expert is unable to change the shape of response but the intervention can allow some adjustment for changes in advertising copy or point-of-sale promotions. Lambin supports the objective first approach by arguing that it is unrealistic to expect judgemental estimates of the different response coefficients from decision makers who do not think that way. Most model builders would agree that managers cannot be expected to estimate response expressions directly but they would hope to derive shapes indirectly by asking a series of decision calculus type questions.

In BRANDAID, Little (1975) takes the opposite approach to Lambin and starts with subjective estimates. One reason for doing this is to prevent people from over-interpreting empirical analyses, which are invariably based on a limited time period and a limited set of variables. 'Statistical results sometimes take on an air of authority because of their seeming objectivity'. Little's experts start by making subjective estimates which they then adjust after empirical analysis, tracking the original model's results against historical data, field experiments and adaptive control after implementation.

One neat and very useful way of combining subjective and objective information is to use regression analysis to define the slope of a relationship, say between sales and advertising, while defining the upper or lower bounds subjectively. The approach has the advantage of allowing essentially non-linear response equations to be solved empirically using regression analysis. For example, the non-linearizable Gompertz becomes linear if a saturation level is assumed. This is very useful because, from Figure 7.1, Gompertz is one of the few expressions with a good set of characteristics. The process will be illustrated.

The original form of a Gompertz expression is:

$$S = a*b^{c^A} \tag{7.11}$$

where a is the saturation level of an S-shaped curve.
Taking logs twice this becomes:

$$\log[\log(S/a)] = \log[\log(b)] + A.\log(c) \tag{7.12}$$

The equation is still non-linear but if the saturation level a is estimated subjectively the equation's other parameters can be estimated by regression.

$$\log[\log(F)] = \log[\log(b)] + A.\log(c) \tag{7.13}$$

where $F = S/a =$ sales as a fraction of the saturation level.

CONCLUSIONS

Subjective estimation has been presented as a technique that can be used when historical data are not good enough to allow empirical methods. It is also thought to have the implementation advantage of allowing decision makers to be closely involved in the model building process.

Subjective estimation has its roots in marketing where there have been many applications and accepted processes are emerging. It has been argued that any managerial estimates of responses are better than none and, if they are guided carefully, managers can provide useful responses.

There are several ways that response curves can be elicited. The most popular is to ask a few indirect questions that allow a 'decision calculus' or 'beta distribution' to be calibrated. Alternatively managers can sketch curves directly, or give a series of incremental estimates that may be fitted to a curve using regression. In this process it is important that an expression is chosen with the right characteristics, and that the analyst is able to distinguish between the character of the data and the character of the chosen expression.

Results can be improved by simply averaging the estimates of several experts. There appear to be no gains from using complex pooling methods although it does pay to use external means of selecting a group of 'real' experts.

Theoretically, Bayesian analysis can be used for combining subjective and objective estimates but it is intractable and rarely used in practice. Various ad hoc procedures of combining estimates have been proposed but, as yet, no front runner has emerged.

FURTHER READING

Edelman, F., 'Art and Science of Competitive Bidding', *Harvard Business Review,* July–August 1965, pp. 53–66.

Kotler, P., 'A Guide to Gathering Expert Estimates', *Business Horizons,* October 1970, pp. 79–87.

Lambin, J. J., 'A Computer On-Line Marketing Mix Model', *Journal of Marketing Research,* vol. IX, May 1972, pp. 119–26.

Larreche, J. C. and Moinpour, R., 'Managerial Judgement in Marketing: The Concept of Expertise', *Journal of Marketing Research,* vol. XX, May 1983, pp. 110–121.

Larreche, J. C. and Srinivasan, V., 'STRATPORT: A Decision Support System for Strategic Planning', *Journal of Marketing,* vol. 45, Fall 1981, pp. 39–52.

Little, J. D. C., 'Models and Managers: The Concept of a Decision Calculus', *Management Science,* vol. 16, no. 8, April 1970, pp. B-466-485.

Little, J. D. C., 'BRANDAID: A Marketing-Mix Model, Part 1: Structure; Part 2: Implementation', *Operations Research,* vol. 23, July 1975, pp. 628–673.

Little, J. D. C., 'Aggregate Advertising Models: The State of the Art', *Operations Research,* vol. 27, no. 4, July–August 1979, pp. 629–667.

Little, J. D. C. and Lodish, L. M., 'A Media Planning Calculus', *Operations Research,* vol. 17, January 1969, pp. 1–35.

Lodish, L. M., 'Sales Territory Alignment to Maximize Profits', *Journal of Marketing Research,* vol. XII, February 1975, pp. 30–36.

Lodish, L. M., 'Experience with Decision-Calculus Models and Decision Support Systems', in R. L. Schultz and A. A. Zoltners, *Marketing Decision Models,* Elsevier, Amsterdam 1981, pp. 165–182.

McIntyre, S. H., 'An Experimental Study of the Impact of Judgement-Based Market Models', *Management Science,* vol. 28, no. 1, January 1982, pp. 17–33.

Naert, P. A. and Wenerbergh, M., 'Subjective Versus Empirical Decision Models', in R. L. Schultz and A. A. Zoltners, *Marketing*

Decision Models, Elsevier, Amsterdam 1981, pp. 99–123.

Simmonds, K. and Slatter, S., 'The Number of Estimators: A Critical Decision for Marketing Under Competitive Bidding', *Journal of Marketing Research,* vol. XV, May 1978, pp. 203–13.

Winkler, R. L., 'The Consensus of Subjective Probability Distributions', *Management Science,* vol. 15, 1968, pp. B-61-75.

8 New product forecasting

Robert Shlaiffer of Harvard is reputed to have said 'Forecasting is like driving a car blindfolded and following directions given by a person who is looking out of the back window'. This is not true for new product forecasting; new products have no sales history so there is no back window to look out of. Fortunately the last decade has brought a revolution in new product forecasting technology that has allowed firms to accelerate significantly their new production processes.

There are three sources of information that can be used to forecast when there is no sales history:

1 What managers say – asking sales people or experts how well a product will sell.
2 What customers say – asking customers if they would buy a product if it were available.
3 What customers do – measuring what customers do in experiments where they can choose the product.

'What managers say' or subjective forecasting is the subject of Chapter 10 where its potential for strategic and technological forecasting will be discussed. This chapter concentrates on the consumer based techniques. It starts by introducing the concepts and methods of new product forecasting and shows how they span the whole new product development process. Each of the methods is then discussed in more depth.

METHODS

The success of new product forecasting methods has led to their proliferation and commercialization by market research and advertising agencies. There is great variety· in the details of their operation but the techniques fall into five classes: early prediction, test marketing, pre-test marketing, product use testing and concept testing. Figure 8.1 shows how the methods tend to follow the new product process.

The earlier methods are less realistic but can be used to test incomplete market offerings. In concept tests customers are asked if they would buy a product after being given a brief description or shown a picture of the new idea. Product use testing may involve a sample of customers testing a product in their own home but to remove bias no attempt is made at branding. Pre-test marketing uses a simulated shopping environment in which new products are branded and sold competitively. In some cases the customers may not be aware they are participating in an experiment. Test marketing is much more realistic and expensive than the earlier methods because it involves trying the whole marketing programme in a test area. Consumers and distributors may not know they are participating in a test area but realism can be lost because managers and sales people may know. In addition, local rather than national media may have to be used. Unlike the other methods early prediction is not experimental; the normal launch procedure is followed but the behaviour of early buyers is tracked in order to produce an estimate of final demand.

ADVANTAGES AND DISADVANTAGES

The diversity of techniques provides little scope for an overall discussion of the advantages and disadvantages of new product forecasting. Some issues are introduced here but each of the methods will be evaluated in more detail when they are described.

The major advantage of experiment based new product forecasting is its track record and ability to give objective results early in a product's life. One measure of success is the number of professional agencies who now offer comprehensive services for data collection and modelling. Competitive pressures have made developments in new product forecasting particularly timely. Early forecasting of sales has helped many companies to improve their product development processes. Escalating product development costs also provide an

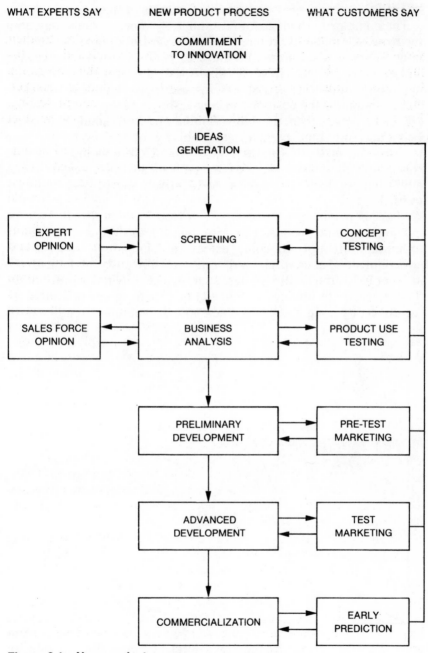

Figure 8.1   New product process

incentive to obtain early and reliable forecasts of sales. The complexity, high cost and timing of some methods may limit their use. All methods require time for organization and data collection. In some cases users may have to choose between forecasting and an early launch. However, this is less of a problem for pre-test marketing, and other techniques for use early in product development. Similarly, the costs of concept testing and pre-test marketing are much lower than the more familiar test marketing approach. Economic and time pressures are causing businesses to gravitate towards the methods for early new product forecasting. The data collection and analysis methods are sophisticated but many agencies now offer services that make them relatively inexpensive and easy to use.

Most new product forecasting methods are designed for fast moving consumer goods. For example, all the pre-test marketing techniques attempt, to some extent, to simulate a supermarket environment. These specialized tools are obviously of limited use in other industrial sectors. Where supermarket buying does not occur the choice of techniques is limited, but there is still a chance to use concept testing and early prediction. In addition, trend analysis

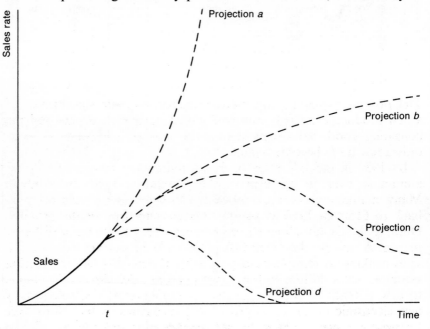

Figure 8.2   Typical new product sales

(Chapter 9) provides several ways of forecasting the demand for durable goods.

BEHAVIOURAL DETAIL

Simple time series analysis cannot be used to forecast new product sales. Figure 8.2 shows the problem; at time t the product is selling well and at an ever increasing rate. An optimistic forecaster may extrapolate the curve as projection a. Readers may consider the optimist naive but such forecasts help explain why many industries have over-capacity and a shake-out following rapid growth (in the home computer market, for example). Projection b is more realistic but still does not portray what happens in many cases. Projection c is close to what occurs with many successful new product launches. In order to forecast new product sales it is necessary to understand what causes the pattern.

All new product forecasting models use a simple model of consumer behaviour to explain sales. The sales rate achieved is the result of a three-stage process:

1 Awareness – by word of mouth, promotion distribution or direct selling, customers become aware of a product.
2 Trial – if customers like what they see they may buy it.
3 Repeat – if what they have bought lives up to expectations they may buy it repeatedly.

The process explains projection c. Advertising, or the interest of a new product, can easily stimulate a high trial rate for a fast moving consumer good. Sales peak then drop back to a lower level when only a few triers become regular users.

By 1980 in the UK sales of Pot Noodles had reached £36m per annum as over 50 per cent of the population tried the product. Many manufacturers were taken by surprise when sales dropped back to £18m in 1982 as many triers became tired of the product. Durable goods can show a similar sales pattern but for a different reason. A new product can diffuse through the market rapidly with sales peaking as many new buyers enter the market. As the market saturates, sales decline and eventually fall as sales can only be made to new potential customers or as replacements. The sales of many new electronic products have followed such sales patterns and have forced companies to be intensively innovative in order to fill the gaps that occur as new product sales peak and trough.

New product managers often go into test markets watching one factor – market share. Many have launched nationally after observing high initial market share only to find out too late that high share was due to an unexpectedly high trial rate. New product forecasting avoids this problem by tracking trial and repeat rates rather than the unreliable market share figure.

Using models before experiments has become increasingly popular. It can give an early indication of sales and helps to identify which variables have to be tracked in the experiment. Prior use of models is particularly useful for test marketing so changes can be made to new products before major resources have been expended on marketing or production.

New product forecasting models

New product forecasting systems have two major components: a data collection method and a data analysis model. For example the pre-test marketing service offered by INBUCON uses a 30-minute video to present new products and competitors' products to consumers and then measures consumers' trial rate by allowing them to select purchases at a 20 per cent discount in a simulated supermarket. Directly after they have been through the shop they are involved in group discussions about their choices. Repeat purchase rate is measured by recontacting consumers after a realistic time lag to allow in-home use. Usually telephone interviews are used to ask the users about their satisfaction with the brand they bought, and to give them another chance to buy the test brand.

Data analysis converts the experimental results into market forecasts. There are many models that purport to do this. Most use some variation on the simple form proposed by Parfitt and Collins (1968):

$$s = prb \tag{8.1}$$

where

$s =$ ultimate brand share;
$p =$ ultimate penetration rate of a brand (percentage of new buyers of this product class who try the brand);

r = ultimate repeat purchases rate of a brand (repurchases of the brand as a percentage of all purchasers who once purchased the brand);

b = buying rate index of repeat purchase of a brand (average buyer = 1.00).

Practical models are usually much more complicated than the one above. One reason for the increased complexity is uncertainty about the ultimate levels of p, r and b. Experiments measure values that have to be projected to their ultimate levels. Another problem is the impact of marketing instruments. For example, price reductions, extra distribution effort or couponing may be used to attract triers. New product forecasters have developed a wide range of models to take these factors into account. One of the best documented of these is the TRACKER test market based new product forecasting model (Blattberg and Golanty, 1978). Figure 8.3 is a flow chart showing how marketing and other variables are fed into the basic awareness, trial, repeat processes.

Because they are commercial, details of many models have been published only in part (Wind, et al, 1981). One of the best documented systems is a test marketing based forecasting model from the N. W. Ayer and Son advertising agency (Claycamp and Liddy, 1969). It has three equations representing 'knowledge about the product' (awareness), 'initial purchase' (trial) and 'repeat purchase'. The specification for awareness is:

$$AR = a_1 + b_{11}(PP) + b_{12}(\sqrt{AMI.CE}) + b_{13}(CP^*) + u \qquad (8.2)$$

where

AR = percentage of housewives able to accurately recall advertising claims at the end of 13 weeks;

PP = judged product positions as expressed in the advertising with respect to existing products in the category;

AMI = average number of media impressions/household;

CE = judged quality of advertising copy executions;

CP^* = coverage of consumer promotions containing advertising messages adjusted for type of promotion;

$a_1, b_{11}, b_{12}, b_{13}$ = parameters to be estimated using regression analysis;

u = error term.

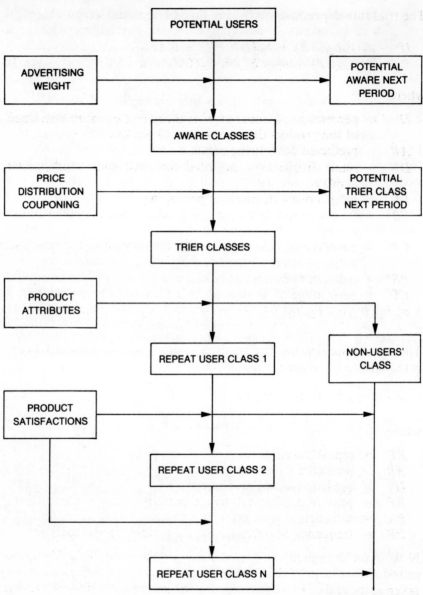

Source: Blattberg, R. and Golanty, J., 'TRACKER: An Early Test-Market Forecasting and Diagnostic Model for New Product Planning' *Journal of Marketing Research*, Vol XV (May) 1978, p. 193.

Figure 8.3   Flow chart of TRACKER

The trial rate depends upon the predicted awareness level:

$$IP = a_2 + b_{21}(A\hat{R}) + b_{22}(DN.PK) + b_{23}(FB)$$
$$+ b_{24}(CP) + b_{25}(PS^*) + b_{26}(CU) + u \qquad (8.3)$$

where

IP = percentage of housewives making one or more purchases of the product during the first 13 weeks;

$A\hat{R}$ = predicted advertising recall;

DN = retail distribution, adjusted for shelf space and special displays;

PK = judged distinctiveness of packaging;

FB = family brand factor, if the product uses a known brand name;

CP = coverage of consumer promotions adjusted for type and value of offer;

PS^* = index of consumer satisfaction with new product samples;

CU = percentage of households using products in the category;

$a_2, b_{21}, b_{22}, b_{23}, b_{24}, b_{25}, b_{26}$ = parameters to be estimated using regression analysis.

The exact specification for repeat purchase is not disclosed but it is thought to be of the form

$$RP = f(A\hat{R}, I\hat{P}, RP, PS, PF) \qquad (8.4)$$

where

RP = repeat purchase level;

$A\hat{R}$ = predicted advertising recall;

$I\hat{P}$ = predicted initial purchases;

RP = price of product relative to other products in the category;

PS = satisfaction with prior purchases;

PF = frequency of purchase for the product in the category.

N.W. Ayer estimated their model using data from 58 new product introductions from 32 different product categories. Consumer surveys taken at the end of 13 weeks were used to estimate levels of advertising recall, initial and repeat purchase, and use of samples and coupons, product specification, category usage, and category purchase frequency. Other quantitative values were obtained using subjective judgements from a panel of marketing and advertising executives.

Results for 35 new products were used to estimate the parameters of equations (8.2) to (8.4) using regression analysis (see Chapters 5 and 6). The other 23 products were retained as a validation sample to test the quality of the model. Results for the validation sample were good. For advertising recall 15 out of the 23 model predictions were within ± 10 per cent of the values measured in the consumer surveys. Results for initial purchase were higher; 20 of the predictions were within ± 10 per centage points of the measured values.

The most meaningful tests of the model are from its use in predicting, before launch, the probable outcome of a given campaign for a specific product. For these the data for the model were taken from test markets and used to forecast results after commercialization. The results were similar to those for the validation sample – predicted initial purchases for five out of eight cases were within ± 5 per cent of the actual level, and only one prediction was more than 10 per cent out.

N.W. Ayer's results are not untypical of those obtained using other new product forecasting models. Using well designed experimental techniques and new product models forecasters have shown a consistent ability to predict new product sales. Despite the new product having no sales history the methods developed appear to give results as good as, if not better than, many conventional forecasts for existing products.

Use of new product forecasting

New product forecasting methods are often used beyond the immediate forecasting role. Because the forecasts are for a product that is not completely commercialized a low forecast can lead to the product being discontinued. Alternatively the result could indicate a product is not yet right for commercialization but development should 'go on' and the product tested again later. In this way new product forecasting is used to make go, no go, or go on decisions.

Another use of new product forecasting methods is experimentation. The speed and low cost of pre-test marketing or product use testing allow several products or packs to be evaluated. The expected sales of the alternatives are measured and used to guide the selection of the product to be launched. Leading manufacturers of fast moving consumer goods – such as General Foods or Procter and Gamble – often spend years test marketing a product before they are sure they have got it right and proceed with a national launch.

Diagnostic information is a final benefit of new product forecasting. Experimentation and the measures of awareness, trial and repeat rates allow the reasons for low sales to be identified. Table 8.1 shows how sales can be low because a company has failed to achieve either awareness, trial or repeat purchase. Raw sales figures would tell a company that a product was failing but offer no guide to corrective action. New product forecasting models can indicate why sales are down and what should be done about it.

Early prediction

Early prediction forecasting uses data from the early part of a product's life to forecast the ultimate sales level (Fourt and Woodcock, 1960). The sales figures are for the real market so there are no experimental problems, but basic questions of new product forecasting remain. What will be the cumulate penetration level of the product (p)? What will be the ultimate repeat purchase rate (r)? And what will be the buying rate (b)? If these are known the ultimate brand share is calculated from $s = prb$. The key to early prediction is estimating the ultimate penetration, repeat and buying rate before they are reached.

Reason and experience lead us to expect the patterns depicted in Figure 8.4. For most heavily promoted brands sales initially rise rapidly as trials are achieved and then asymptotically approach an ultimate level. After the first few periods' sales the shape of the cumulative penetration curve should become apparent and allow the penetration line to be projected visually or using trend analysis. Trend analysis is an approach using mathematical curve fitting that will be discussed in detail in Chapter 9.

Many market research agencies have established consumer panels that allow trial, repeat and buying rate to be tracked. These panels are groups of several thousand consumers who, every week or so, complete a diary listing their purchases. Where panels do not occur forecasters may be forced to rely on ad hoc surveys or commission a special panel for the duration of a launch. Alternatively, businesses who are not in mass markets may be able to use their own records to track sales.

The cumulative penetration curve (Figure 8.4a) applies particularly

Table 8.1

Reasons why sales are low, and solution

Awareness	Trial rate	Repeat rate	Problem	Action
High	High	High	Too much demand	De-market Subcontract
Low	High	High	People don't know it	Increase promotion Change media
High	Low	High	People don't like the sound of it	Reposition
High	High	Low	People can't buy it People don't like it People didn't get what they expected	Intensify distribution Reformulate Reposition
Low	Low	High	Promotional problems	Re-think promotions
Low	High	Low	High impulse purchase product	Maybe distribute widely to make a fast buck
High	Low	Low	Dud product	Try again
Low	Low	Low	?	Let someone else try

to brands in established markets, e.g. a new brand of toothpaste or soup. If a company is forecasting sales of a new product group such as occurred with colour TVs – or more recently with compact disk players – penetration may not be so quickly achieved. Cumulative penetration may follow the S-shaped curve traditionally associated with the early stages of the product life cycle. Innovation diffusion models have been used to forecast such markets successfully. These

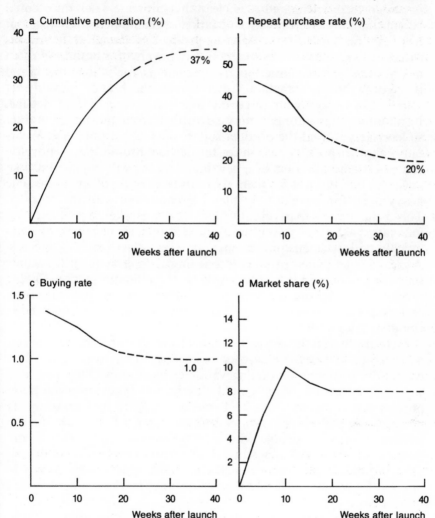

Figure 8.4   New product sales projection

are similar to the cumulative penetration part of the new product forecasting methods but do not attempt to represent repeat purchases. They are sometimes classed as new product forecasting models but they are more realistically grouped with the trend analysis techniques discussed in the next chapter.

Experience with new product launches leads one to expect repeat purchase rates and buying rates to decline with time. If the decline is not correctly estimated it is clear that ultimate sales rates could be substantially overestimated. Market segmentation and wear-out help explain the decline. After a product is launched it reaches successive segments of customers. Early buyers of a brand are often heavy users, or the largest market segments for whom the brand is a good choice. Sometimes after launch the brands may attract some lighter users who force the average buying rate to decline. In addition later adopters may be further from the target market so less likely to find the product suitable for repeat purchase. Wear-out is another possible reason for the decline. Promotion, or novelty, can easily generate triers of a new brand. Some will buy the product once and find it is not for them. Novelty may cause others to become heavy users for a while until they become bored with the product. This behaviour is particularly likely for a market segment called innovators who are adventurous buyers of new products but can quickly be lost as customers when an even newer product appears. A great danger of new product forecasting and marketing is to assume that the heavy user innovators will be the ultimate market for the product. By tracking the penetration, repeat and buying rate forecasters are able to project to their ultimate rates and forecast the resultant sales level.

It is paradoxical that early prediction forecasts rarely relate marketing activity to sales. Researchers who have tried to enhance their models by including marketing variables have found their forecasts were not improved. Why should this be so? Innovation adoption processes may be the reason. Evidence suggests that mass media do not have a direct effect on consumers but work through opinion leaders – these are people who rapidly assimilate information and because of their social position influence the opinions of others. Once a product has been launched and the spontaneous group of opinion leaders have started the ball rolling, marketing activity has little effect.

The position of early prediction forecasts in the new product process limits their use beyond forecasting. Tracking a new product's sales can provide diagnostic information but often not in enough time to do anything. Similarly, early prediction can give forecasts of ultimate sales levels but not in enough time to set the correct production capacity. Its major value is as a tracking tool for monitoring performance and providing medium term forecasts of the sales of new products.

Test marketing

Whereas early prediction uses early sales data to forecast sales, test marketing uses information from a large scale experiment in the market place. Often, if a test market is successful, a company can 'roll out' a product from the test area and so make a test market indistinguishable from a rolling national or global launch. The difference is intent – a test market takes place before a company is committed to a full launch.

The role of test marketing has changed over the years. Once test markets were used primarily to make go/no go decisions. If the forecast indicated the tested product would not make money, the product would not be launched. Now test markets are more often used diagnostically. They allow the whole marketing mix to be fine tuned before a national launch.

Test markets are the only test of the full marketing mix but they are very expensive and demanding of expertise. In designing a test market several critical decisions have to be made: What to test? What test areas? What duration of test? What information to gather?

What to test? Test markets provide forecasts for the whole marketing mix, not just the product. The simplest approach is to test launch a product and see what happens. Parts of the marketing mix may have been tested separately but they may not behave in the same way when combined in the market place. Consumer panels or ad hoc surveys can be used to track the performance of a product and see what, if anything, is wrong. Alternatively, a company may use several test areas to try an alternative marketing mix. The cost of test markets limits the number of tests that can be carried out but by using experimental designs several components can be changed simultaneously. The most advanced use of test marketing is the calibration of new product forecasting models that allow alternative marketing programmes to be simulated. Such models are complex so are usually only used in conjunction with agencies who have developed them e.g. SPECS from N. W. Ayer (Dodson, 1981), NEWS from BBDO (1971) or TRACKER (Blattberg and Golanty, 1978).

Choosing test areas is not trivial. No town, city or region is a microcosm of the nation as a whole. Often some towns thought to be particularly typical become very popular for test markets but by their frequent use they become untypical. Other areas may be chosen because they are not typical but they contain a high proportion of the target market, e.g. ethnic groups, income or age groups. If businesses desire to test using TV advertising it is likely that one of the smaller TV regions is chosen. They may be untypical of the country as a whole but a lot cheaper than testing in a larger area.

It is rare that only one test area is used. By using more than one the bias of individual areas can be reduced. Multiple tests also allow more marketing strategies to be tested. Costs increase with the number of areas but by conducting tests in sequence a small pilot plant can be used to supply all the markets.

The dynamics of penetration, repeat and buying rate show the importance of the duration of test decision. The product's average repeat purchase rate and the number of repeats before ultimate levels are reached dictate the length of test necessary. Prior knowledge of product group behaviour can give a test duration but the ideal may be longer than competitive pressures allow.

The information to be gathered depends upon the objectives of the test market. Usually factory shipments, store audits and consumer panels are monitored to provide forecasting data. The availability of established panels is often a reason for the selection of test areas. Ad hoc survey of retailers and consumers can also be used to locate any problems or marketing opportunities.

Test marketing is the only realistic experimental sales forecasting method but, as its detractors have often said, it has several problems. Schlackman Research point them out. Full test markets:

1 Are expensive to conduct given full scale production processes and advertising expenditure needed for the test situation.

2 Can take a considerable amount of time.

3 Offer opportunities for competitors' interference.

4 Can 'telegraph' future marketing strategy.

5 Are subject to a high failure rate (over 50 per cent of products fail in area tests or subsequent national roll out).

However, it should be remembered that the most vociferous critics of test marketing are those promoting alternative new product forecasting methods. Many excellent companies are intensive users of test marketing.

As a manager from Crown Zellerbuck, a competitor of P & G in some paper products said, 'P & G test and test and test. You can see them coming for months, often years. But you know when they get there, it is probably time for you to move to another niche, not to be in their way. They leave no stone unturned, no variable untested'.

Pre-test marketing

Pre-test marketing methods use simulated stores to gather information for new product forecasting. The demand for speedier new product development and advances in pre-test marketing technology is leading to their increased use as an addition to, or as an alternative to, full test marketing. James Figura, the corporate director of marketing of the health and beauty aids company Richardson-Vicks, gives a typical reaction to the new techniques. 'It was met with intense scepticism when first introduced, but a few companies invested in learning how well it worked. The result for them has been a significant acceleration of the new product process'.

Pre-test marketing services are sold by a number of market research agencies. Each has its own way of simulating the market although several use similar market models to forecast demand. To give an insight into pre-test marketing five leading services will be described. Table 8.2 is a brief summary. Each of the services has a method of choosing a sample of consumers, a way of simulating mass media advertising to create awareness, a simulated buying situation and a method of gauging repeat purchase.

SHARESCALE

SHARESCALE is offered by Mass Observation. The object is to discover as soon as a brand has passed its product test what market share it will achieve. To do this a panel of between 120 and 180 consumers representing the new brand's largest market are recruited. In groups of 10–15 they are then invited to a hotel where the exercise is explained and they meet the interviewer who will be looking after them. They are then shown the test brand, its advertising and the

Table 8.2
Pre-test marketing

Company	Sample	Awareness	Trial	Repeat
Mass observation	120–180 chosen	Hotel display + TV adverts	From catalogue	From catalogue
Schlackman Research	50–100 chosen	Video	Simulated shelf	In home interviews
RBL	500 housewives	In store magazine	Mobile store	Mobile store
INBUCON	50 chosen	Video	Simulated supermarket	Intention to buy survey
TNA	300–500 outside stores	Direct mail 'tip ins'	10–20 major outlets	Diary

advertising for its competitors. The interviewers then ask if they may shop for them in the production field for between 10 or 20 weeks, depending on the purchase frequency of the product. Mass Observation claim most consumers agree to cooperate and stay in the panel throughout the experiment.

Every week or fortnight the interviewer then goes to a supermarket, finds out current prices for every size and brand in the product field, including special offers, and marks the catalogue accordingly. The catalogue is then shown to the consumers in their home and orders are taken. Next day the goods are delivered and paid for by the respondent. The test product comes from special stocks, the rest are bought from supermarkets. The process is repeated about a dozen times to check repeat purchase rate.

At the end of the test brand share is forecast using the original Parfitt–Collins model (1968). Diagnostic information is obtained by interviewing respondents singly or in groups and asking about their reaction to the product and advertising.

SHARESCALE is the most unrealistic of the pre-test marketing methods described here. Consumers are obviously very aware of their participation in an experiment. It is 'leaky' so panelists may top up their purchases outside the periodic meetings or make impulse purchases while on their normal shopping trips. Nevertheless the service offers a great degree of flexibility in the choice of target customers and diagnostic interviewing.

The method can be described as a 'sales wave' technique. Its focus is on repeat purchase (sales waves) rather than the realistic representations of an initial purchase situation. Whereas other pre-test marketing methods usually track one or two repeat purchases, SHARESCALE follows around a dozen waves.

PREDICTOR

PREDICTOR is offered by Schlackman Research. Technically it is an enhanced version of ASSESSOR (Silk and Urban, 1978). It has central location interviews for the original contact followed by in-home interviews to measure repeat purchase waves.

Respondents are recruited near the central location and screened on demographics and product group usage. They are then taken to the central location where they are interviewed to find their brand awareness and preference. After being shown a video of adverts for the test brand and competition, the respondents are given a cash voucher which they can trade for products displayed on a simulated supermarket shelf. A free gift is given to them all and a free sample of the test product is given to those who did not choose it.

In-home interviews are used to access repeat purchase. After they have had chance to use the product, interviewers visit the respondents' home and again check awareness and preference. Prompted by a photographic display with realistic pricing the consumer is given an opportunity for repurchase using their own money. Where necessary in-home purchases may be repeated. Finally the trial impressions of the brand are elicited.

PREDICTOR has the great advantage of being based on ASSESSOR – probably the most widely accepted and validated pre-test marketing system (Urban and Katz, 1983). In addition PREDICTOR has tried to correct for the lack of diagnostics which were a disadvantage of the earlier model. Like SHARESCALE it provides a very flexible pre-test marketing facility but at the expense of being an unrealistic and obvious experiment.

RBL

RBL mini-test market differs from the other services in monitoring sales using a fleet of mobile self-service stores that visit a fixed panel of 500 housewives in two major cities at about the same time every week.

Panel members are not aware that they are on a panel, merely that they are members of a 'shopping club'. Test products are promoted in a number of ways. The main one is RBL's own free magazine which carries realistic press advertising. In-store promotions can also be provided using posters, audio commercials or demonstrations. Below the line support can also be simulated.

Test products are sold in the mobile stores alongside about 1,500 other grocery products, including own brands. Panel members make their purchases in the normal way but use a membership card to gain access to the store and to identify themselves at the check out. Individual customer sales and repeat purchases are tracked using an automatic cash register and data capture machine. Cumulative penetration, repeat buying and average purchase quantity are recorded and used to forecast demand using Parfitt–Collins' method.

RBL's pre-test marketing facility is very sophisticated. It is secure and offers a realistic shopping environment. In addition it can provide detailed shopping information on a large panel who are unaware they are participating in an experiment. In this respect the panel is better than the usual consumer panelist who has to complete a diary.

The rigidity of the panel and the shopping habits the mobile stores demand is a major limitation of the techniques. The panel is a segment of shoppers who are willing and able to use mobile shops. The system does not allow shoppers who do not fit into this class to be included.

Another limitation is forced by the need to retain a pretence of reality. Other pre-test markets provide diagnostic information by post-purchase interviewing. Since RBL use a permanent panel this cannot be done without sacrificing their advantage of realism.

The diagnostic limitations of RBL mini-test markets can be overcome using Research International SENSOR. The company offer a range of services ranging from concept testing, through SENSOR mix research which uses a process very similar to PREDICTOR mini-test markets.

INBUCON

INBUCON's laboratory test market (LTM) is based on the LTM estimation procedure of Yankelovich, Skelly and White Inc. (1981). Their first facility in Perivale, Middlesex, UK is typical of those now available in other parts of the world. It contains a small supermarket where products are sold to customers, a theatre–auditorium where customers can be exposed to promotional material, rooms for interviewing customers after their purchases and telephone facilities for after-use interviewing.

Typically a new panel of 50 people are recruited and paid a small amount for participating in a survey. After screening and completing a background questionnaire providing demographic, behavioural and attitudinal data they are taken to the theatre–auditorium where they are shown a 30-minute television show interspersed with commercials including the test brand.

In small batches they are then taken to the appropriate section of the simulated store where they indicate the product they would like to buy. Purchases are encouraged by all products being offered at a 20 per cent discount. To avoid influencing other respondents products are not taken from shelves but given to them after the store session.

After making their purchases, respondents complete a post-purchase questionnaire or are involved in motivational research interviews or group discussions. They are finally told that they will be contacted again once they have had a chance to try the test product.

After some time has elapsed they are re-interviewed by telephone or in person to determine the reaction of the family to the product. Those who intend to rebuy the product can be given an opportunity to purchase at the full retail price. Repeat calls can be carried out to determine usage and repurchase over a period of time.

INBUCON's simulated supermarket and RBL's mobile stores offer an interesting contrast. Both offer a realistic shopping environment for first purchases but there the similarity ends. RBL gain by not appearing to be an experiment but lose because of the loss of diagnostics that the pretence demands. They do, however, offer a very good record of customers' buying history and repeat purchase. INBUCON gain on the quality of their diagnostics and flexibility in the sample drawn. Customers may not be aware which product is being tested but the overall buying situation is far from realistic.

TNA

TNA use real retail outlets to provide information for sales forecasts using Parfitt–Collins' model.

For each test between 10 and 20 retail outlets are selected to take a new product for a trial period. The number and location vary depending upon the requirements of the client. The retail outlets all use a common merchandising policy.

For the trial a sample of between 300 and 500 customers from the defined target market are recruited from directly outside the stores in question. The panellists are required to maintain a diary across all purchases including one containing the test brand.

While the test is on, the respondents can be exposed to special promotions, such as direct mail or money-off coupons. Additionally, advertising can be simulated by 'tip-in' advertisements which IPC can place in some of its weeklies.

After a four-week 'run-in' period the test product is introduced to the store. Total store sales are recorded but the panel provide the necessary information for tracking penetration, repeat purchase and usage. Usually the experiment runs for five or six purchasing cycles so that the ultimate sales rate can be estimated.

Apart from the initial recruitment and diary, TNA's mini-test markets are very realistic. Shoppers use their store over the whole experiment. In addition detailed diagnostic information can be obtained from the diary or interviews. There are, however, two main problems. Like full test markets the system is not secure; competitors can observe and damage experiments. Also the methods need enough of the test product to stock the stores being used. Many other customers will buy the product besides the panel. This contrasts with other services where sales are restricted.

Product-use testing

Product-use testing (Crawford, 1983) gauges consumers' reactions to a product without attempting to simulate market conditions. Typically respondents are given a sample of a product to use and are questioned about their attitude towards it. A forecast of likely demand can be obtained by asking the respondents their intention to buy the product or offering them the chance to obtain further samples. In product testing a distinction should be drawn between alpha testing where a product is tested by a manufacturer's employees, and beta testing where potential customers test products in their own home, factory or office. Many products have been known to work perfectly in-house but fail completely in a realistic setting.

Product-use testing is less expensive and complex than pre-test marketing and there are many ways it can be used. There is no attempt to represent market conditions but respondents can be sent samples by mail or given the product after a personal interview. usually the 'halo' effect of source is removed by conducting blind tests where the minimum of packaging decoration is used. Packs are usualy plain except for an identity mark and usage instructions – just like the famous brand X. Often the relative merit of a new product is tested by asking customers to compare the new product with existing brands. When this is done it is necessary to present the alternatives anonymously and use identity marks that do not give a systematic bias – a problem usually overcome by randomizing identity marks. After use respondents are questioned about their preference for the test brand and may be given the opportunity for repeated use. Once usage trials are over the identity of the manufacturer may be revealed and users again asked about the product.

The main application of product-use testing is to check the formulation of new products and provide diagnostic information to allow ideas to be refined. However, by asking about intentions to buy and tracking reported use against competitive products the results can be used to make forecasts of repeat purchase and usage rates.

Concept testing

Concept testing (Moore, 1982) is used to estimate customers' reaction to a product idea early in product development. It is often conducted before any samples of a product exist but the trend is towards obtaining customers' opinions using cheaply and quickly made prototypes.

Typically customers are shown a simple description of a concept sometimes accompanied by a line drawing showing the product in use. Respondents are then asked a series of questions. The primary question is usually 'intention to purchase'. This is often followed by questions used to check respondents understood the concept. Finally diagnostic and classifications are asked. If samples are available, product-use tests can be tried with consumers who responded positively to a concept.

It is rare that a company gets a concept right the first time. Often a series of concept tests will take place with the first few used to refine the concept statement or generate more ideas.

Opinion is split over whether 'bland' concepts should be presented. 'Promotional' concepts are more realistic but opponents argue, first that they want a reaction to a pure concept; second that personal experience has found relatively small difference between 'bland' and 'promotional' concepts; and third, that it is impossible to tell whether the consumer is responding to the concept, positioning or copy. Tests show that concepts presented promotionally will outperform bland concepts but the results are monotonic – that is, in comparative tests the same winners appear independent of the type of test. Preferences vary but users agree that care should be taken in the preparation of promotional concepts. Not only does the use of promotion change acceptability of a concept, but the success also depends on the copy used. As a general rule concept writers should use the minimum amount of sell required and concepts to be compared should be described by the same writer.

CONCLUSIONS

New product forecasting is a series of techniques that tracks customer behaviour in order to produce early forecasts of new product sales. Usually the trial rate, repeat purchase rate and usage rate of products are measured in order to compute sales using a mathematical model. The last few years have seen a rapid development in new product forecasting technology. There is now an almost continuous spectrum of techniques that cover all stages of the product development process. The range stretches from concept tests, that can be used to forecast likely product sales before a product exists, to early prediction methods, for soon after the full launch of a product.

Competitive pressures are leading to more extensive and earlier new product forecasting. The major development is pre-test marketing which is less expensive, quicker and more secure than conventional test markets. They sacrifice reality, but gain in flexibility and control they give to forecasters. Test marketing is still used more widely than pre-test marketing, but the shift to the earlier methods is being led by such inveterate test marketers as P & G as they try to reduce their typical product development time from eight to four years. A striking case of the advantages of pre-test marketing is provided by Van den Berghs. While Kraft were test marketing Carousel margarine Van den Bergh were able to sample and test them for competitive effect using RBL's mini-test market service. They were quickly able to forecast the product would not be a major threat because of low repeat purchase rates. It is likely they had accurate results even before Kraft did.

A reason for the shift to earlier new product forecasting is the accuracy that users claim to have found. The most widely publicized results are those for ASSESSOR which is very similar to Research International's SENSOR and PREDICTOR by Schlackman Research. In a retrospective study of 74 products tested 63 per cent of those classified as definitely or probably GO by ASSESSOR were successful in test markets. The figure can be compared with A.C. Nielsen's study which concluded that the average success rate of test market products was 35.5 per cent.

It is to be expected that concept tests are less accurate forecasting tools than other methods. Their lack of predictive power can be attributed to: products failing to deliver the benefits tested; changes in the concept tested; and changes in the environment. However, empirical evidence on concept testing is encouraging. Companies conducting concept tests just before launch have found about 80 per cent of their forecasts to be accurate. Others talk of results so good as to be 'uncanny' or 'scary'.

New product forecasting methods are most widely used by the fast moving consumer goods businesses. They were developed there and based on buyer behaviour found in the industry. They do, however, have potential for use in other sectors. Concept testing and product-use testing can be used with almost any product. In many cases the forecasting task is less difficult than that facing fast moving consumer good manufacturers. Most products do not take off so quickly and do not have the complication of repeat purchase and usage rates. The problem reduces to measuring cumulative penetration over a long period. In such cases the trend analysis techniques of the next chapter can be used to advantage.

FURTHER READING

BBDO, *The Theoretical Basis of NEWS*, New York, BBDO, Management Science Department, 1971.

Blattberg, R. and Golanty, J., 'TRACKER: An Early Test-Marketing Forecasting and Diagnostic Model for New Product Planning', *Journal of Marketing Research*, vol. 15, May 1978, pp. 192–202.

Claycamp, H. J. and Liddy, L. E., 'Prediction of New Product Performance: an Analytical Approach', *Journal of Marketing Research*, vol. 6, 1969, pp. 414–20.

Crawford, C. M., *New Product Management*, Homewood, Ill, Irwin, 1983.

Dodson, J. A., 'Application and Utilization of Test-Market-Based New-Product Forecasting Models', in Wind, Y., Mahajan, V. and Cardozo, R. N., *New-Product Forecasting*, Lexington, Mass, Lexington Books, 1981.

Fourt, L. A. and Woodcock, J. W., 'Early Prediction of Marketing Success Grocery Products', *Journal of Marketing*, vol. 25, 1960, pp. 31–38.

Moore, W. L., 'Concept Testing', *Journal of Business Research*, vol. 10, 1982, pp. 279–294.

Parfitt, J. and Collins, B., 'The Use of Consumer Panels for Brand Share Prediction', *Journal of Marketing Research*, vol. 5, 1968, pp. 131–45.

Silk, A. J. and Urban, G. L., 'Pre-Test Market Evaluation of New

Packaged Goods: a Model and Measurement Methodology', *Journal of Marketing Research,* vol. 15, May 1978, pp. 171–91.

Urban, G. L. and Katz, G., 'Pre-test Market Models: Validation and Managerial Implications', *Journal of Marketing Research,* vol. 20, 1983, pp. 21–34.

Wind, Y., Mahajan, V. and Cardozo, R. N., *New Product Forecasting,* Lexington, Mass, Lexington Books, 1981.

Yankelovich, Skelly and White, Inc., 'LTM Estimating Procedures' in Wind, Y., Mahajan, V. and Cardozo, R. N., *New-Product Forecasting,* Lexington, Mass, Lexington Books, 1981.

9 Trend analysis

Trend analysis is the most widely used and abused method of strategic forecasting. It is popular because it is quick and easy to use. Abuse occurs when it is employed thoughtlessly to give results that appear to be statistically reliable but are, in fact, naive.

The approach generally uses regression analysis to find a curve of best fit through time series data (Chapter 5). Figure 9.1 is a typical case where the objective is to use the sales history from 1980 to 1984 to produce a forecast for 1985 and 1986. Table 9.1 contains the data.

Table 9.1
VCR sales forecast using quadratic trend analysis

Year	History*	Sales (1,000,000 units) Forecast	Lower	Upper
			95% limit	95% limit
1980	0.5	0.44	−0.07	0.95
1981	1.5	1.64	1.31	1.97
1982	3.2	3.14	2.76	3.52
1983	5.0	4.94	4.61	5.27
1984	7.0	7.04	6.53	7.55
1985	−	9.44	8.27	10.61
1986	−	12.14	9.98	14.30

*Source: The Economist, 'Television' (5 February 1983), p. 35.

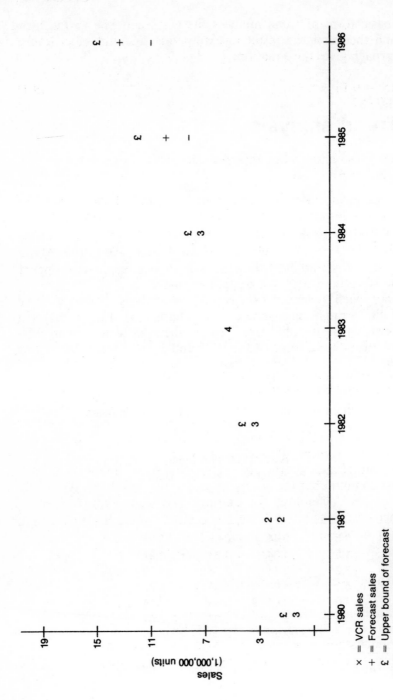

Figure 9.1 VCR sales forecast using quadratic trend analysis

× = VCR sales
+ = Forecast sales
3 = Upper bound of forecast
— = Lower bound of forecast
2,3,4 = Multiple points where 2, 3 or 4 points coincide

The basic form of trend analysis fits a straight line to the time series and then uses the result to extrapolate to future sales levels. The approach gives the equation:

$$VCRS = 0.14 + 1.65*T \qquad (9.1)$$
$$R^2 = 0.987$$

where

$VCRS$ = estimated video tape recorder sales in year Y.
$T = Y - 1980$.

The R^2 value indicates a reasonably good fit but the validity of the result is questionable since it fits a straight line to a series that curves upwards. A quadratic expectation can be used to produce a better shape. It allows regression analysis to produce an equation with a better fit and shape:

$$VCRS = 0.44 + 1.05*T + 0.15*T^2 \qquad (9.2)$$
$$R^2 = 0.999$$

Substituting $T = 5$, for 1985 and $T = 6$, for 1986 in (9.2) produces the sales forecasts in Table and Figure 9.1. The results also show the upper and lower limits (95 per cent) of the estimate – figures that are a useful by-product of regression analysis.

Typically time series analysis uses several years of data to forecast up to three years hence. However, as will be shown later, there are occasions when just a few years of data can provide enough information to forecast decades ahead.

There are several useful applications of trend analysis. Sales is the most common but the adoption rate of new products, the substitution of one technology for another and technology forecasting are other areas where trend analysis is effective. All the applications will be described later.

ADVANTAGES AND DISADVANTAGES

Trend analysis inherits several advantages from regression analysis. It is relatively quick and easy to use and, because it is based on a well understood technique, it provides statistical measures of the reliability and validity of the results. Two such measures are the

R^2 statistics and confidence limits of the forecast that were used in the introduction. Although they are not discussed in this chapter, the statistics used to examine regression analyses (Chapters 5 and 6) can also be used to validate trend analyses. The availability of validation statistics contrast with arbitrary time series analysis (Chapter 3) where fewer measures are available.

Using transformations trend analysis can produce forecasts from data showing a range of patterns, for example, straight line progressions, exponential growth, S-shaped curves or patterns that show a gradual approach to a saturation level. Those available within ORION are described and illustrated in Table 9.2 and Figure 9.2. It will be noticed that some expressions can take up different patterns depending on the estimated coefficients. Unfortunately the benefit of being able to fit almost any shape to a curve can also be a disadvantage. When fitting a chosen curve to data regression analysis can produce a trend line that gives stupid results. Such errors can be compounded by the 'scientific look' that validation statistics can give.

Table 9.2
Trend expressions and characteristics

No. Curve	Equation[1]	L	R	D	E	S	SL	SS
					Characteristics[2]			
1 Linear	$S = a + bT$	√						
2 Constrained hyperbola	$S = T/(a + bT)$						√	
3 Exponential	$S = ae^{bT}$		√		√			
4 Log-log	$S = aT^b$		√	√	√			
5 Semi-log	$S = a + b\log(T)$			√				
6 Modified exponential	$S = ae^{b/T}$						√	
7 Hyperbola	$S = a + b/T$					√		
8 Modified hyperbola	$S = 1/(a + bT)$	√						
9 Quadratic	$S = a + bT + cT^2$							√
10 Log quadratic	$S = e^{(a + bT + cT^2)}$				√			√
11 Gompertz[3]	$S = ab^{cT}$				√	√		

[1] $S =$ dependent variable, usually sales	[2] $L =$ Linear
	$R =$ Reducing
	$D =$ Decaying
$T =$ time	$E =$ Exponential
$e =$ universal constant	$S =$ S-shaped
(2.718)	$SL =$ Saturating to a limit
$a,b,c =$ coefficients to be found using regression analysis	$SS =$ Supersaturating

[3]Not linear so cannot be estimated using regression analysis

Although trend analysis can look sophisticated it retains the major limitation of all time series analyses — it examines the patterns of historic data and makes a forecast by assuming the patterns will continue into the future. Trend analysis is often used for medium to long range forecasting where past sales contained no clue that major changes may be about to occur. The bland use of long range time series analysis can be very dangerous indeed unless overlaid with a subjective assessment of alternative futures. Trend analysis also retains the truncation problem of moving average forecasting and gives equal weights to all data. This can be problematical if there is a sudden change at the end of a series. Regression analysis will try to fit a curve to all the data so a forecast may pay little attention to new and important variations. There are no rules to suggest how many data points should be used so trial and error must predominate.

Trend analysis is limited by its reliance on the extrapolation of historic patterns to produce forecasts. It may sometimes look nice to use because it appears to produce strategic forecasts almost automatically, but the view is mistaken. Thoughtlessly produced forecasts may be accurate for most of the time but they are prone to major errors because of environment changes or the vagaries of regression analysis. Curve fitting methods should not be used blindly. Forecasters should choose the shape of the curve to be projected before using analytical methods to find the best fit. Finally, trend analysis should always be used in conjunction with subjective forecasting. Methods that depend on historic data cannot be expected to identify the weak signals that precede major changes in markets or technology.

FIT AND SHAPE

Trend analysis is best viewed as a three-part process. The first part

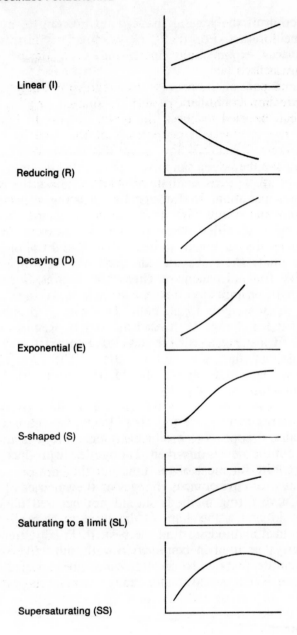

Linear (I)

Reducing (R)

Decaying (D)

Exponential (E)

S-shaped (S)

Saturating to a limit (SL)

Supersaturating (SS)

Figure 9.2   Typical trend patterns

is the selection of the general shape or expression to represent the trend to be forecast. For the *VCR* example the historic pattern, or shape, was exponentially increasing so a flexible quadratic expression was used.

The second part of the process uses regression analysis to fit the chosen expression to a historic pattern. *R*-squared, or other validation statistics, can be used to check the quality of the fit but the most important test is a visual comparison of the time series and the forecast. Figure 9.3 shows how equations can have a satisfactory fit but still have the wrong shape.

The final stage of trend analysis produces a forecast by extrapolating the trend equation. It is dangerous to collapse parts one and two of trend analysis. ORION can automatically fit ten curves to a data series; Table 9.2 contains details of the expressions and the shapes they produced. When applied to the *VCR* series the automatic process produces the equations on Table 9.3. It should be noted that the first four all produce a reasonable fit but do not produce the same shape or long term forecasts (Figure 9.3).

Table 9.3
Automatic fit of VCR sales series

Curve No.	R-squared	Equation
9	.999	$VCRS = .44 + 1.05^*T + .15^*T^2$
10	.999	$VCRS = EXP(-.67249 + 1.1727^*T - .13112^*T^2)$
1	.987	$VCRS = .14 + 1.65^*T$
3	.945	$VCRS = .66348^*EXP(.64821^*T)$
8	.730	$VCRS = 1/(1.5006 - .4181^*T)$

Curves 9 and 3 both increase exponentially but the latter is at such a rapid rate that it produces a forecast of over 30,000,000 units in 1986 – more than one per household in the UK. Curve 1 is a straight line – a forecast that has already been disregarded. Unfortunately, the two curves with the best fit give the most contrasting forecasts. While curve 9 suggests a reasonable exponential increase, curve 10 forecasts declining sales after 1984.

The results show the danger of collapsing the shape and curve fitting parts of trend analysis. Curve fitting should be attempted

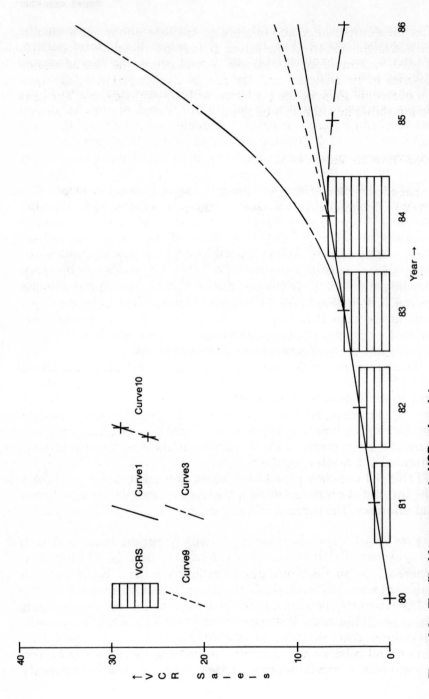

Figure 9.3 The fit of four curves to VCR sales data

after the desired shape and expression has been chosen. If in doubt, use a straight line to fit the series. It may be obviously wrong, but at least its limitations are known. Alternatively the careful choice of series to be analysed and the use of constrained trend analysis càn overcome some of the problems with wayward curves. The next section shows how this can be done.

CONSTRAINED TREND ANALYSIS

S-shaped time series, or curves that saturate to an upper limit, are particularly suited to time series analysis. In technology and sales forecasting there is often an upper limit beyond which performance or sales can never go. Take, for example, the motor car engine. There is a theoretical limit to the thermal efficiency that the internal combustion engine can ever achieve, so it is expected gains from spending on R and D would decline as the theoretical limit is approached. Similarly, for VCR sales, there is obviously some upper limit to the sales that can be made. By taking into account these rational or practical constraints the quality and reliability of trend analysis can be significantly increased.

When forecasting the potential of a new product group, like a VCR, it is easier and more reliable to forecast penetration rather than sales. This is because penetration always follows a particular type of curve that has an upper limit. For domestic appliances the absolute upper limit must be 100 per cent of households although there are some goods, such as tumble driers, that appear to have saturated at a much lower level.

Table 9.4 contains penetration figures and a forecast for VCRs. The forecast is produced using a Gompertz curve which is S-shaped and saturates. The expression has the form

$$Y = a_0 * a_1^{a_2^t} \tag{9.3}$$

Where a_0, a_1 and a_2 are parameters and t is time. After solution a_0 is the saturation level, and $a_0 * a_1$ is the Y value when $t = 0$.

Unfortunately (9.3) is not linear so has to be solved using non-linear estimation techniques rather than regression. These are iterative procedures that use rules to guide the search for the coefficients that would otherwise be estimated using regression analysis. There is a wide range of procedures but they are not all robust. Fortunately, many forecasting packages automatically use one of the more reliable methods whenever non-linear estimation is necessary.

Table 9.4
Penetration of VCRs: % of households

Year	Penetration (%)*	Forecast (%)	Change (%)
1980	2.50	2.49	2.49
1981	7.50	7.61	5.12
1982	15.90	15.69	8.08
1983	24.90	25.07	9.38
1984	34.00	33.95	8.88
1985	–	41.31	7.36
1986	–	46.91	5.60

*Source: The Economist, 'Television' (5 February 1983), p. 35.

The Gompertz equation for the VCR penetration series (see Figure 9.4) is:

$$VCRP = 59.231 * 0.042043^{0.64738^T} \tag{9.4}$$

where T = the year $-$ 1980.

This suggests a saturation level of penetration to be 59 per cent of households. It is interesting to note that, like the curve 10 forecast for sales, the result shows the market declining after 1984. As an alternative to using non-linear estimation (9.3) can be solved using regression analysis if a saturation level (a_0) is assumed. Then the equation becomes:

$$z = a_1^{a_2^t} \tag{9.5}$$

where $z = Y/a_0$.

Taking logs twice gives:

$$\log(\log z) = \log(\log a_1) + t.\log a_2 \tag{9.6}$$

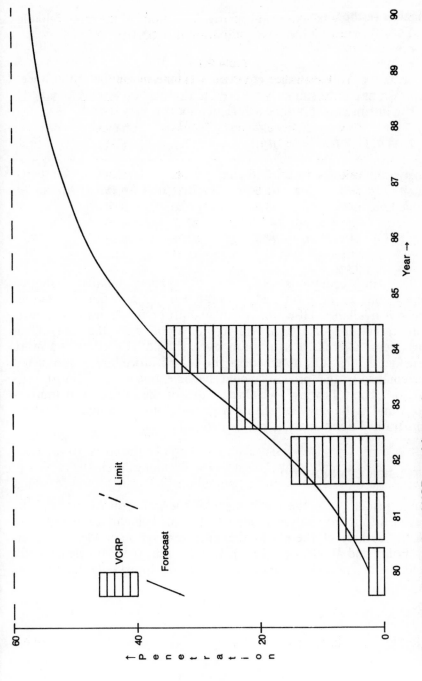

Figure 9.4 Penetration of VCRs and forecast

which is of the form:

$$Y = a + bx \tag{9.7}$$

so can be solved using regression analysis. Other non-linear expressions can be similarly reduced if a saturation level is assumed. The intrinsically non-linear logistic model is very useful:

$$Y = a_0/(1 + \exp[a_1 + a_2 t]) \tag{9.8}$$

This produces a saturating S-shape very similar to the Gompertz curve. Again a_0 is the saturation level. If it is known (9.8) can be made linear as

$$\log[(1 - z)/z] = a_1 + a_2 t \tag{9.9}$$

where $z = Y/a_0$.

The transformations (9.6) and (9.9) allow reliable S-shaped expressions to be estimated if non-linear optimization techniques are not available. However, if an inappropriate saturation level is chosen the transformations will provide a poor fit to the data. When this occurs alternative saturation levels should be tried until a more satisfactory result is obtained. If the search procedure is conducted systematically the process would become one of non-linear estimation. The following specialized cases of the diffusion of innovations and technology substitution provide other examples of where constrained trend analysis can be profitably used.

DIFFUSION OF INNOVATIONS

Some insights into the mechanism of the diffusion of innovations have led to trend analysis models with some behavioural detail. One of the earliest of these was the pure innovation model proposed by Fourt and Woodcock (1960). It holds that the extra penetration achieved in a period is proportional to the untapped potential remaining.

$$Q_t = r\bar{Q}(1 - r)^{t-1} \tag{9.10}$$

where

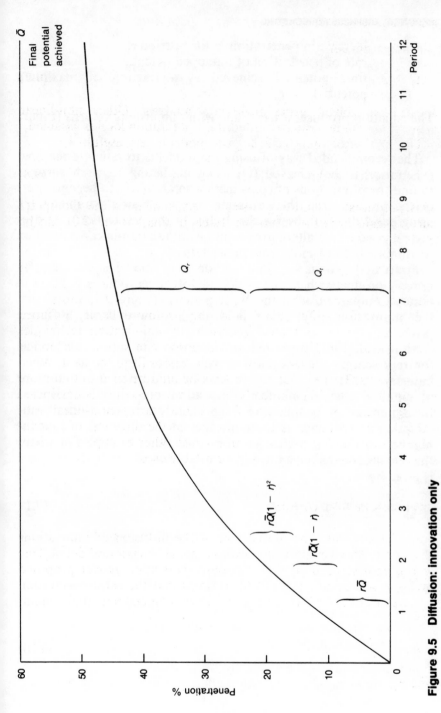

Figure 9.5 Diffusion: innovation only

Q_t = increase in penetration in time period t;
r = rate of penetration of untapped potential;
$\bar{Q}$ = final potential achieved as a fraction of maximum potential.

The equation produces a trend line with diminishing returns (Figure 9.5).

The recommended way of using the model is to estimate the final penetration to be achieved ($\bar{Q}$) using marketing research surveys, to find the proportions of consumers who are likely to become users of the product, and then estimate the penetration parameter (r), using panel data to observe the decline in the penetration rate over several periods. An alternative would be to use non-linear estimation to estimate both Q and r from panel data.

Fourt and Woodcock's 'innovation only' model is designed for grocery products where the rapid take-off it reproduces is likely to occur. Comparison with the VCR pattern (Figure 9.4) shows that the 'innovation only' shape is wrong for more slowly diffusing products.

Mansfield (1961) suggested an alternative 'imitation only' model for representing the adoption of new technology or products by industry. It assumes that the process of innovation is actually one of imitation where the number of new adopters in a period is dictated by a number of people who have already adopted. Initially the adoption rate is slow as there are few adopters to imitate. As the number of users increases so does the adoption rate. Eventually the rate declines as the untapped potential diminishes. The behaviour is given by:

$$Q_t = p(\bar{Q} - Q_T) \quad Q_T/\bar{Q} \tag{9.11}$$

untapped   relative number of adopters available
potential   to be imitated

where

Q_t = increase in penetration in time period t;
Q_T = the cumulative number of adopters to date;
p = the imitation rate.

Again forecasts can be made by using the first few observations to estimate p and Q by regression analysis and then using the model to project future sales.

The 'innovation only' and 'imitation only' models were combined by Bass (1969) to produce a new product growth model for consumer durables.

$$Q_t = r(\bar{Q} - Q_T) + p(\bar{Q} - Q_T)Q_T/\bar{Q} \qquad (9.12)$$

    innovation   imitation
    effect   effect

This makes the realistic assumption that some individuals make their adoption decision independently (innovators) while others (imitators) are influenced by the number of people who have already adopted. The shape of the cumulative penetration curve depends upon the relative magnitudes of the innovation rate (r) and the imitation rate (p). If $r < p$ the penetration curve will decay continuously as in Figure 9.5. However, if $r > p$ an S-shaped curve will occur.

Once sufficient data have been collected (9.12) can be estimated using regression analysis. Rearranging (9.12) it becomes:

$$Q_t = r\bar{Q} + (p - r)Q_T - (p/\bar{Q})Q_T^2 \qquad \text{or} \qquad (9.13)$$
$$Q_t = a + bQ_T + cQ_T^2 \qquad (9.14)$$

which can be solved by regressing Q_t on Q_T and Q_T^2. Alternatively, once three periods data have been collected, (9.14) can be solved exactly as three simultaneous equations.

Bass notes that because the three coefficients of (9.14) are not independent estimates, and therefore the derived values for r, p and $\bar{Q}$, are biased and should be corrected to:

$$r' = [0.97r]/[1 + 0.4(1 + g)r]$$
$$p' = [0.97r]/[1 + 0.4(1 + 4g)p]$$
$$\bar{Q}' = [\bar{Q}]/[0.98 - 0.4(p + r)]$$

where $g = p/r$.

The diffusion equations are a useful variation on conventional trend analysis. Unlike other time series methods, they are based on hypotheses about consumer behaviour. Actual diffusion processes are obviously far more complex than the simple dichotomy into innovators and imitators suggests but the resulting equations are robust and can produce reliable forecasts.

There have been attempts to produce more sophisticated diffusion models by adding extra dimensions but these have met with limited success. Most add the effect of one or two marketing variables (usually advertising and promotion) but there is no unified theory of how to incorporate marketing or exogenous variables. The few comparisons that have been made tend to show that the extra sophistication offers little improvement over the simple models. A major limitation of the more sophisticated models is their need to be estimated early in a product's life when little data are available.

Technology substitution

Technology substitution is a special case of the diffusion of innovation that occurs when a new technology is replaced by an old one; for example, the substitution of air for sea/rail travel, or the replacement of conventional 'black' albums by pre-recorded tapes or compact disks. Substitution can be forecast in the same way as conventional diffusion processes but the very neat method devised by Fisher and Pry (1978) make it well worth covering separately.

The Fisher–Pry process will be followed for a series showing the change in the per capita consumption of margarine and butter in the USA (Figure 9.6).

Using an alternative representation the imitation only model of diffusion (9.11) becomes:

$$df/dt = b(1 - f)f \qquad (9.15)$$

where

f = the fraction of the market having adopted the new technology ($Q_T/\bar{Q}$),
b = growth constant for a particular technology ($p\bar{Q}$),
df/dt = the rate of change of the fraction adopting (Q_t).

When (9.15) is integrated it produces the logistic expression

$$f = 1/(1 + e^{b(t - t_0)}) \qquad (9.16)$$

So, the imitation diffusion model (9.11), the logistic model (9.8) and Fisher–Pry's substitution model are, in fact, very similar. Fisher–Pry's trick is to manipulate (9.16) so that it can be rewritten as:

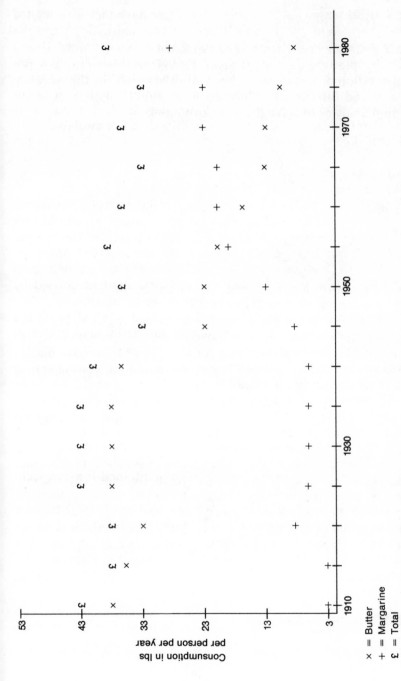

x = Butter
+ = Margarine
З = Total

Source: National Research Council, USA

Figure 9.6   Trends in US butter and margarine consumption

Consumption in lbs
per person per year

$$f/(1 - f) = e^{d+bt} \qquad\qquad (9.17)$$

where d and b are coefficients to be estimated.

Then by plotting $f/(1 - f)$ against t on semi-log graph paper the substitution process approaches a straight trend line that is easily visualized and forecast. The forecast in Figure 9.7 was made using regression analysis to solve the transformation:

$$F = d + bt \qquad\qquad (9.18)$$

where $F = \log_e f/(1 - f)$

The result:

$$F = -0.261 + 0.284\ t \qquad\qquad (9.19)$$
$$r^2 = 0.928$$

shows the proportion of margarine consumed continuing to increase from 81 per cent in 1985 to 91 per cent by 1995.

The Fisher–Pry method is a simple way of looking at a very complex process. Over the decades covered by the substitution economic, trade and health reasons for the change must have undergone many changes. An attempt to causally model the change would have to find some way for representing all the mechanisms involved. Like the other trend analysis methods, the Fisher–Pry approach observes the aggregate effect of all the influences and assumes that together they will produce the same pattern of substitution in the future as they did in the past. However, sometimes one of the major influences does undergo a major change and effect the rate of substitution. The substitution of colour televisions for monochrome sets in the UK is a case in point (Figure 9.8). The change coincided with a major oil crisis, whose ensuing recession may have changed consumers speed of upgrading to colour once and for all. Such shifts can render early substitution forecast inaccurate but the television case is typical in following a second steady straight line once the perturbation is over.

TECHNOLOGY TREND ANALYSIS

Technology trend analysis seeks to forecast changes in technological

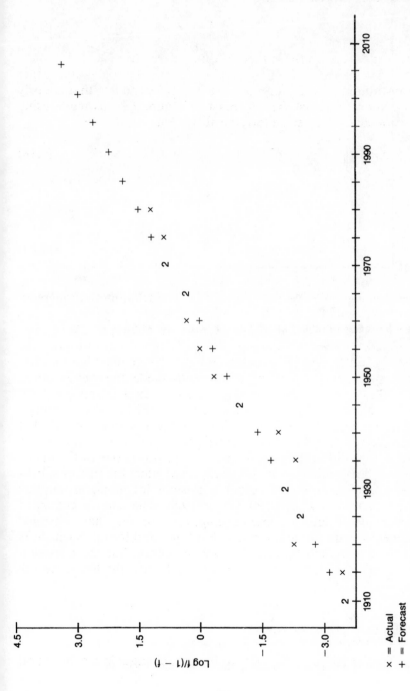

Figure 9.7 Fisher–Pry substitution

x = Actual
+ = Forecast

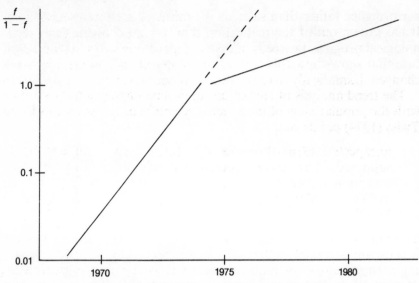

Source: Twiss, B., *Forecasting Market Size and Market Growth Rates for New Products,* Elsevier Science Publications, North Holland, 1984.

Figure 9.8   Substitution colour TVs for black and white in the UK

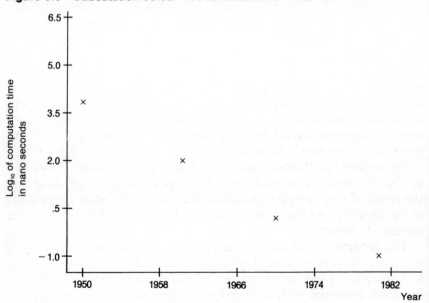

Source: *The Economist,* Science and Technology Brief (3 April 1982), p. 129.

Figure 9.9   The decrease in computation time for computers

performance rather than sales or the diffusion of a new technology. It has grown out of the realization that, for most of the time, technological progress proceeds at a steady pace. Figure 9.9 is a modern case that shows how this is true for computational speeds that have changed dramatically over the last 30 years.

The trend analysis of technological progress appears to be at odds with the popular view of unexpected scientific progress but, as Brian Twiss (1974) points out:

> unexpected break-throughs are much rarer than commonly supposed. The much quoted example of penicillin is the exception rather than the rule. Most of the innovation in the 1980's and 1990's will be based upon scientific and technological knowledge existing now.

The pattern of technological progress tends to be uniform because it is usually achieved as the result of designers selecting and integrating a large number of innovations from diverse technological areas to produce the higher performance achieved.

Often the impact of a radically new innovation is swamped by the steady progress of evolutionary developments in related areas. This is shown by the change of computational speeds in Figure 9.9. The period covers major discontinuous innovations (from vacuum tubes in 1950 to transistors in 1960, silicon chips in 1970 and gallium arsenide in 1980) but the progress is regular. The transistor itself provides a good example of the relative impact of break-throughs. It is often credited with being responsible for the size reduction in electronic equiment, yet without the parallel development of ancillary technologies, it is estimated that transistor based electronic equipment would be only marginally smaller (about 10 per cent) than a vacuum tube version.

So, technological trend analysis is based on the same assumption as the Fisher–Pry approach to technological substitution. Both are the result of very complex processes, but their cumulative effect tends to be regular, and the past trends can be a good indication of the immediate future.

The recognition of the S-shaped path of technological progress is a major feature of technology trend analysis (Figure 9.10). Initially technological progress is slow, maybe because few people are involved, basic scientific knowledge must be gained, and engineering obstacles cleared. Conventional wisdom and the establishment can hold back development for a long time. Combat aircraft technology progressed rapidly in the First World War but then became almost frozen for 20 years as military budgets were cut and the senior services resisted flying machines.

Advances start to accelerate exponentially once the importance of a technology is realized and technological effort and funds are expanded. The threat of the Second World War stimulated the rapid increase in combat aircraft performance that continued after the end of the war and the introduction of radically new jet engine technology.

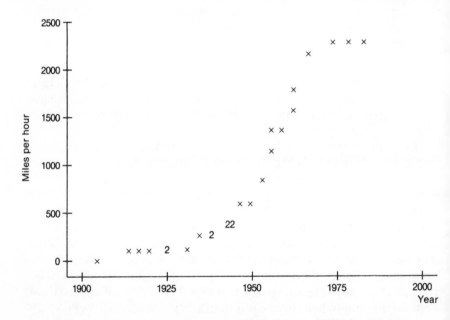

Figure 9.10   Maximum speed of operational military aircraft

Finally, the technological advances cease to accelerate and may stop growing altogether. There are two reasons why the rapid technological progress ends. First, there may be an absolute limit to the technology. Figure 9.11 shows how the maximum speed of operational helicopters has saturated at just above 220 mph. This is near the limit of conventional helicopters. Above that speed either the forward moving rotor becomes supersonic (so loses lift), or the rearward moving rotor stalls (also losing lift). By using radically new technology the barrier can be overcome, but not satisfactorily or

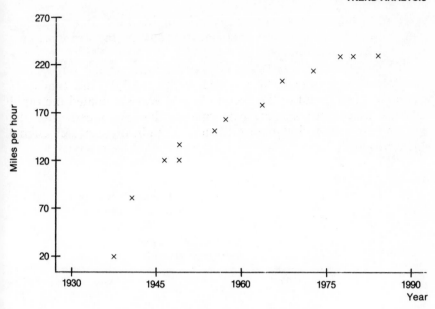

Figure 9.11   Maximum speed of operational helicopters

economically for most helicopter roles, even with military R and D budgets.

Sometimes the barrier is purely economic. For example, the 'sound barrier' did not slow combat aircraft development, so why should civil aircraft be not supersonic? Concorde and the Tu-144 (maybe) have shown there is no technological barrier but all economically successful aircraft are subsonic (Figure 9.12). Practical technologies stop advancing when rapidly diminishing returns set in. At the moment, the limited economic value to the customer of supersonic air travel, in conjunction with its high economic and social costs, make the speed of sound an economic barrier. Even combat aircraft appear to have reached a non-technological barrier to their development (Figure 9.10). Faster combat aircraft could be built but at too great a cost to other performance criteria.

The S-shaped curve of technological trends is more prone to uncertainty than that of sales trends. The initial slow growth may not exist if the potential of a new idea is grasped quickly. Both helicopter and laser technology developed rapidly from the start because their significance was obvious and they were no challenge to established power bases.

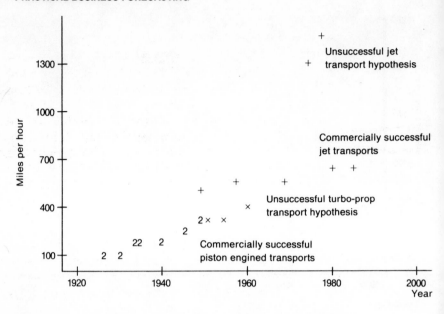

Figure 9.12   Economic cruise speed of commercial aircraft

Levelling of development is usually due to a combination of technological and economic factors. Often the trend line continues across
several major technological innovations but new technologies can
sometimes cause rapid changes. The development of typesetting technology (Figure 9.13) shows how competition can change what
appears to be a technological limit. First, the development of photo
and electronic typesetting completely changed the rate of technological development in the industry. Second, up to 1940 the 'hot metal'
technology appeared to have reached a technological limit. However,
under the threat of the new technology, it broke through the old
barrier in a desperate attempt to compete. Such last ditch fights
are typical when new technologies threaten established ones. The
behaviour is important because it can slow down the speed by which
new technologies are accepted.

USING TECHNOLOGY TREND ANALYSIS

The normally regular pace of technological development makes tech-

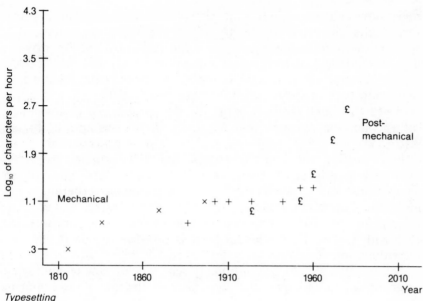

Typesetting
× = Cold
+ = Hot
£ = Photo
− = Electronic

Source: Mohn, 'Application of trend concepts in forecasting typesetting technology', *Journal of Technology Forecasting and Social Change*, vol. 3, no. 2, 1972.

Figure 9.13   The advance of typesetting technology

nology trend analysis a useful planning tool. It can help set realistic performance targets for new developments and prevent heavy expenditure on technologies when the likely returns are diminishing. However, it is a tool that can be dangerous if used thoughtlessly.

Often it is not obvious which performance trends are central. It is reported that US aero engine manufacturers, and the British government, initially rejected jet engines for transport aircraft because some experts were preoccupied with specific fuel consumption as the criterion for comparing aero engines. Relative to piston engines, jet engines still have poor specific fuel consumption but they are supreme in terms of passenger miles per unit cost. To overcome this myopia, Bright (1978) suggests identifying at least half a dozen attributes or, more likely, twice that. The criteria should then be used, compared and reviewed periodically.

Technology trend lines are often fitted manually rather than using regression analysis. Regression analysis is limited because transformations are often unable to follow the rapid saturations that sometimes occur. In the experience of the authors, it usually provides a good statistical fit to the data but produces a shape which overshoots natural or economic barriers. A second disadvantage of regression is the need to envelope data points rather than fit a line of best fit through them. It is usually the extremes of performance, rather than the average, that are tracked, for example in Figure 9.10.

The direction and limits of trends should be explored carefully. It is easy to neglect the limits to performance improvement when competition has focused attention on a particular criterion for a long time. Potential technical, economic, social, political and ecological reasons for barriers should be considered. Often, as was the case with Concorde, the actual limit is not due to one factor, but a combination.

The horizon should be continually scanned for new technologies, or groups of technologies, that may increase the rate of development or remove barriers. Most technological progressions are smooth but history shows that few businesses are able to survive major technological changes. The improved performance in electronics has been rapid but regular. However, over the last 30 years each shift in technology has brought new business to the fore. None of the leaders in the old vacuum tube technology are now leading silicon chip makers and it looks as if the Japanese, rather than the Americans, will lead the world in gallium arsenide chips. Forecasting technological change is one thing; reaction to change is something completely different.

FURTHER READING

Bass, F. M., 'A new product growth model for consumer durables', *Management Science,* vol. 15, January 1969, pp. 215–227.

Bright, J. R., *Practical Technology Forecasting: Concepts and Exercises,* The Industrial Management Centre, Austin, 1978.

Fisher, J. C. and Pry, R. M., 'A simple substitution model of technological change', *Technological Forecasting and Social Change,* vol. 3, 1978, pp. 75–88.

Fourt, L. A. and Woodcock, J. W., 'Early prediction of market success of new grocery products', *Journal of Marketing,* vol. 24, October 1960, pp. 31–38.

Mansfield, E., 'Technological change and the rate of imitation', *Econometrics,* vol. 29, October 1961, pp. 741–765.

Twiss, B. C., *Managing Technological Innovation,* Longman, London, 1974.

10 Subjective forecasting

Subjective forecasting uses the systematic assessment of informed opinion to make predictions. Those involved are asked to make direct estimates of what they think the future will bring. It contrasts with subjective estimations where experts are asked to guess the relationship between variables in a forecasting model.

Subjective forecasting can be used to answer many types of questions. Typical ones could be:

1 What events may occur in the next ten years that could have a critical effect on products or markets?
2 By what year will event A have occurred?
3 How far will a technology have evolved by year n?
4 What will sales be in year n?
5 What is the interaction between events A and B?

This chapter is about subjective methods of exploratory forecasting. The term exploratory covers those forecasting techniques based upon an extension of the past through the present and into the future. By this definition all the forecasting techniques in this book are exploratory.

Technology forecasting literature contains exploratory and normative techniques (Twiss, 1981). Normative approaches start with a postulation of a desired or possible future event and then trace backwards to determine the steps necessary to reach the end point. Usually they generate a large number of alternative paths that have to be evaluated. Typical techniques are morphological analysis and relevance trees. Normative techniques are not covered here because they are tools for ideas generation and technology planning rather than forecasting. This chapter, like the rest of this book, concentrates on assessing what the future might be, rather than how it can be achieved.

After discussing the advantages and disadvantages of subjective forecasting the remainder of this chapter looks at three areas. The first part contains brainstorming, leading indicators and monitoring. These can be used to identify potentially important events. The next section examines ways of combining subjective forecasts. It covers miscellaneous methods, Delphi, cross impact analysis and scenario writing. Finally, ad hoc and Bayesian methods of combining subjective and analytical forecasts are described.

ADVANTAGES AND DISADVANTAGES

Subjective forecasting has major advantages over other forecasting methods. Experts' opinions form forecasts so there is no need for structured and perfectly maintained data bases. The methods are usually used for strategy forecasting where the time horizon is over two years and there are not enough historical data to support an analytical method. Also, as time horizons extend, there is a decreasing likelihood that past patterns will be reproduced in the future.

Expert knowledge and opinions can capture much wider and diverse sources of information than analytical methods. Often the major events that shape established industries, and shape new ones, come from unexpected directions. The signals are not necessarily weak, but they often come from sources that are not normally monitored. For example, most major innovations originate in small firms rather than the major incumbents in the industry. Many subjective forecasting techniques are designed to try to capture such potentially vital bits of information.

There is a positive and negative side to involving managers in subjective forecasts. An advantage is the commitment and enhanced awareness that participation can stimulate. This must be balanced against their bias. Often it may be logical for them to be less than honest. Salesmen or managers who know their forecasts will be used to set targets are behaving rationally if they consider the implications of their figures. Similarly when forecasting technology, managers or engineers with backgrounds in an old industry find it hard to forecast the relative decline of the tools they know.

The psychological literature on human judgement abounds with examples of the information processing limitations and biases in performing tasks associated with forecasting. In particular the illusion of control, accumulation of redundant information, failure to seek possible disconfirming evidence, and overconfidence in judgement are liable to induce serious errors (Hogarth and Makridakis, 1981).

Human limitations are the main disadvantages of subjective forecasting. Frequently a company's experts are the people most likely to be biased and least able to contribute unorthodox information of strategic importance. Numerous studies have shown that the predictive judgements of human beings is frequently less accurate than simple quantitative models but often problems are so inexact, and data so scarce that even simple time series models cannot be used. In addition, subjective techniques are the only ones with any chance of capturing the unforeseen signals that may precede a significant change.

IDENTIFYING CRITICAL EVENTS

Creative organizations are more likely to identify and respond to new opportunities or threats than bureaucratic ones. So the cultivation of a creative environment is as important to strategic forecasting as the use of techniques. Creative organizations usually tend to be open companies where intensive informal communication is the rule and a free flow of information is encouraged. Vertical and horizontal communications are equally important. In particular it is realized that much valuable information can be gathered by people at the sharp end of the business, for example, service engineers, salesmen or production workers. Horizontal communications are important because the cross fertilization of ideas and knowledge from different areas is essential to evaluating information. Often the very layout of firms and their functional organizations seem designed to ensure that casual communications and creativity are minimized.

It is difficult to separate the failure to forecast events from the failure of an organization to act on the event forecast. In this respect the need for an entrepreneurial organization is equal to the need for a creative one. When people are encouraged to use their initiative, to experiment and to innovate, they are likely to be sensitive to the opportunities that the environment creates.

The cultivation of an entrepreneurial and creative environment is the most effective way of ensuring an organization identifies and responds to changes. Subjective forecasting is a body of knowledge than can help organizations make strategic forecasts but they are likely to be of little use if used in a barren environment.

Brainstorming

Brainstorming can be a useful first step in subjective forecasting. It is a group based technique where participants are asked to use a set of rules designed to stimulate the free flow of ideas. The emphasis is on quality, rather than quantity of ideas with the contributions of individuals being encouraged by permitting no critical comment during the session. Osborn (1953) invented brainstorming as a means of reducing the environmental and emotional blocks that inhibit the exchange of ideas, to some extent, in all organizations. A typical session brings together a group of about a dozen people with diverse backgrounds and experience, and from within and outside the sponsoring organization. The session then follows four major rules:

1   No judgement of ideas is permitted. This prevents people being inhibited by potential criticism.
2   The wildest of ideas are sought. They may not be of immediate practical value but they may seed more useful ones.
3   The aim is to produce a large number of ideas; a target of 120 is typical. This may require a lengthy session but it is necessary in order to go beyond the first few obvious suggestions.
4   Participants are encouraged to build on or modify earlier ideas. This frequently leads to concepts that are better than the original ones.

Groups can brainstorm to try to identify events of potential value or danger to a company. Negative brainstorming can be particularly useful. Here participants are asked to think how things could go wrong. There is a chance that in a freewheeling brainstorming session someone may ask a question that everyone has been pushing to the back of their minds, such as 'Why should people buy video disc players when VCRs are cheaper and more flexible?'

Leading indicators

Leading indicators, either tied, economic or precursor trends, can provide an early warning of future sales. Tied indicators can be reliable and easy to follow because there is a known relationship between the indicator and the item to be forecast; developed countries are now able to forecast the increased demand for hospital services and pensions that will occur in the twenty-first century because they know the current age profiles of their populations.

Usually sellers of raw materials or components will find it easier to forecast primary demand than their own sales. Sales of finished goods to consumers by retailers are a tied indicator of factory sales of the goods, or the components from which they are made. Consumer purchases of goods such as washing machines often follow quite regular patterns while factory sales of the same goods can be very difficult to forecast. The further a manufacturer is away from the end consumer, the greater is the variation he is likely to feel as panic buying and stock adjustments by intermediaries amplify any slight irregularities in consumer sales. Tracking tied indicators of consumer demand for washing machines would not enable a manufacturer of washing machine motors to predict the exact twist and turn of their sales but it would give him an early warning of major demand shifts.

The original purchase dates of durable goods in service can be a good tied indicator. Users can choose to bring forward or delay the replacement of equipment but the age profile, with likely replacement ages, can be a useful guide to future demand. When a new product is adopted quickly sales can suddenly diminish once all potential buyers have made their first purchase. Sales can then remain low for a few years until the original goods are replaced. The second wave of high sales can sometimes be almost as large as the first, and often takes many manufacturers completely by surprise. UK colour TV manufacturers completely failed to predict the replacement surge for colour TV that started in the 1980s (Figure 10.1). There was simply no excuse for not reading such market dynamics when the tied leading indicators of the replacement market were so easy to see.

Economic leading indicators are more general, but less reliable, than tied indicators. They originated with the realization that certain economic variables, such as profits, factory building approvals, machine tool orders etc., tend to move up or down before the rest of the economy. The argument is that by following the movements of several of these leading indicators movements in the rest of the economy can be forecast.

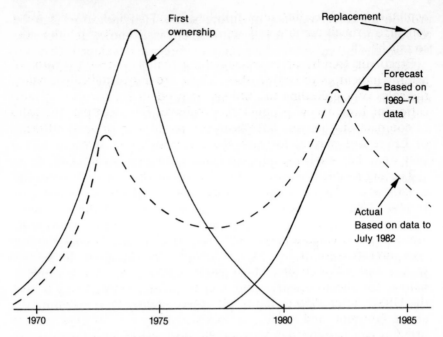

First
ownership

Replacement

Forecast
Based on
1969–71
data

Actual
Based on data to
July 1982

1970　　　　　1975　　　　　1980　　　　　1985

Source: Twiss, B., *Forecasting Market Size and Market Growth Rates for New Products*,
Elsevier Science Publications, North Holland, 1984.

**Figure 10.1　First ownership as a tied leading indicator of replacement
colour TV sales – UK market**

Unfortunately there are problems. The economic leading indicators
are prone to error. Company profits is one published leading indicator which the Central Statistical Office expect to be wrong by between
3 per cent and 10 per cent. This is because final figures come from
company accounts, which are audited and published only after considerable delay. While this is happening the Central Statistical Office
tries to make estimates but their figures are usually low. For example,
their first guess at profits for 1978 was £29.13 billions but by 1984
the figure had been revised upwards by 21 per cent.

To reduce individual errors the Central Statistical Office publishes
its composite longer term leading index that combines five statistics
into a single indicator that is supposed to predict turns in the economy
about a year ahead. Sadly the index itself is prone to error because
it has to be published quickly. Sometimes the first published indicator
contains only two components so it can be expected to change as
more information is added. For example, after nine months the

September 1983 leading indicator had been reduced by over 3 per cent. How much can one rely on indicators whose re-estimates vary so much?

Precursor trends, or curve matching, will be the final form of leading indicators to be described. These are untied indicators where the sales of a preceding technology or product are used as an indication of how a new product may behave. For example, the sales of compact disk players have been compared with original diffusion of LP record players to show that, although CDs are not selling very well, they are being adopted faster than their predecessors.

The big problem with precursor trends is that no two trends are exactly alike. Two examples will be used to illustrate the problem. In the 1960s a forecast showed combat aircraft maximum speed as a precursor trend for transport aircraft speed. At the time combat aircraft had reached a maximum speed of about 2,000 mph whereas civil aircraft were at just over 600 mph and the trend of the two speeds had followed an almost parallel path since 1925. Unfortunately, for the forecasters and taxpayers in France, the UK and the USSR, after 1960 civil aircraft speeds stabilized at a figure little above 600 mph and no longer followed its precursor. The margin of error can be judged from the 1985 forecast of civil aircraft with a speed of 2,500 mph.

Black and white TVs as a precursor of colour TVs is another example of failed forecasting. Manufacturers tooled up for colour sales on the assumption that the product would be adopted at the same speed as black and white. In reality colour diffused more rapidly leaving unfilled demand that allowed the Japanese to penetrate the European and American markets. The Japanese seem to have made a better job of forecasting the potential. With hindsight it can be seen why the precursor trend did not work. Black and white TV was a totally new product which diffused slowly as networks were enlarged, programming improved and people adapted to a different lifestyle. Conversely colour TV was an obviously improved technology product substituting for an old one. There was relatively little learning required in knowing what to do with a colour TV.

In summary, the first impression shows curve matching is a simple and effective way of forecasting. In reality it is prone to error because the trends are not tied. Where market research companies have taken a more sophisticated view of precursor trends they have reported successes. New product forecasting models, calibrated using experience with earlier products, are sometimes used to provide very reliable early forecasts of new product sales.

Monitoring

> The future doesn't descend upon us on some prophetic day like the Messiah ... It grows out of forces which are now turbulently in motion ... Whatever warning we're going to get we already have.
>
> *Theodore Levitt*

This being true, it should be possible to detect coming trends by observing the environment and tracking occurrences that may signal changes to come. Monitoring is a systematic way of doing so. It has four activities (Bright, 1978):

1 *Searching the environment* for signals that may be the forerunners of change. These could be a combination of technological, economic, social, political and ecological events or progressions that could all flag events to come. For example, the slow-down of the nuclear energy programmes in several western countries can be related to several preceding trends: the growing concern for safety as illustrated by Ralph Nader's campaign against some American cars; the growing concern for ecology; the anti-bomb movement and the increase in energy saving triggered by a series of oil crises. In addition, the economic recession of the 1970s reduced the need for the extra capacity that nuclear energy would add.

2 *Identifying alternative possible consequences* if the trends are true and continue. Will the 'no nukes' debate cool once the new generation of theatre nuclear weapons has been deployed? Will the accelerated nuclear energy programmes of some aggressively commercial countries, like France, Japan and Korea, force other countries to go nuclear in order to compete?

3 *Choosing the parameters,* policies, events and decisions to be followed in order to monitor the true direction of change. What variables are critical indicators of change? That is, the speed of decline of the cost of nuclear power and the changing balance from social to economic arguments as western governments move right of centre.

4 *Presenting the evidence* to decision makers so that the information can be assimilated. Typically a table of events with dates or graphs of time series data is used.

COMBINING SUBJECTIVE ESTIMATES ANALYTICALLY

It is generally agreed that, in subjective forecasting, a number of heads are better than one. The question then arises, how should the disparate views of experts be combined? The answer is by either analytical or group methods.

A few simple and many complicated ways of combining estimates have been proposed. Winkler (1968) groups them as: assigning equal weighting to the judgements, assigning weights proportional to an expert self-rating, assigning weights proportional to someone else's rating of the experts, or assigning weights that are proportional to an expert's past predictive accuracy. In practice, there is little point in going beyond an equal weighting (simple averaging) scheme. There are two reasons for this. First, as any simple experiment will show, subtle changes in weights have very little effect on the averages that are produced. Second, research shows that simple averages of group opinions can be remarkably predictive compared to other combinational schemes (Larreche and Moinpour, 1983).

Delphi

Delphi is a group method of combining judgements that is designed to have the advantages of group interaction while removing some of the problems. Like trend analysis, it is one of the most popular means of strategic forecasting.

Group forecasts are theoretically superior to analytically combined forecasts because they allow experts to exchange information and ideas about the future. However, committee based approaches have their own shortcomings. The views of some contributors may dominate because their position or reputation gives them authority. Even when everyone is of equal status there is likely to be bias because dominant individuals, or those who are more articulate, may have influence greater than their cases justify. There is also a bandwagon effect where once a group of people start to agree, others are disinclined to put an opposing view. A final practical problem is the difficulty and expense of getting experts together at the same time.

Delphi is a technique developed at the Rand Corporation to overcome the problems. It uses a panel of experts who are kept in ignorance about the composition of the rest of the panel or the source of the opinions. The process is an iterative one where forecasts and opinions are exchanged until they converge or freeze.

Delphi is widely used for long range forecasts. Often the dimension forecast is time to an event but it can also be used to forecast sales or levels of technological achievement.

The true validation of Delphi time scaling is a long term process but the Rand Corporation have conducted 'almanac' studies where experts were asked about phenomena with a known answer. They found that consensus grew towards the correct answer as the study progressed. Real Delphi studies show a similar gain in consensus but their results are not so easily checked. Validatory tests are few but some results indicate the method has a systematic bias away from the medium term. There is a tendency for forecasts to be optimistic in the short term as development times are underestimated, while long term forecasts can be pessimistic because of people's inability to appreciate the accelerating pace of development.

Cross-impact analysis

While the technique so far discussed attempts to combine the judgements of individuals, cross-impact analysis is used to examine the potential interaction between forecasts. Some events may interact to reduce the impact of either, while others may interact to facilitate accelerated development or a disaster. For example, Malthus' (1777–1834) prediction, that the world would starve because of exponential population growth with finite land resources, was wrong because the population growth has been more than balanced by agricultural productivity. Two developments that have had a mutually amplifying effect were liquid crystal and silicon chip technology. Without the other, neither would have revolutionized the watch or calculator industries in the way they did.

In its simple form cross-impact analysis involves cross tabulating possible events on a matrix which allows the interaction between every pair of events to be reviewed (Figure 10.2). The matrix is then examined asking, if event 1 is true, what would be the impact on events 2, 3, 4, etc? Typically, three forms of impact are considered:

1 Impact – will event 1 amplify or diminish the impact of events 2, 3 . . . ?
2 Timing – will it accelerate or retard the occurrence of the other events?

(i) If these events occur

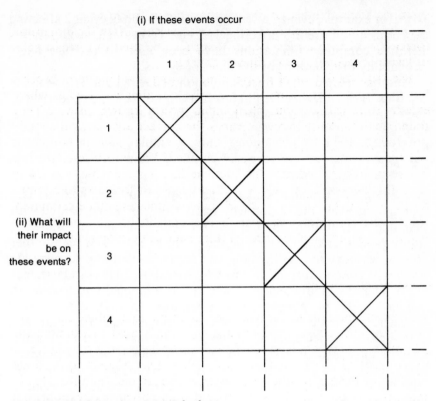

Figure 10.2   Cross-impact analysis

3   Probability – will it ensure, require or prevent the other events occurring?

It is sometimes imputed that the evaluation should be conducted by an analyst but the process is one that is likely to be enhanced by team work. In a first pass through experts may be asked the likely level of cross-impact for each cell, and then required to give more information where interactions are high. Cross-impact analysis could stop at this stage having forced participants to consider the complex dynamics of events. Even at this level the technique has a potential for improving the internal consistency of forecasts and clarifying assumptions.

Cross-impact lends itself to the development of more sophisticated analyses (Bright, 1978). It is obvious that interactions are likely to be more than one to one. The whole matrix therefore becomes active with, for example, event 1 affecting events 2, 5 and 6; event 2 affecting 5, 7 and 9; and event 5 affecting 1, 2 etc. To evaluate such patterns iterative computer simulations have been used to produce likely probability distributions of the times of events.

Another refinement is the conjunction of Delphi and cross-impact analysis. It can improve Delphi forecasts and enhance the understanding of interactive relationships between future trends and events.

Scenario

According to Cornelius Kuiken, the head of strategic analysis and planning at Shell, the reason why many firms are disenchanted with planning is that they committed themselves too much to specific future predictions. To overcome the problem Shell, and many other companies including G.E., now use scenario planning to generate a series of possible futures against which strategic plans can be tested.

The subset of individual forecasts to be combined into a scenario can be chosen in many ways. Cross-impact analysis can be used to generate a single 'most probable' scenario although this approach is limited by its dependence on the forecasts making up the matrix. Once a most probable scenario has been chosen other 'boundary scenarios' can be generated by examining deviations from the core. Alternatively several 'individual theme scenarios' can be chosen automatically or by groups. The military were one of the earliest users of scenario planning and they have used a process where events and trends are combined randomly to produce alternative views. A more popular managerial approach brings a group of imaginative experts together to discuss a pre-prepared series of trends, topics and hypotheses. Each scenario is then developed around a theme and given a title that focuses attention on their major features. For example, 'the violent society' where crime and civil disobedience grow exponentially, or 'the limits to growth' where the world economy and population collapse when material limits are reached.

How many scenarios should be produced? The answer is a few – a single most probable scenario is likely to retain too many of the problems of myopic planning. It is also obvious that the strategic planning process would be ridiculous if there were dozens of scenarios against which each strategy had to be tested. So, the number chosen must be a compromise between a desire for safety and a need for simplicity.

The ad hoc combining of subjective and analytical forecasts

The ad hoc combining of forecasts is an inevitability. A manager's job has little meaning if he has to live with forecasts that are mechanistically produced. His job is to shape the future so a dispassionately produced forecast may become a starting point from which he plans to exert his will on the future. The familiar hockey stick effect is one result of the interplay between where history indicates a market will go, and where managers would like it to go.

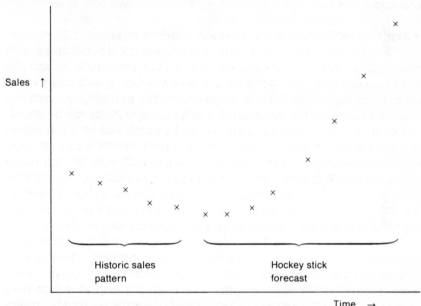

Figure 10.3 The hockey stick effect

The story goes, 'sales have been in decline but our plan (for which extra funds are required) will stop the rot. Next year is too soon to arrest the decline but the following year the trend will have bottomed out and will be followed by a rapid rise'.

The following year the argument is likely to be much the same, except an extra line has been added to explain why the expected recovery has been forced back a year – usually because of some 'one-off' event that no-one could have foreseen. Year after year the same pattern can continue until a whole team could be provided with jolly hockey sticks. This King Canute-like belief that managers can turn the tide of a declining product is probably the major reason why simple time series methods usually produce better forecasts than subjective judgements.

Besides the cynical view of how analytical forecasts and judgements are combined, subjective forecasting provides many opportunities for combining the two. Customarily Delphi, cross-impact analysis and scenario start with analytical forecasts that are viewed by panels of experts who then add their own judgement. Where managers have a vested interest in forecasts, there is a chance of bias but, by screening the experts, and maintaining some of the anonymity of Delphi, the bias may be reduced.

Although it is common practice to start subjective forecasting exercises with analytical forecasts there is a case against doing so. The sophisticated statistical presentation of analytical forecasts can give them an exaggerated aura of authority and reliability. In addition, they may narrow the focus of attention to the area of the pre-prepared forecasts. Giving everyone a full set of identical analytical forecasts at the start of a subjective forecasting session can reduce confusion and speed up the process but there is a danger that it limits discussions and reduces originality.

Formally combining subjective and analytical forecasts

In one sense, given the problems with combining forecasts, it is surprising that formal means are not used more widely. On the other hand the subtlety of Bayesian analysis makes the method inaccessible to most managers. However, once the unfamiliar terms and processes are mastered the method can be usefully applied.

The forecast starts with a subjective forecast of what a product's sales may be before analytical evidence is gathered. These original estimates are called a prior distribution because they are prior to statistical evidence and expressed as a probability distribution $f(p)$, rather than a point forecast.

Next analytical forecasts, say pre-test markets may be carried out to give experimental evidence of likely sales. The result is a sampling distribution $f(x/p)$.

Now using Bayesian analysis a posterior distribution can be calculated to give an estimate that combines the subjective and analytical data.

$$f(p/x) = \frac{f(p)f(x/p)}{\int f(p)f(x/p)dp}$$
(10.1)

Usually the posterior distribution has a variance smaller than the original prior distribution and a mean that is a compromise between the subjective and objective estimate.

Bayesian analysis can be applied to combining subjective and analytical estimates as well as forecasts. It is usually applied to simple linear regression although the process can be extended to multivariate Bayesian regression. The approach has also been applied to the estimation of decision calculus type models but the results are very complicated. Readers interested are referred to specialist books on the very extensive topic (Zellner, 1971). Oh that the world were more simple!

FURTHER READING

Bright, J. R., *Practical Technology Forecasting: Concepts and Exercises* (3rd edition), Industrial Management Center Inc, Austin, Texas, 1978.

Hogarth, R. M. and Makridakis, S., 'Forecasting and planning: an evaluation', *Management Science,* vol. 27, no. 2, 1981, pp. 115–138.

Larreche, J. C. and Moinpour, R., 'Managerial Judgement in Marketing: the concept of expertise', *Journal of Marketing Research,* vol. XX, May 1983, pp. 110–121.

Osborn, A. F., *Applied Imagination: Principles and Procedures of Creative Thinking* (3rd edition), Charles Scribner, New York, 1953.

Twiss, B., *Managing Technological Innovation* (2nd edition), Longman, London, 1981.

Winkler, R. L., 'The consensus of subjective probability distributions', *Management Science,* vol. 15, no. 1, 1968, pp. 61–75.

Zellner, A., *An Introduction to Bayesian Inference on Econometrics,* Wiley, New York, 1971.

Appendix: Software for business forecasting

ORION is Comshare's data management, analysis and forecasting decision support system for time related data. It is used because it provides a good example of a state-of-the-art software that contains all the facilities that a practical forecaster is likely to need. The main forecasting routines include:

1 Smoothing
   Moving average
   Single exponential smoothing
   Double exponential smoothing
   Triple exponential smoothing
   Winter's exponential smoothing
   Adaptive exponential smoothing
2 Trend analysis
   Trend curve fitting
   (10 regression curve fits)
   Gompertz
   (Non-linear curve fit)
3 Regression analysis
   Multiple regression
   Multiple classification regression
   Polynomial distributed lag regression
   Stepwise regression
   Cochrane–Orcutt regression
4 Seasonal adjustment methods
   The Census Bureau's X-II version of the Census method II procedure. This is suitable for identifying trends, cyclical, seasonal and irregular patterns.

5 Box–Jenkins
Univariate
Multivariate

Thus ORION includes a large number of the time series methods described in Chapter 3, the regression techniques covered in Chapters 5 and 6 and a variety of trend curves whose application is discussed in Chapter 8. It also deals with Box–Jenkins methods but, in our judgement, these are still too difficult for the non-specialist to apply successfully and have therefore been omitted from this book along with a number of other more complex techniques, e.g. state space forecasting, that in our opinion are not yet easily comprehended by the manager.

Other facilities within ORION are:

1 A built-in calendar allowing data of different time periods and variable number of values to be stored and analysed collectively. tively.
2 A multidimension data base structure that allows data to be gathered and organized for a range of reporting needs, i.e. by product group, region, sale territory, etc.
3 Data management operations for preparing, manipulating, selecting and validating data.
4 A reporting system that can produce reports, graphs, charts or histograms at a computer terminal or high resolution laser printer of graphics device.

In the chapter on ratio models, the planning decision support system SYSTEM W is used.

Though ORION and SYSTEM W are very convenient to use, there are many similar packages, so that the manager should have no great difficulty in implementing the methods that we ran using these two packages, using packages available to him. There are in fact three major sources of such software:

1 Most larger data processing installations will have the SAS library of statistical routines available. The SAS economic and time series routines contain routines for most common time series methods along with those for regression and trend curve fitting. In addition, there are also facilities for constructing ratio models.
2 Managers in large organizations are likely to have access to companies like Comshare that offer time sharing facilities.

Many of them offer access to the SAS system. Given the importance of forecasting to managers, most offer software comparable to that embodied in ORION and SYSTEM W.

3 There is now a large amount of forecasting software available on microcomputers. Thus, on the IBM PC, Forecast Plus, PC Sybil and Statgraphics amongst other packages, all offer similar facilities to ORION. The number of spreadsheet packages suitable for the construction of ratio forecasting models now runs into dozens for the IBM PC.

FURTHER READING

Dobbins, R. and Witt, S. F., *Portfolio Theory and Investment Management,* Basil Blackwell, Oxford, 1983, 201 pp.

'Forecast Plus' literature available from: Walonick Associates, 6500 Nicollet Ave S., Minneapolis, MN55423, USA.

'PC-Sybil' literature available from: Temple, Barker and Sloane Inc., 33 Hayden Ave, Lexington, MA 02173, USA.

'SAS–ETS' manual available from: SAS Institute Inc., Box 8000, Cary, N. Carolina, 27511–8000, USA.

'Statgraphics' literature available from: Statistical Graphics Corporation, 2 Wall St, Princeton, NJ, 08540, USA.

Wisnell, Phil 'The Great Spreadsheet Face Off', *PC Magazine,* vol. 4, no. 11, 1985.

Index

accounts, company 125
ADBUG 237, 239
adjustment coefficient 208
advertising 158, 160, 205, 229, 234, 237
  agencies 258, 263, 271
  expenditure 5, 35, 170, 189, 190, 272
  levels 205, 229, 237
  recall 263, 265, 266
  'tip-in' 278
  TV 272
aggregation 14, 42–3
agricultural industry 145
aircraft technology 305–8, 319
Almon distributed lag 205–6
alpha testing 279
Annual Abstract of Statistics 32
ASSESSOR 275, 276, 281
assets, current 131, 132
assets, fixed 129, 130, 132
assets, total 127, 131
assumptions
  additional (for significance tests)
    179–80
  classical 166–7
audit 15
autocorrelation 211–18
  analysis 48
  coefficient 44–6, 48, 216, 217
  function (ACF) 71
autoregressive models 63, 95–7
autoregressive scheme, first-order 212,
  216, 218
awareness, product 263, 265, 267, 275,
  276

Ayer, N. W., and Son 263, 265, 266, 272

balance sheet 125, 126, 127
Bass, F. M. 299
Bayesian analysis 252–3, 255, 326–7
beta distribution 248–9, 254
beta testing 279
bias
  personal 252, 314, 315, 321, 326
  statistical 17, 194, 299, 322
bidding, competitive 247
bounds, upper and lower 253
brainstorming 314, 316
BRANDAID 251, 253
brands, mature 234
brand share 262
Brown's method 63, 88–9, 98
budgeting 5, 114
Business Statistics Office 32, 33
buying rates 263, 267, 270, 272

calendar effect 43–4
Cambridge Econometrics 36
capacity planning 84
capital, working 131, 132
cash flow 115–22
causal models 16, 38, 156
census information 31
Census of Distribution 33
Census of Production 32, 33
Census XII 63, 73–7, 92
Central Statistical Office 31, 32, 33, 318
chemicals industry, bulk 145, 146, 149

cigarette demand model 195–7, 201–3
CIPFA 33
Cochrane-Orcutt iterative technique
   214–17, 218
Collins, B. 262, 275, 276, 278
commercialization 266
commodity market 2
Companies' House 33
company financial data 33
company sales, individual 150–1
complements 189
computational speeds 305
computer software 48, 113, 118–21, 324,
   329–31
   for regression 165, 191, 195, 214, 217
Comshare 329, 330
concept test 258, 260, 277, 280, 281–2
confidence intervals 96, 97, 134, 138,
   190, 288
constant level 79, 88, 90, 94, 99, 100
consumer behaviour 261, 277, 282, 299
consumer goods 260, 261, 266, 282
consumer industry 145, 147, 149
consumer panels 267, 271, 272, 273,
   276, 277
consumer surveys 265, 266, 267, 271
consumer tastes 158
contingency planning 4, 6, 113, 114,
   121–2, 141
corporate models 113
correlation, serial 211–18
correlation coefficients 219–20, 221
cost of forecasting method 21, 23
cost of goods sold 129
covariance 166
creditworthiness 114
cross-impact analysis 322–4, 326
curve fitting
   in subjective forecasting 240, 243,
     246, 254
   in trend analysis 288, 289, 291, 309
curve matching 319
customs statistics 32
cycles 13, 55, 67, 73

data, cross-section 211, 219, 221, 222
data, model 119–20, 127, 132, 133
data, primary 29–30
data, quality of 38–9, 226, 227

data, secondary 29, 30–8
data, time series, *see* time series, data
data, variability of 227
data analysis model 262
databases 29, 30, 36–8, 247
data collection 56, 258, 260, 262
data patterns 99
data points, missing 42
debt, short term 131, 132
decision calculus 235, 236, 237, 239,
   254, 327
decision model, advertising 225
decomposition methods 49, 63, 66–77
   Census XII 63, 73–7, 92
   classical 63, 67–71, 77, 90, 92
Delphi method 252, 321–2, 324, 326
demand forecasting 145–52, 273
determination, coefficient of (R^2), *see*
   R-squared
deviations 177, 179
diagnostics 275, 276, 278, 279, 280
differences, generalized 216, 217
differencing 46–8, 55, 57, 80, 83–7
distributed lag regression models 203–7
distribution systems 160, 170, 190
disturbance term 161, 163, 164, 165,
   190, 193
   autocorrelation of 211
Dobbins, R. 3
'driver series' 133, 135
d statistic 212, 213, 214
Durbin-Watson test 212–14

earnings, retained 129
earnings survey 32
econometric forecasting models 32, 36,
   80, 155
econometrics 155
economic adjustment processes 204
economic forecasting 152
economic leading indicators 317–19
economic statistics 31–2
economic theory 169
economy sectors 145–6, 152
elasticity 194, 195, 196–7, 223
electronic products 261–2, 305, 310
empirical methods, limitations of 226–9
employment related statistics 32
engineering company orders 59

environmental changes 227–8, 289, 320
equations, forecasting, accuracy and
    significance of 177–84
equations, quadratic 243
equations, simultaneous 149
equity 126, 127, 130–1, 132
errors (in forecasting) 39, 70, 79, 80, 315
    cumulative 74, 91
    estimation of 135, 190
    measurement 163, 211
    random 136–41, 161, 212, 216, 217
    smoothed forecast 87
error term 161–3, 180, 194, 210, 211,
    218
estimates, expert 225
    combining 250–5
    obtaining 236–50
estimates, incremental 240, 254
estimates, moving average 42, 63, 66
estimates, objective 253
estimates, parameter 166, 189, 198, 217,
    219, 288
    interpretation and evaluation of
        168–77
estimates, point 239, 246
estimates, probability 247–50
estimation 16–17
    of ratios 122–4
estimation, non-linear 293–4, 296, 298
estimation, subjective 225–6, 229–55
    advantages and disadvantages 226
    combining estimates 250–5
    obtaining estimates 236–50
    shape of response in 229–36
estimation error 42
estimators 166, 167
    best linear unbiased 167, 194, 219
    biased 194
    ordinary least squares (OLS) 163–7,
        171, 189, 190, 194, 210–12,
        216–19
ex ante forecasting 19, 57, 74
expected values 166, 167
experimentation 3, 266, 267, 279
    see also marketing, test
experts
    identifying 236
    questioning 237–46, 249
    self-rating 236, 250–1, 321

see also forecasting, subjective
ex post forecasting 19, 70, 74
extrapolation of trend equation 289, 291

Family Expenditure Survey 31
feasibility study 14
financial modelling 113
financial planning languages 113, 122,
    136
financial planning packages 135, 149
financial press 35
Financial Statistics, MA4 33
Fisher, J. C. 300, 302, 305
forecast accuracy 17–19, 190–1
forecast horizons 23, 56, 98–9, 313
forecasting, demand 145–52, 273
forecasting, ex ante 19, 57, 74
forecasting, exploratory 313
forecasting, ex post 19, 70, 74
forecasting, moving average 289
forecasting, new product, see product
    forecasting, new
forecasting, process of 13–15
forecasting, strategic 226, 285, 313
forecasting, subjective 225, 257, 289,
    313–27
    advantages and disadvantages 314–15
    combining subjective and analytical
        forecasts 325–7
    combining subjective estimates 321–4
    curve fitting in 240, 243, 246, 254
    identifying critical events 315–20
forecasting competitions 54, 98
forecasting method, selection of 15–24
forecasting packages 21
forecasts
    classification of 7
    production of 184–91, 217–18
    reliability of 56
forecasts, combined 106
    see also forecasting, subjective
forecasts, composite 80
    see also forecasting, subjective
forecasts, best linear unbiased 189, 190
forecasts, moving average 42, 63, 66
Fourt, L. A. 296, 298
freedom, degrees of 181, 182, 190, 204,
    243
F test 180–1, 210, 221

functional form (choice of) 197, 216
funds, flow of 125, 127–41

Gauss–Markov Theorem 167
General Household Survey 31
Gompertz expression 253–4, 293, 294, 296
goods, complementary 158
goods, consumer 260, 261, 266, 282
goods, durable 261, 299, 317
goods, quality of 157
government statistics 31–3, 34
grocery products 298
group methods 251, 252
Guide to FT Statistics, The 35

hardware systems 2
helicopters 306–7
hockey stick effect 325–6
holiday demand models 197, 208
Holt's method 89–94
Holt–Winter's method 63, 89–94, 98
household demand function 221
hypotheses, tests of 180, 181

IBM PC 331
identification 16
imitation 298, 299, 300
INBUCON 262, 277–8
income, disposable 157, 194, 195
income distribution 158–9
income statement 125, 126
incremental estimates 240, 254
independence, linear 200, 203
indicators, leading 314, 316–19
indicators, tied 316, 317
indicator variables 197
industry-by-industry forecasts 152
industry sectors 145–6, 152
industry statistics 32
inflation, effects of 114
inflation adjustment 39, 195
infrequent events 13, 55
Inland Revenue Statistics 32
innovations, diffusion of 269–70, 296–302
innovators 270, 299
input/output coefficients 152
input/output models 33, 36, 145–52

insurance 2–3, 145
intercepts 161, 168, 198, 199, 216
International Financial Statistics 34
irregular component 67, 70, 74

Koyck distributed lag 206–7, 208, 210, 222–3
Kuiken, Cornelius 324

laboratory test market 277–8
lags 156, 203–11, 219, 239
 Almon distributed 205–6
 Koyck distributed 206–7, 208, 210, 222–3
 polynomial distributed 205–6
Lambin, J.J. 253
Larreche, J.C. 236
leads 156
least squares estimators, *see under* estimators
liabilities, current 131, 132
liabilities, total 131
linear regression models, *see under* regression models
liquid crystal technology 322
Little, J. D. C. 225, 229, 237, 239, 253
local government 33–4
logistic model 296, 300
log-linear functional form 195, 209, 223
log-linear regression models 193–7, 209
log transformations 49–50, 82–3, 228, 231, 294
London Business School 37

MA4 Financial Statistics 35
McIntyre, S. H. 236
macroeconomic forecasts 37
Mansfield, E. 298
manufacturing industry 145, 146
market, efficient 3
market, replacement 317
market demand function 157, 159, 198, 203–4, 208, 221, 223
market growth curve, S-shaped, *see* S-shaped curves
marketing, pre-test 258, 260, 262, 266, 273–9, 281, 326
marketing, test 258, 260, 262, 263, 266, 271–3, 281
marketing effort 229

marketing mix 271
marketing mix model 253
marketing variables 300
market planning 106
market research 35, 258, 298
  agencies 258, 260, 267, 273, 319
markets, mature 229
market segmentation 270
market share forecasting 156, 159–61,
    169–77, 184, 189–90, 237, 273
  see also product forecasting, new
market size forecasting 156, 157–9, 189,
    194–7
Mass Observation 273
mean absolute deviation 17, 79
mean square error 17, 77, 79
means, sample 190
mode (of distribution) 248, 249
models
  advertising decision 225
  autoregressive 63, 95–7
  causal 16, 38, 156
  corporate 113
  econometric forecasting 32, 36, 80,
      155
  identification of (suitable) 15–16
  input/output 33, 36, 145–52
  non-causal 38
  updating 19, 74–6
  use of, for forecasting 17
  'vehicle park' 114, 141–5
  see also market share forecasting;
      forecasting; ratio models;
      regression methods; time series
      models
Moinpour, R. 236
monitoring 15, 314, 320
moving average forecasts 42, 63, 66
multiclient studies 35
multicollinearity 218–24

naive methods 63, 64–6, 87
  basic naive model 64
  seasonal naive model 63, 65–6
new trier effects 234
Nielsen, A. C. 281
noise 10
non-causal models 38
normal distribution 180, 210, 248
normative techniques 313, 314

nuclear energy 320

OECD 34
official bodies 34
opinion leaders 270
ORION 73, 77, 206, 240, 288, 291,
    329–31
outliers 42, 85, 87
panels, see consumer panels
Parfitt-Collins model 275, 276, 278
Pass, C. L. 195, 201
patents 37
pattern, historic 289, 291
penetration
  cumulative 267–9, 270, 276, 282, 299
  forecasting 293–300
  level 267
  parameter 298
  rate 262, 272, 278
performance appraisal 4, 5–6
petrol station sales 59
photocopying agency sales 59
plant maintenance 145
point events 7, 8
policy determination 4, 5, 156
polynomial distributed lags 205–6
pooling methods 251, 252, 254
population 157, 158, 189
population statistics 31
precursor trends 316, 319
prediction, early 258, 260, 267–71
prediction interval 190–1
PREDICTOR 275–6, 277, 281
price forecasts 189
prices, relative 160, 169, 265
probability analysis 247–50, 323, 324,
    326
problem definition 13–14
process industry output 63
product forecasting, new 257–82
  advantages and disadvantages 258–61
  behavioural detail 261–2
  conclusions 281–2
  methods 258
  models 262–6, 271–2, 319
  regression analysis in 263, 266
  use of 266–7
product group, new 269, 293
product growth model, new 299

production planning 106
product life cycle 234, 269
product process, new 257, 258, 266, 273, 281
product quality 160, 170, 190
product use testing 258, 266, 279–80, 282
profit computations 129
profits 246
promotional concepts 280
promotions (sales) 231, 232, 234, 261, 270, 300
  consumer 263, 265
  point-of-sale 253
Pry, R. M. 300, 302, 305
purchase rate, repeat 261–3, 265, 267, 270, 272–3, 275–81

qualitative factors 198
quality control 145

R^2, *see* R-squared
Rand Corporation 252, 321, 322
ratio models 5, 6, 24, 33, 54, 111–53
  advantages and disadvantages 152–3
  cash flow 118–21
  computing 112–13, 132–3
  funds flow 127–41
  input/output 33, 36, 145–52
  uses of 114–22
  'vehicle park' 141–5
ratios, predicting 112
raw material costs 33
RBL 276-7, 278, 281
re-estimation 57, 76, 77, 97
reference category 200
regression analysis 5, 38, 155–91
  advantages and disadvantages 155–6, 226–9
  applications 156–61, 243, 246
  in new product forecasting 263, 266
  in trend analysis 285, 287, 296, 298, 299, 310
regression methods 24, 95, 143
  see also regression analysis
regression models 6, 49
  accuracy and significance measures 177–84
  assumptions of 166–7, 201, 210–11, 218

  autoregressive 63, 95–7
  distributed lag 203–7
  final form 184, 221
  log-linear 193–7, 209
  multiple linear 165–6, 169–77, 193, 216, 221
  parameter estimates in 166, 168–77
  partial adjustment 208–9
  producing forecasts using 184, 189–91
  simple linear 161–5, 178, 327
regression packages 96, 191
regular differencing 83–7
report generation 121
Research International 277, 281
residuals 164, 165, 217, 218
resource allocation 4–5
resource needs 152
responses, sales
  changes of 234, 236
  equations 237, 239, 253
  shape of 229–36, 237, 240, 253
Retail Price Index 39
returns, diminishing 231, 232, 237, 239, 298, 307
robustness 21, 23, 57, 228, 239, 299
  testing 81–2
R-squared 177–9, 195, 211, 219, 221, 243, 287
  corrected 191
  test for significance of 181

sales
  as 'driver series' 135
  as trend analysis application 287, 289
  new product, pattern of 261, 267
  non-zero 231
  original equipment 142, 143, 144
  spares 141–5
sales forecasting 156–7
sales responses, *see* responses, sales
sales waves 275
sample error 74
SAS 330, 331
saturation 10, 63, 99, 103, 237, 243, 310
  levels 229, 231–2, 239, 254, 293–4, 296
scenario planning 314, 324, 326
Schlackman Research 272, 275, 281
seasonal difference 81, 96

seasonal effects 90, 200
seasonality 10, 44, 48–9, 65, 67, 99
  test for 71
sensitivity analysis 122, 133–41, 144, 151
SENSOR 277, 281
services industry 145
shape, selection of 291
shape of response 229–36, 237, 240
SHARESCALE 273–5, 276
Shell 324
Shlaiffer, Robert 257
shops, mobile 276, 277, 278
significance, statistical 46, 48, 184
  levels 212
  tests 179–84
silicon chip technology 322
Simmonds, K. 250
single differencing, see regular
  differencing
Slatter, S. 250
slope 161, 168, 199, 253
smoothing methods 63, 77–94
  adaptive 63, 87-8
  Brown's double exponential 63, 88–9,
    98
  Brown's triple exponential 63, 94–5
  Holt-Winters double exponential 63,
    89–94, 98
  single exponential 55, 63, 77–87, 92
socio-political forecasting 8
software, computer, see computer
  software
spares sales 141–5
spatial effects 198
'spreadsheet' packages 6, 111, 113, 331
S-shaped curves 232, 237, 293, 296, 305,
  307
standard deviation
  of β distribution 248
  of forecast error 190
  of normal distribution 248
  proportionality to mean 49–50
  test 85, 104
standard error test 181–4
  see also t-test
steps 10, 55, 88, 99, 101
Standard Industrial Classification 32, 33
stationarity 44, 46, 47, 48
stochastic term 161, 163

stocking effect 234
strategic planning 4, 6, 152, 156
subjective methods, see estimation,
  subjective; forecasting, subjective
substitutes 189, 195
supermarkets 260, 262, 275, 276, 277,
  278
supersaturation 232, 243
system definition 14
SYSTEM W 113, 330, 331

target setting 114, 314
taxation 129, 130, 132
technology, limits of 305, 310
technology forecasting 37, 287, 293,
  298, 313, 319
technology substitution 300, 319
technology trend analysis 302–8
  using 308–10
telephone interviews 262, 278
televisions, colour 302, 317, 319
temporal effects 197–8
threshold effects 232
tied indicators 316, 317
time scaling 322
time series 7, 8
  constant level 79
  data 54, 55, 211, 219, 221–2, 227, 285
  examples 57–63
  inflation adjustment 39
  length of 55, 99
  nature of 7, 10–13
  stationarity 44, 46, 47, 48
  turning points in 10
  see also seasonality
time series models 53–106
  advantages and drawbacks 105–6
  applications 53–4
  choosing a time series method 54–7,
    97–105
  data considerations 54, 55
  types of method 63–4
  univariate 53
  see also autoregressive models; Census
    XII; decomposition methods;
    moving average forecasts; naive
    methods; smoothing methods
time span of decisions 7, 8, 23
TNA 278–9

TRACKER 263, 272
trade associations 34–5
trading day adjustments 43–4
transformations 57, 98, 193, 216, 217, 288, 296, 301
   log-linear 193–7
transformed data 80
trend, extrapolation of 85, 89
trend, removal of 84
trend, time 219
trend analysis 38, 267, 282, 285–310
   advantages and disadvantages 287–9
   constrained 293–6
   diffusion of innovations 296–300
   fit and shape 289–93
   regression analysis in 285, 287, 296, 298, 299, 300
trend curves 6, 24, 126, 288, 308, 309
trends, mean level 44–8
   linear 10, 46–7, 67, 88, 90, 102, 287
   non-linear 10, 73, 77, 94, 97, 103
   quadratic 47, 94, 287
trials, customer 261, 262, 263, 265, 267, 281
Trigg and Leach approach 87
t test 181–4, 190, 196, 201, 210
two-tail test 182
typesetting 308

UK Treasury Model 36
unbiasedness 167, 210

validation sample 266
validation statistics 288, 291
Van den Bergh 281
variance
   of error terms 166, 210, 211

estimated 182
   minimum 167, 198, 211
   non-stationarity in 49–50, 83
   of parameter estimates 211
   of posterior distribution 327
'vehicle park' models 114, 141–5
variables
   balance sheet 125, 126
   convention for names of 116
   dependent 161, 162, 165, 168, 171, 189, 193, 217
   determining 156, 159
   dummy 171, 195, 197–203, 227
   forecast 7, 155, 165
   income statement 125, 126
   independent (or explanatory) 96, 161, 165, 168, 171, 189, 193, 218–19
   indicator 197
   lagged 203–11, 213, 219, 222
   omitted 211, 214
   'plug' 131
   qualitative 198
   quantitative, broad bands of 198
   random errors in 136–41
   relationships between 155
VCR sales 287, 291, 293, 294
volatility 10

wear-out 270
Winkler, R. L. 321
Witt, S. F. 3, 195, 201, 209
Woodcock, J. W. 196, 298
write-offs, exceptional 127, 131, 135

Yankelovich, Skelly and White Inc. 277
Yearbook of International Statistics 34